무함마드의
계시는
왜 자꾸 바뀔까?

Why Muhammad's revelations are

changing repeatedly?

- by Lee Man Seok -

이 도서의 국립중앙도서관 출판시 도서목록(CIP)은
e-CIP홈페이지 (http://www.nl.go.kr/ecip)에서 이용하실 수 있습니다.

국립중앙도서관 출판사 도서목록(CIP)
무함마드의 계시는 왜 자꾸 바뀔까? / 이만석 지음. 서울 : 4HIM
192p. ; 225x152cm.
ISBN 978-89-964279-0-2 03280

하나님의 영광을 위하여
그 분의 뜻인 인류 구원을(무슬림들을 포함한)
성취하기 위해 이 책이 쓰임 받기를 기도합니다.

무함마드의 계시를 기록한 꾸란에 사용된 언어는 아랍어(Arabic)
이다. 이 아랍어가 현대 사회에서 사용되는 아랍어가 아니라 7세기
무함마드 시대의 문어체로 기록된 아랍어이다. 그래서 아랍어가
모국어가 아닌 지역의 무슬림들은 꾸란의 언어를 이해하지 못한다.
심지어는 아랍어가 모국어인 국가의 무슬림들 가운데 중 · 고등
교육을 받은 사람들조차 꾸란을 읽어 보면 무슨 말인지 이해할 수
없는 부분이 많이 있다고 한다. 철저한 무슬림 집안에서 태어나
12세 때에 이미 꾸란의 전체를 암송한 이집트 출신의 마크 (Mark
G.)박사도 신학교를 졸업할 때까지는 꾸란의 내용을 이해할 수 없
었다고 말한다. 그러므로 꾸란의 언어인 아랍어 본문을 이해하
는데 제한이 있음을 고백하지 않을 수 없다. 그러나 감사한 것은
한국어로 번역된 3 종류의 한글 꾸란들(한국외국어대학교 아랍어과 교수

인 김용선 교수가 제일 먼저 번역했으며 그후 이슬람 국제출판국에서 수정 · 보완한 것이 있다. 최근에는 명지대학교 아랍지역학과 최영길 교수가 사우디아라비아의 지원을 받아 번역한 것이 있다 -편집자 주)이 있으며 영어로 번역된 10 종류의 꾸란(Shakir 역, Yousuf Ali 역, Pickthel 역, Hilali 역, Sher Ali 역, Khalifa 역, Arberry 역, Palmer 역, Rodwell 역, Sale 역, 등이 있다 -편집자 주) 과 이란어로 번역된 꾸란(역자가 누군지 밝히지는 않았지만 이란 종교성에서 번역하여 인터넷에 올려놓은 것으로 보인다 -편집자 주)이 있기에 상호 비교하면 거의 정확하게 본문이 의도하는 의미를 유추해 낼 수 있다고 본다.

무슬림들이 사용하는 신앙용어는 주로 아랍어를 사용한다. 그런데 그 아랍어들이 서로 발음이 다른 경우를 종종 보게 된다. 이는 아랍어가 자음만 쓰고 모음을 기록하지 않는 것이 보편적 현상이기에 지역마다 그 발음상의 차이가 있는 것은 당연한 현상이다. 예를 들면 이슬람의 창시자 무함마드의 이름을 이란에서 사용하는 발음처럼 모함마드라고 쓸 것이냐 아니면 서방에서 오랫동안 사용해 오던 마호메트라고 쓸 것이냐 혹은 무함만(실제로 아랍에서 사용하는 발음은 이 발음이 가장 유사함)이라고 쓸 것이냐 하는 문제가 발생한다. 이럴 경우는 아랍권의 어느 지방의 발음이 아니라 꾸란의 발음을 기준으로 표기하고자 한다. 아랍어의 신문이나 서적들은 모음을 붙이지 않고 자음만 기록하기 때문에 지역에 따라 습관상 여러 가지 모음을 붙여서 읽게 되므로 발음상의 차이가 있을 수 있지만 그들의 경전인 꾸란은 정확하게 모음을 붙여 놓았기 때문에 어느 지역에서 읽어도 동일한 발음으로 읽힌다. 그러나 외국어를 한국어로 표기하는 표기법의 기준에 의해서 정해진 것이 있다면 그것을 사용하기로 한다. 예를 들면 중동에서는 '무함맏' 이라고 발음하지만 한국어 표기법에서는 '무함마드' 라고 표기하기로 정해졌으므로 그것을 사용하기로 한다.

또한 꾸란의 인물들은 혼돈을 피하기 위해 아랍어 발음 그대로 표기할 것이며 성경적 이름을 괄호 안에 병기할 것이다.

예를 들면 예수는 한역이나 영역 꾸란에서는 예수 혹은 Jesus 라 하고 아랍어에서는 "이싸"라 한다. 반면 성경의 모세는 아랍어 원문의 발음 그대로 "무싸"라고 표기했다. 이는 성경의 예수나 모세와 꾸란의 이싸나 무싸는 서로 매우 다른 인물 묘사적 특징들을 가지고 있기 때문이다. 특히 한글 번역 꾸란 중 이슬람 국제출판국에서 번역한 것과 명지대 아랍지역학과 교수인 최영길이 번역한 꾸란에는 알라(Allah)를 "하나님" 이라고 번역하고 있으나(21세기 중동 이슬람 문명권 연구사업단, 『중동 종교 운동의 이해2』 (파주: 한울, 2005), 15p. -편집자 주) 이 책에서는 이들을 인용할 때도 다시 알라(Allah)로 고쳐서 인용할 것이다. 왜냐하면 기독교와 유대교의 하나님과 알라(Allah)를 같은 신으로 생각하게 되는 혼동을 피하기 위해서이다.

무함마드 계시의 변화 추이를 비교 설명함에 있어서 매우 심각한 한계가 있는 또 한 가지 이유는 꾸란의 수라는(Surah) 계시된 연대순으로 묶여져 있는 것이 아니라 장의 길이 순서로 묶여져 있지만 반드시 그런 것도 아니며 또한 대부분의 메디나의 수라(Surah)와 많은 메카의 수라(Surah)들이 각기 다른 시기에 행해졌던 이야기들을 한데 묶어 놓은 복잡한 복합물이라는 것 때문에 어려움은 가중된다. 따라서 꾸란의 계시의 정확한 연대를 가늠할 수 있는 중요한 근거는 일반적으로 무슬림 학자들도 그 양식과 내용을 가지고 기준을 삼는다.

이 책은 요즘 급격히 관심이 높아지고 있는 이슬람에 대해서, 그리고 그들이 주장하는 평화와 관용의 종교인 이슬람에 대해서 그 정체가 과연 무엇인지를 근원부터 밝히고자 노력했다. 무조건 그들이 믿는 종교와 교리가 나쁘고 우리가 믿는 종교가 옳다고 일방적인 주장을 하려는 것이 아니다.

다만, 그들의 경전인 꾸란이 나중에 받았다고 하는 계시에 의해 처음의 계시가 왜 취소되는지와 무함마드의 말과 행동의 기준이 왜 자꾸만 변천되어 가는지를 중점적으로 설명하고자 했다.

이슬람 학자들은 반드시 아랍어로 된 꾸란만이 진정한 알라의 계시이며, 각국어로 번역된 것은 단지 참고자료인 해설서에 불과하다고 주장한다. 그래서 꾸란은 번역하지 말라고 하며 아랍어 그대로 읽어야 하며 하루에 다섯 번 씩 하는 이슬람식 기도도 아랍어로 드려야 한다는 것이다. 그런데 코란의 아랍어는 현대인들이 사용하는 아랍어가 아니다. 아랍어가 국어인 아랍지역의 사람들도 너무 어려워서 비록 고등교육을 받은 사람일지라도 꾸란을 따로 공부하지 않으면 꾸란의 본문 내용을 쉽게 이해할 수 없다는 것이다. 마치 고어(古語)를 공부하지 않은 사람은 15세기 궁중 언어로 기록된 훈민정음 원본이나 용비어천가를 이해할 수 없는 것과 같이 7세기 문어체 아랍어로 기록된 꾸란을 아무나 쉽게 이해할 수는 없는 것이다.

요즈음 같이 문학이 발달되고 표현 기법이 고도로 발달된 21세기에 번역해 놓으면 그 원문의 의미가 손상될 것이 두려워 번역을 금지시킨다는 것은 납득이 가지 않는다.

오히려 비 아랍권에서 무슬림들이 7세기 문어체 아랍어로 읽으면 0-1% 밖에 이해가 안 되는 꾸란을, 최선을 다해 번역해 놓으면 아무리 번역에 오류가 있다고 해도 95-99%는 이해할 수 있지 않을까? 그런데 왜 95-99% 대신에 0-1 % 밖에 이해할 수 없는 방법을 택할까?

짐작컨대 꾸란 5장 101절에 말하고 있듯이 "꾸란의 계시는 자세히 알고 보면 오히려 해가 될 것도 있으니 질문하지 말라"고 하는데 이는 그 내용이 너무 혐오스럽기 때문에 감추고 싶은 부분이 있다는 말로 이해할 수 있을 것이다.

알라(Allah)

이슬람의 유일, 절대, 전능의 신. 원래 아랍인들 사이에 꾸리이시 종족의 신을 알라라고 불렀으며 '달의 신' 을 '알라' 라고 부르기도 했는데 무함마드가 이슬람의 유일신으로 만들었다. 번역서에는 하나님으로 번역이 되어 있으나 기독교에서 말하는 유일신 여호와 삼위일체 하나님과는 전혀 다른 신의 이름이다.

이슬람(Islam)

단어의 의미는 "복종" 이라는 뜻으로 주후(AD)570년 아라비아의 메카에서 태어난 무함마드가 만든 종교로서 꾸란과 하디스 등 샤리아(율법)를 기초로 함.

무슬림(Muslim)

복종하는 자들이라는 뜻으로 이슬람을 믿는 사람들을 뜻한다.

꾸란(Quran)

지브리일(가브리엘)천사를 통해 내려왔다고 주장하는 알라의 계시를 무함마드가 전달한다고 말한 것들을 그가 죽은 뒤 그의 세 번째 후계자(칼리프들) 우트만이 수집 · 정리해 놓은 것.

하디스(Hadith)

꾸란이 불완전하여 그것만으로는 이슬람 공동체를 다스릴 수가 없자 무함마드가 죽은 지 200여년 후에 부카리(Bukhari) 혹은 무슬림(Muslim)등의 추종자들이 '무함마드가 말했다고 믿어지는 문장들을 수집해 모은 것들' 을 책으로 엮은 것으로 꾸란과 더불어 이슬람 율법의 기초를 이룬다.

알 라트, 알 우짜, 알 마나트(Al Lat, Al Uzza, Al Manat)

알라의 세 딸들이라고 부르며 메카 사람들이 섬겨오던 여신들로서 무함마드가 그들과 알라의 관계를 끊어버렸다.(꾸란53:19-23)

순나(Sunnah)

이슬람의 창시자 무함마드의 전통.

시아파(Shiah)

시아파는 무함마드의 혈통만이 그의 후계자(칼리파)가 될 수 있다는 생각으로 무함
마드의 사위 알리 이븐 탈립을 따라 갈라져 나온 분파이다. 알리의 후손 중 어렸을 때
실종 된 마흐디(Mahdi)를 숨어 있는 이맘으로 간주하고 예수와 함께 재림한다고
믿고 있다. 전세계 무슬림들의 15% 정도를 차지하는 소수 종파로 여겨지고 있으나,
이란에서는 90% 이상이 시야파이며, 이라크에서는 약 60퍼센트에 해당하는 인구
다수가 시아파이다.

순니파(Sunni)

꾸란과 함께 무함마드의 언행록(하디스)을 포함한 순나(Sunnah 관례, 전통)를 따라
무함마드의 삶을 본받아 그대로 지키고자 하는 무슬림들을 말한다.
오늘날 전 세계 무슬림 인구의 85 퍼센트가 순니파이고 나머지 15퍼센트 정도가
시아파이다.

히즈라(Hijra)

무함마드가 메카의 우상숭배자들의 핍박을 피해 자신의 추종자들을 데리고 서기
622년 메디나로 옮겨간 것을 의미. 이 해가 이슬람력의 원년이다. 보통은 이주, 이동
혹은 이민 등의 뜻으로 번역되기도 하며 헤지라(Hejira)라고도 표기된다.

적그리스도

신약 성경에서, 마지막 시대에 나타난다는 예수와 그 사역을 대적, 방해하는 자.

피트나(Fitnah)

분쟁, 소동, 투쟁 혹은 불일치 등의 뜻을 가진 단어로 비무슬림들이 이슬람의 통치를
거부 혹은 대적하는 모든 활동을 의미한다.

서기(기원 후: A.D.(라틴어 Anno Domini의 약자)

기원 원년 이후. 예수가 태어난 때를 원년으로 하여 햇수를 헤아린다.
또는 주후라고도 한다.

과격한 이슬람 무장단체들

알 가마 알 이슬라미야(al-Gama' a al-Islamiya)

이슬람 집단(Islamic Group, IG). 1970년대에 주로 이집트 감옥에서 나타났고 후에 이집트 대학 몇 군데에서 나타났다.

함마스(Hammas)

팔레스타인에 위치한 이슬람 과격한 원리주의자이자 저항 운동.

헤즈볼라(Hezbollah) 또는 히즈볼라(Hizbollah)

"알라의 당(Party of Allah)"을 의미함. 레바논 남부에 근거를 가지고 이스라엘과 미국을 비롯한 기독교 세력을 대적하고 있음.

이슬람 구원전선(Islamic Salvation Front, FIS)

북아프리카 최초의 합법적인 이슬람 정치 당으로, 1988년 알제리 정부에 의해 처음 인정되었다. 후에 온건파 집단과 좀 더 호전적인 당파인 이슬람 구세군(Islamic Salvation Army)로 나뉘었다. 알카에다의 또 다른 이름이다.

무슬림형제단(Muslim Brotherhood)

여러 국가와 이슬람 집단을 아우르는 이슬람 조직.

팔레스타인 해방을 위한 인민 전선(Popular Front for the Liberation of Palestine)

팔레스타인의 진보적인 노동계층의 당, 마르크스주의와 레닌주의를 따른다.

탈레반(Taliban)

아프가니스탄의 이슬람 원리주의자 집단으로 그 의미는 '학생들' 이라는 뜻임.

알 카에다(al-Qaeda)

오사마 빈 라덴이 이끄는 원리주의자 이슬람 조직.

자마아티 이슬라미(Jamaat-i-Islami, 이슬람회(Islamic Society))

아부니달(Abu Nidal)

이 조직은 함마스, 이슬람지하드와 함께 팔레스타인 3대 과격단체로 불리기도 했으며 서방 언론들은 오사마 빈 라덴이 등장하기 전까지 세계에서 가장 위험한 테러리스트 지도자로 아부니달을 지목하기도 했다. 5명의 사망자와 29명의 부상자를 냈던 1986년 김포공항 테러는 북한으로부터 5백만 달러를 받은 아부니달의 조직에 의해 서울 아시안 게임을 방해하기 위해서 개막 일주일 전에 저질러진 것이라고 한다.(월간조선 2009년 3월호)

이 기사에 의하면 아부니달이 북한의 청부를 받고 김포공항 테러를 자행했다는 충격적인 사실이다. 이런 사실은 스위스 베른신문사의 무라타 기자가 김포공항 폭파사건을 조사한 보고서를 베를린의 '구(舊)동독 정보기관 슈타지(STASI) 자료관리 연방정부 특명센터'에서 찾아냈다. 김포공항 테러직후 독일의 프란츠 대령이 지휘하는 슈타지의 한 부서(22국)가 김포공항 폭파사건에 대해 조사했는데 심문과정에서 북한의 청부를 받고 조직원을 시켜 테러를 저질렀다고 자백했다고 한다. 이 테러는 당시 서울아시안게임 1주일전에 폭발물이 터져 5명이 사망하고 29명이 부상을 입은 충격적인 사건이었으나 정부는 범인을 밝혀내지 못했지만, 서울아시안게임을 방해하고 종국적으로는 88서울올림픽을 저지하기 위해 북한 공작원이 저지른 것으로 추정된다고 발표했었다. 청부거래는 아부니달과 김일성의 친분 때문에 가능했으며, 그는 오사마 빈 라덴이 등장하기 이전까지 이슬람권에서 가장 잔인한 테러리스트로 널리 알려졌었다.

Contents

한국에 이슬람이라는 종교가 들어온 지도 벌써 50년이 지났다. 한국의 이슬람 확산 운동은 그들의 계획대로 성공적으로 진행되고 있는 중이지만 이슬람에 대한 한국교회의 연구는 심히 부족한 상황이다. 2001년 9월 11일에 있었던 뉴욕의 세계 무역센터에 테러를 가한 사람들이 무슬림들이었다는 사실을 알고 이슬람에 대한 관심을 가졌으나 그 관심은 오히려 이슬람은 좋은 종교이고 평화의 종교인데 다만 몇몇 테러리스트(광신자)들의 테러행위로 이미지가 손상되고 있을 뿐이라고 홍보할 기회를 주는 결과를 가져왔다.

그 결과 세계적으로 무슬림들의 숫자는 더욱 늘어나게 되었다. 9 · 11 테러는 충격적 사건이기는 했지만 한국과 너무 먼 거리에서 일어난 사건이었고, 한국인들과 상관이 없었던 사건이었기에 그 충격은 쉽게 잊혀져갔다.

그런데 그 후 3년이 지난 2004년 6월 이라크에서 김 선일이라는 한국인이 무슬림들에게 참수를 당하는 사건이 발생했다. 이 사건은 한국인도 이슬람의 테러 대상이 될 수 있다는 사실을 우리에게 일깨워 주었다. 이때도 한국인들은 이슬람이라는 종교가 도대체 어떤 종교이기에 사람들의 목을 정육점의 고기 자르듯이 잘라 죽일까? 온 국민들이 격분하고 비탄에 빠졌었지만 한국의 이슬람중앙회에서는 이 충격을 이슬람 홍보의 기회로 삼기 위해 발 빠르게 움직였다. 고조된 이슬람에 대한 관심 때문에 신문과 방송 등 언론들은 이슬람을 소개하기 위해서 덩달아 바쁘게 움직였다. 한국의 이슬람에 대한 전문가가 부족하기에 이슬람중앙회에 가서 이슬람의 이맘들이나 무슬림 학자들에게 마이크를 대고 이슬람의 참수에 대해 질문을 했다.

그러나 한국의 무슬림들은 대학교수에서부터 무명의 신자까지 일관된 목소리로 "이슬람은 평화의 종교이며 그런 일을 저지른 살해범들은 테러범들이며 진실한 무슬림들이 아니며 이슬람에서는 사람의 목을 잘라 죽이라는 교리는 어디에서도 찾아볼 수 없다"고 주장했다. 사실은 꾸란 9장 5절처럼 "이교도들을 발견하는 대로 살해하라"(꾸란 9:5) "불신자들의 목을 쳐 죽이라"(꾸란 8:12)등 여러 구절들이 있음에도 불구하고 대부분의 한국인들이 꾸란을 찾아가며 확인하지는 않을 것이라는 것과 만일 꾸란을 찾아 확인할 사람들이 있더라도 그 수는 미미할 것이며 이미 사람들의 머릿속에 각인된 첫 인상을 지우기에는 시간이 걸릴 것이라는 것을 계산에 넣은 것이라고 보인다. 그들의 그런 주장들은 전혀 진위를 확인하는 절차 없이 그대로 대중언론 등을 통해서 홍보되었다. 그 결과 한국의 무슬림들의 숫자는 그런 흉악한 테러사건이 있었음에도 불구하고 점진적으로 증가되어 갔다. 한편 그 사건의 피해자가 무명의 한 사람에 국한되었던 탓에 시간이 지나면서 이슬람에 대한 관심이 차츰 줄어들었다.

그로부터 다시 3년이 지난 2007년 7월 한국의 샘물교회에서 23명의 한국인 청년들이 아프가니스탄으로 단기선교 여행을 떠났다가 2명이 순교하고 21명이 6주간 동안 탈레반이라는 무슬림 지하드단체에 포로로 끌려 다니다가 풀려나는 사건이 발생했다. 이 사건은 온 세계에 매일 톱뉴스를 장식한 사건이었다. 납치된 인원수나 납치기간에 있어서 세계적으로 손꼽힐만한 규모의 사건이었다. 이제 한국인들은 그 사건에 놀라기는 했지만 가해자들인 이슬람이나 탈레반을 비난하는 대신에 피해자들인 한국 기독교 쪽으로 공격의 화살을 돌렸다는데 문제의 심각성이 있는 것이다.

그 후에도 예멘테러 등 한국인들이 테러에 노출되어 피해를 입고 있는 상황이 계속되고 있음에도 한국의 무슬림 박사들은 이슬람은 평화의 종교라고 강력하게 주장하며 많은 홍보 자료들을 만들어 배포하고 있다.

그럼에도 불구하고 이슬람에 대한 바른 연구가 부족한 탓에 일반인들이 이슬람에 대한 관심이 있을지라도 홍수처럼 쏟아지는 이슬람 측에서 제공하는 홍보 자료를 쉽게 손에 넣어 그들이 주장하는 정보만을 읽고 있는 상황을 보면서도 막상 그들의 정체를 밝히는 자료가 많지 않아 안타까워하던 중 이 책을 쓰게 되었다.

이슬람이 평화의 종교인가?

아니면 폭력의 종교인가? 하는 질문 중에서 단순히 어느 한 쪽만을 고집한다면 이는 다소 성급한 판단이라고 본다. 왜냐하면 이슬람의 경전인 꾸란에는 평화도 언급하고 있지만 동시에 폭력도 명령하고 있기 때문이다. 정리를 해보면 이슬람은 평화로 시작했지만 결국은 폭력을 명하는 쪽으로 결론을 짓고 있으며 이슬람의 나씨크 교리에 의하면 꾸란의 평화로운 계시들은 후에 과격한 폭력적 계시에 의해서 취소된 것이며 무슬림들이 삶의 지침으로 삼고 있는 무함마드가 행동으로 보여준 모범도 역시 그렇다는 것을 이슬람의 경전을 연구한 정직한 사람들은 부인하지 않을 것이다.

이슬람은 무함마드라는 한 사람이 서기 610년부터 632년까지 23년 동안 소위 계시를 받았다고 하는 꾸란(Quran)이라는 책을 경전으로 하는 종교다. 이 꾸란은 하늘에 원전이 보관되어 있으며 그것을 이슬람의 신 알라(Allah)가 가브리엘(Gibrieel) 천사를 통해서 무함마드에게 계시 해주었다고 주장한다.

한편 기독교의 성경은 1,600년 동안에 40여명의 저자에 의해서 기록되었으며 역사적·지리적 혹은 문화적 검증을 통하여 만인의 진리로 인정된 반면 꾸란의 계시는 어느 누구의 검증도 받은 일이 없으며 무함마드 혼자서 진리라고 주장하고 있는 것이다.

그 당시 기독교인들이나 유대교인들뿐만 아니라 무함마드가 계시를 받았다고 말하는 것을 들었던 많은 사람들도 그것이 진리가 아니며 그를 미친 자가 하는 헛소리라고 불렀던 사실은 이슬람 역사가들도 동의하고 있다.

그러나 무함마드는 꾸란이 이전의 경전들을 폐기(Abrogating)하는 최후의 경전이라고 주장하며 그것을 믿는 자들만이 무슬림이라고 했다. 그렇다면 그 계시가 과연 어떤 영에 의한 계시인가 하는 것을 밝혀볼 필요가 있는데 이를 위해서 많은 연구가 있었던 것이 사실이다.

이 책에서는 무함마드의 계시의 근원을 확인하기 위해서 그 영의 정체를 직접 관찰하며 연구하기 보다는 그 계시라고 하는 것이 상황에 따라 변화된다는 사실에 주목하였다. 무함마드는 어떤 사건이 발생했을 때 자신이 결정을 내려야 하는 중요한 입장이 되면 '계시' 라는 방법을 통해서 문제를 해결하곤 했다(H.A.R Gibb『이슬람』, 55p, 여기서 저자 자신은 무함마드가 문제를 풀기 위하여 계시를 교묘히 이용했다는 사실에 대한 견해에 대해서 유감을 갖고 있다고 설명하고 있지만 그러한 시각이 많이 있다는 사실을 인정하고 있다-편집자 주). 이것이 '자신의 결정' 이라고 말하는 것보다 당시 아라비아 사람들이 최고의 신이라고 생각하던 '알라(Allah)께서 내리신 계시' 라고 하면 더 권위가 부여된다는 것을 이용한 것으로 보인다.

그러므로 그의 계시라는 것은 일관성이 없고 상황에 따라서 변하게 되며 문맥과 화자(話者)가 아무 예고도 없이 수시로 바뀌며 역사적으로도 세상의 역사가들이 말하는 것과 상호 모순되며 과학적으로도 세상의 과학자들이 말하는 것과는 모순된다는 점을 무슬림 자신도 인정하고 있다(최영길,『성꾸란 의미의 한국어 번역』(서울파하드 국왕 꾸란 출판청, 1996), 꾸란 개요 참조 -편집자 주). 따라서 이 책에서는 상황에 따라서 변화되는 무함마드의 계시의 상호 모순성과 추이를 살펴보면서 이슬람의 영의 정체를 확인하고자 하는 것이다.

지금까지 무함마드의 계시의 변화 추이에 대한 연구는 서방의 학자들의 것들은 간혹 보이지만 한국에서는 미미한 것 또한 사실이다. 오히려 한국은 이슬람 측에서 제공하는 홍보자료가, 중동 산유국에 가서 그들의 장학금 혜택을 받으며 유학을 하여 학위를 받고 돌아온 한국인 무슬림 학자들에 의하여 저술되거나 혹은 번역되어 서점가를 점령하고 있는 상황이다. 이슬람 측에서 제공하는 홍보자료는 심지어 교회와 신학교에서 조차 무분별하게 채택되어 읽히고 있는 실정이며 돈만 있으면 얼마든지 책을 만들 수 있는 대한민국 헌법이 보장한 언론과 출판의 자유를 마음껏 활용하고 있는 이슬람의 공격에 한국교회가 효과적으로 대처하기 위해서는 이슬람의 교리대로 꾸란과 하디스에 있는 원래의 이슬람에 대해서 바른 정보를 찾아내어 대중적으로 알리는 것이 무엇보다도 시급한 상황이다.

　　이슬람에서 무함마드가 받았다고 하는 "계시"라는 것은 즉 꾸란을 말하는 것이다. 이슬람에서는 무함마드가 알라(Allah)의 계시를 받았다고 하는 것을 꾸란이라는 이름으로 수집하여 제 3대 칼리프인 우트만이 집대성하여 한 권의 책으로 묶었다. 물론 내용상의 차이가 있는 무함마드 계시의 다른 수집들도 있었지만 그들 중 하나를 표준으로 정하고 나머지를 모두 모아서 불태워 없애 버렸다고 한다.

　　그래서 지금 우리가 확인할 수 있는 무함마드의 계시들 즉 꾸란 구절들은 무함마드가 하늘에 있는 원본을 가지고 그대로 전달 받은 것이 아니라 이슬람의 3대 칼리프인 우스만이 모아 엮은 꾸란이라는 것이다.

　　무슬림들이 지켜야 하는 이슬람의 율법의 근거는 무슬림들이 무함마드의 계시라고 주장하는 꾸란 뿐 아니라 하디스(Hadith)와 순나(Sunna)도 있다. 우리가 흔히 이슬람의 율법(Sharia:샤리아)이라고 하는 것은 꾸란과 하디스와 순나를 모두 합친 것을 말한다. 이슬람에는 샤리아라는 책이 따로 있는 것이 아니다. 이슬람의 율법을 연구하자면 무함마드의 언행록이라고 하는 하디스와 무함마드의 행위를 본받아 배워야 하는 순나를 함께 살펴야 하지만 그렇게 하자면 얘기의 폭도 넓어지고 분량이 방대함으로 이 책에서는 특수한 몇 가지 부분을 제외하고는 주로 무함마드의 계시라고 하는 꾸란과 하디스를 살펴 비교하는데 국한시키고자 한다. 또한 무함마드의 계시의 변화 추이를 연구함에 있어서 주로 꾸란과 하디스를 참고하는 방법을 사용하고자 한다고 밝혔다.

이슬람 학자들의 견해를 비교하는 것도 바람직한 연구 방법이라고 생각하는 이들이 있을지 모르지만 이슬람 학자들의 견해는 통일되어 있지도 않을 뿐 아니라 상호간에 현격한 견해 차이를 보이는 분야들도 적지 않으며 심지어는 사우디아라비아를 필두로 하는 순니파(Sunni)파와 이란을 필두로 하는 시아파(Shiah)는 정반대의 견해를 주장하는 경우도 흔히 발견할 수 있기에 여기에서는 순니와 시아를 불문하고 이슬람 학자들이라면 아무도 부인할 수 없는 그들의 경전인 꾸란(Quran)과 하디스(Hadith)를 참고하면서 다음 장부터는 무함마드의 계시의 변화 추이를 계속 살펴보고자 한다.

SECTION 1

초기 무함마드 계시

Why Muhammad's revelations are
changing repeatedly?

이슬람의 역사를 보면 무함마드는 서기 610년에 알라(Allah)의 계시를 받았다고 주장한다. 물론 무함마드가 계시를 받았다는 상황에 대한 묘사는 꾸란에 기록되어 있지 않다. 이는 하디스를 참조해야 한다. 하디스(Hadith)란 무함마드가 계시를 받았다고 언급하지는 않았지만 그의 추종자들과 몇몇의 아내들에 의해서 무함마드가 직접 말했다고 믿어지는 어록들을 수집·정리 해 기록해 놓은 것을 말한다. 이를 수집한 사람의 이름을 따라서 부카리(Bukhari)의 하디스 혹은 무슬림(Muslim)의 하디스 혹은 다우드(Dawoud)의 하디스 등으로 불리게 된다. 이슬람의 역사를 연구함에 있어서 하디스를 참조할 때 무슬림들은 부카리(Bukhari)와 무슬림의 하디스를 가장 신빙성 있는 하디스로 인정하고 있다.[1] 부카리의 하디스에 기록되어 있는 그의 첫 계시의 상황은 아래와 같다.

(신실한 무슬림들의 어머니) 아이샤(Aisha)[2] 가 말하기를[3] 신의 계시가 알라의 메신저에게 내려오기 시작한 것은 밝은 낮의 빛처럼 좋은 꿈의 형식으로 이루어 졌는데 그에게 은밀한 사랑이 내려왔다. 그는 여행을 위하여 음식을 준비해서 며칠 씩 알라(Allah)께 예배하며 히라(Hira) 동굴에서 명상을 하다가 음식이 필요하게 되면 다시 그의 아내 카디자(Khadija)와 가족들에게 돌아오곤 했다. 그런데 그가 히라 동굴에 있을 때 갑자기 진리가 그에게 임했다. 천사가 내려와 그에게 "읽으라![4] 그는 "저는 읽을 줄 모릅니다."[5] 라고 대답했다. 무함마드는 "그 천사가 나를 너무 강하게 사로잡아서 짓누르기에 나는 도저히 견딜 수가 없었다. 그 천사는 나를 놓아주더니 다시 읽으라고 했고, 나는 다시 저는 읽을 줄 모른다고 대답했다. 그랬더니 그는 다시 나를

---

1. 부카리(Bukhari)나 무슬림(Muslim)이 무함마드의 어록집을 수집하여 하디스를 펴낸것은 무함마드가 죽은 지 200년이 지난후의 일이다. 무함마드는 서기 632년에 죽었고 부카리는 서기 810년에 태어나서 870년에 죽었다(위키백과 사전).

2. 아이샤는 하디스를 구성하는데 가장 중요한 첫 번째 인물 고리로서 무함마드로부터 그녀가 직접 들었다고 하는 말들을 수집한 것들이 많다. 아이샤는 무함마드가 가장 사랑하는 아내이며 그녀가 6살 때 50세의 무함마드와 결혼하였으며 그녀의 나이 18세 때 무함마드는 62세의 나이로 죽었다. 무함마드는 그녀를 비롯한 자신의 아내들을 모두 무슬림들의 어머니라고 부르도록 했으니 그녀는 어린 나이에 모든 무슬림들의 어머니가 되었다.(꾸란33장6절).

3. 아래 인용문은 부카리(Bukhari의 하디스 제1권 1번 책 제 3항에서 인용한 것임.

4. 최영길, 『이슬람문화사』(서울: 송산출판사,1990),21p 읽으라는 말은 아랍어로 이끄라아(Iqraa)로 표기한다." 고 했다.

5. 무함마드가 문맹이라고 하는 사실은 무슬림학자들의 공통된 주장이나 이를 꾸란과 하디스에까지 기록한 것은 꾸란이 누구에게 교육 받아 기록한 것이 아니라 '직통계시' 임을 강조하기 위한 것으로 보인다. 이슬람 역사에 보면 무함마드는 정직하게 장사를 하여 주인에서 '무우민' (믿을 만한 자)이라는 칭호를 들었다고 한다. 글을 모르는 자가 어찌 장사를 잘하여 정직하게 보고하고 신뢰를 얻을 수 있었을까 하는 점에 의문을 제기하는 학자들도 많이 있다.

견딜 수 없을 정도로 심하게 짓눌렀다. 그런 후 다시 나를 놓아주더니 읽으라고 했다. 나는 다시 읽을 줄 모른다고 했다(혹은 무엇을 읽으란 말이냐고 물었다). 그랬더니 세 번째로 나를 짓누르다가 다시 놓아주더니 '응혈(clod:엉긴 피)로 인간을 창조하신 네 알라의 이름으로 읽으라'고 했다. '읽으라. 네 알라는 자비로우시니라'(꾸란 96:1, 96:2, 96:3)."알라의 메신저는 그 영감을 받고는 가슴이 심히 방망이질을 했다. 그는 카디자[6] 에게 돌아와서"나를 덮어주시오. 나를 덮어주시오."라고 말했다. 그들은 그의 두려움이 사라질 때까지 그를 덮어 주었고 그 후 그는 일어났던 모든 일들을 그녀에게 말하면서 "내게 무슨 일이 일어날 것 같아 두렵소."[7] 라고 했다. 카디자는 "알라(Allah)의 이름으로 맹세코 절대로 그런 일은 일어나지 않을 거예요. 알라(Allah)께서는 당신에게 부끄러움을 주시지 않을 거예요. 당신은 친척들과 가족들과 좋은 관계를 유지해 왔고 가난한 사람들을 도와주었고, 손님들을 정중히 대접했고 재난 당한 사람들을 도와주었지요." 카디자는 그를 데리고 사촌인 압둘 우짜(Abdul Uzza)의 증손이며, 아사드(Asad)의 손자이며, 나우팔(Naufal)의 아들인 와라까(Waraqa)에게 데리고 갔다. 그는 이슬람 이전 시대에 기독교인이었으며 히브리

---

6. 카디자(Khadija)는 무함마드가 25세 때 결혼한 첫번째 아내였으며 그녀는 매우 부유한 아라비아의 대상 무역 상단의 여주인이었고 그녀가 무함마드와 결혼할 때는 40세 였으며 그녀는 이미 여러 번 결혼에 실패한 경력이 있는 여자였다.
7. P. J. 스튜어트, 『펼쳐보는 이슬람』, 김백리 역 (서울: 풀빛, 2004), 67p. : 이 때 무함마드의 두려움은 극도에 달하여 여러 차례 절벽에서 뛰어내려 자살하려고 했으나 천사가 만류하였다고 한다.

어로 글을 쓰던 사람이었다. 그는 알라께서 허락하시는 대로 히브리어로 복음(Gospel)을 기록하곤 했다. 그는 늙어서 앞을 보지 못했다. 카디자(Khadija)가 와라까(Waraqa)에게 "당신 조카의 말을 들어보세요."라고 하자 그는 "오 조카여. 무엇을 보았소?"라고 물었다. 무함마드는 자기가 본 것을 그에게 모두 말했다. 와라까는 "이분은 알라(Allah)께서 모세(무싸Musa)에게 보내셨던 그 비밀을 간직한 분(천사가브리엘)이시오. 내가 젊었더라면 당신의 백성들이 당신에게 돌아오는 것을 볼 수 있었을 것이오." 라고 말했다. 무함마드는 "그들이 나를 배척할까요?"라고 물었다. 와라까는 확신에 찬 어조로 "누구든지 당신이 받은 것과 같은 것을 받는 자들은 배척을 받을 것이요. 당신이 배척을 받을 때까지 내가 살아 있다면 내가 당신을 강력히 도와 줄 것이요."라고 말했다. 그러나 며칠 후 와라까(Waraqa)는 죽었고, 얼마 동안 신의 영감도 중단되었다.[8]

압둘라의 아들 자비르(Jabir)가 계시가 중단되었을 동안에 무함마드가 말한 것을 전하기를 "내가 걸어가고 있었을 때 갑자기 하늘에서 음성이 들렸다. 위를 올려다보니 내가 히라 동굴에서 보았던 그 천사가 하늘과 땅의 가운데서 의자에 앉아 있었다. 나는 두려워서 집으로 돌아와 (담요로) '나를 덮어주오'라고 말했다. 그 때 알라(Allah)께서 아래와 같은 구절들(꾸란)을 계시하셨다. '오 겉옷을 걸치는 자(무함

8. Al-Imam Zain-ud-Din Ahmad bin Abdul-Lateef Az-Zubaidi, Summarized Sahih Al-Bukhari, translated by Dr Muhammad Muhsin Khan (Riyadh Saudi Arabia : Maktaba Dar-us-Salam, 1996), 51p.

마드)여! 일어나서 경고하라. 그리고 그대 알라만을 찬양하고 그대의 망토를 청결케 할 것이며 부정한 것을 피하라. - 꾸란 74:1-5 최영길 역

이 후 계시가 강력하게 정기적으로 종종 내려오기 시작했다."고 말했다.[9] 무슬림들이 가장 신뢰하고 있는 부카리(Bukhari)가 전하는 하디스의 내용 중 무함마드가 최초로 계시를 받는 장면을 묘사한 것을 보면, 마치 샤머니즘의 박수나 무당에게 신이 내리는 장면과 흡사하며[10] 한국의 이슬람 최고의 학자라고 자타가 인정하는 최영길 교수도 그의 『꾸란의 이해』에서 그 당시 사람들이 무함마드를 제정신이 아닌 미친 사람으로 취급하였으며 꾸란을 더러운 악마의 책으로 혹은 거짓된 영의 역사로 기술하고 있다는 것을 인정하고 있으며 심지어는 꾸란에도 아래와 같은 기록이 있다.

"이 때 그들은 말했더라. 그대에게 꾸란이 계시되었다니 실로 당신은 미친 사람이라."-꾸란 15:6

"제정신이 아닌 시인을 위해 우리의 신들을 버려야하는가? 라고 말하더라."-꾸란 37:36 [11]

---

9. Ibid, 52p
10. 미르치아 엘리아데, 『샤머니즘 고대 접신술』, 이윤기 역 (서울: 까치글방, 1992), 50~75p.
11. 최영길, 『꾸란의 이해』(서울: 성천문화재단, 1995), 16~17p.

무함마드 계시의 전달자

무함마드에게 알라(Allah)의 지시를 받아 계시를 전달한 천사는 과연 누구일까? 부카리의 하디스에 의하면 계시를 받은 당사자인 무함마드는 그가 누군지 몰랐다는 것이다.[1] 이는 이슬람의 경전인 꾸란을 이해하는데 매우 중요한 의미를 부여한다. 무함마드는 나중에 자신의 아내 카디자(Khadija)가 기독교인이었던 사촌 와라까(Waraqa)에게 데리고 가서 그가 계시를 받았던 상황을 자세히 들려주었더니

---

1. Al-Imam Zain-ud-Din Ahmad, Summarized Sahih Al-Bukhari, 51p : 무함마드는 첫 번째 계시를 받았을 때 자신에게 계시를 내려준 실체가 누군지 몰라서 집으로 뛰어 와서 "내게 무슨 일이 일어날 것 같다"고 하면서 두려워 할 때 그 아내 카디자(Khadija)가 "알라(Allah)에게 맹세코 그렇지 않을 것이며 알라(Allah)께서는 절대로 당신에게 부끄러움을 주지 않을 것이라"고 말했다는 기록을 보면 카디자(Khadija)의 종족이 이미 알라(Allah)라는 신을 믿고 있었다는 것을 증명해 준다.

그가 말하기를 이는 무싸(모세)에게 계시를 내렸던 바로 그 천사라고 알려 주었다는 것이다. 그는 늙어서 앞을 보지 못하는 소경이라고 했다. 이 와라까의 신앙에 대해서는 많은 정보가 있지 않으나 그는 카디자의 사촌이었고, 무함마드와 같은 도시 메카에 살고 있었다. 그는 히브리어 성경을 복사하는 사람이었다고 하는 부카리(Bukhari)의 하디스 내용을 그대로 믿는다면, 어느 정도 성경적인 지식이 있었던 사람으로 볼 수 있을 것이다. 무함마드의 아내 카디자(Khadija)에 의하면 무함마드는 친척들과 좋은 관계를 유지해 왔다고 하는데 그렇다면 한 도시에 사는 카디자의 친척인 와라까(Waraqa)는 자주 만났을 가능성이 짙다. 무함마드가 첫 계시를 받은 때는 서기 610년이었으며 무함마드가 카디자와 결혼을 한 것은 서기 595년 이었다. 그러므로 무함마드는 카디자와 결혼을 함과 동시에 와라까(Waraqa)와는 친척 관계가 되었으며, 그들은 메카에서 15년을 같이 살고 있었다. 그래서 무함마드는 와라까로부터 성경에 대해서 가끔 들었을 가능성이 있기는 하지만 꾸란에 나타난 무함마드의 성경 지식은 매우 불완전하고 오류가 많은데 그 이유는 무엇일까?[2] 자료가 불충분하기는 하지만 몇 가지 생각해 볼 수 있는 점이 있다.

첫째는 와라까(Waraqa)가 무함마드에게 성경을 가르치고자 하는 열정이 없었던 것이라고 추측해볼 수 있다.

둘째는 무함마드가 성경말씀을 들을 때 중요하게 생각하지 않고

---

2. 마크 G, 『이슬람과유대인 그 끝나지 않은 전쟁』, 131~132p.

귓전에 흘러들었을 가능성도 있다. 그런데 종교적인 현상이 자신에게 일어나자 그런 현상을 상담할 수 있는 사람은 와라까(Waraqa) 밖에는 없다고 생각하고 아내와 함께 찾아간 것일 수 있다. 그러나 그 때는이미 그가 눈이 안 보이고 기력이 쇠하여 며칠 후 숨을 거두었다고하니[3] 실제적으로 무함마드가 와라까의 지도를 받았을 가능성은거의 없었을 것으로 보인다.

---

3. Sahih al Bukhari, Volume 1, Book 1, chapter 3.

무함마드의 계시는 왜 자꾸만 바뀔까?
Why Muhammad's revelations are changing repeatedly?

무함마드가 처음 계시를 받은 때는 라마단 월이라는 데는 이견이 없는 듯하다. 라마단은 아랍 달력으로 9월을 말하는 것이다.[1] 이는 아래 꾸란의 구절을 통해서도 확인할 수 있다.

진실로 알라는 거룩한 밤에 이 계시를 내리나니 거룩한 밤이 무엇인지 그대에게 설명하여 주리요 거룩한 이 밤은 천개월보다 더 훌륭한 밤으로 이 밤에 천사들과 가브리엘 천사가 알라의 명령을 받아 강림하여 아침 동녘까지 머무르며 평안하소서 라고 인사하더라.

- 꾸란 97:1~5 최영길 역

---

1. 이슬람의 달력은 월력(月曆)으로 각 달의 명칭은 1월: Muharam, 2월: Safar, 3월: Rabi Awwal, 4월: Rabi thani, 5월: Jumada Ula, 6월: Jumada Akhira 혹은 Thanya, 7월: Rajab, 8월: Shaban, 9월: Ramadan, 10월: Shawal, 11월: Dhul Qadah, 12월: Dhul Hijjah 이다.

보통은 금식하는 달로 더 잘 알려진 라마단 달 27일 째 되는 밤은 권능의 밤(Night of Power)이라고 불린다.[2] 이슬람 지역에서는 이날 밤에 특별한 축제들이 많이 열린다. 신실한 무슬림들은 온 밤을 지새우며 모스크에 머물며 꾸란을 읽거나 기도하면서 그날 알라로부터 특별한 은총을 경험하기 위해서 노력한다. 특히 이날 밤에 꾸란이 무함마드에게 처음으로 계시되었다고 한다.[3] 이 밤에는 전 세계 모든 무슬림들이 꾸란 97장 3절(거룩한 이 밤은 천개월보다 더 훌륭한 밤으로 이 밤에 천사들과 가브리엘 천사가 알라의 명령을 받아 강림한다)을 외우면서 자신들이 알라의 은총을 입고자 최선을 다한다. 특히 기독교 측에서는 이슬람에서 신앙적 축제를 벌이는 라마단 달에 특별 기도회로 모여 소위 역라마단 기도운동을 펴기도 한다.[4] 그런데 이슬람의 상징이라고 하는 초승달 문제를 생각해 보자면 이것이 왜 이슬람의 상징이 되었을까? 하는 의문을 갖게 된다.

이슬람권 최고의 권위를 가지는 알 아즈하르(Al-Azhar)이슬람 신학대학교에서 "이슬람의 역사와 문화"를 연구하여 박사학위(Ph.D)를 획득하고 그 대학에서 이슬람 역사를 가르치는 교수로 재직하다가 개종한 마크 G. 박사는 "알라(Allah)라는 명칭은 이슬람이 창시되기

---

1. 김정위, 『이슬람 입문』, 35p. 여기서 저자는 꾸란을 처음 계시 받은 밤은 라마단 달의 그믐 경으로서 이 밤을 결정의 밤이라는 용어로 불렀다고 기록하고 있다.
3. 정수일(간슈), 『이슬람문명』(서울: 창작과 비평사, 2002), 151p.
4. 조종을, "라마단 권능의 밤을 기억하고 꼭 기도합시다. 늘사랑교회 홈페이지 참조 (http://www.everlove.or.kr/community/?kind=7&cate=77&mod=2&page=1&idx=625&searchKind=&searchText=&subCate=)

전에 이미 아라비아 반도에서 메카의 카아바 신전의 360개 우상 가운데 하나를 지칭하는 말로 사용되었으며 몇몇 부족들은 '달의 신'을 알라(Allah)라고 부르기도 했다"고 한다.[5] 한편 이슬람 측에서는 히라(Hira)동굴에서 무함마드가 명상에 잠겨 있다가 첫 번째 계시를 받았을 때 하늘에 초승달이 떠 있었기에[6] 그것이 이슬람의 상징이 되었다고 주장하기도 한다.[7] 만일 그 말이 사실이라면 계시의 시기와 이슬람의 상징은 서로 모순이 있다는 것을 확인할 수 있을 것이다. 무함마드가 첫 번째 계시를 받았다고 하는 것은 라마단(이슬람력 제 9월) 달의 27일째 밤이라고 한다.[8] 그런데 무함마드가 첫 번째 계시를 받고 히라(Hira)동굴에서 나오니 초승달이 떠 있었다고 하는 것은 논리적으로 모순이 있다. 왜냐하면 초승달은 음력으로 매월 초순인 1~5일에 하늘에 보이는 것인데 월력(月曆)을 사용하는 아랍의 제9월 라마단 달 27일에 달이 보였다면 그것은 초승달이 아니고 그믐달이 되는 것이다. 그러므로 만일 이 주장이 맞는다면 이슬람의 상징은 초승달(Crescent)이 아니고 그믐달(Decrescent)이 되어야 한다. 이런 논리적인 모순이 있기에 일부 이슬람 학자들은 이슬람의 상징으로서 초승달을 거부해야 한다고 주장하기도 하지만[9] 아무도 이를 실천에

5. 마크 G, 『이슬람과유대인 그 끝나지 않은 전쟁』, 132p.
6. '이슬람선교, 웹사이트 참조(http://www.islammission.org/islam/introduct/islam.htm)
7. 이희수, 『만화, 초등학생이 꼭 알아야 할 이슬람의 모든 것』, (서울:주니어김영사, 2009), 53 p.
8. http://www.islammission.org/islam/ramadan/2001_ramadan/011212.htm.
9. Sheikh Muhammed Salih Al-Munajjid, '이슬람Q & A' http://www.islam-qa.com/en/ref/1528.

옮길 수 있는 사람은 없을 것으로 보인다.

무함마드가 첫 번 계시를 받고 동굴에서 나올 때 하늘에 초승달이 떠 있었기 때문에 그것이 이슬람의 상징이 되었다는 주장이 논리상 모순이 있어서 사실이 아니라면 초승달이 이슬람의 상징이 된 진짜 이유는 무엇일까? 많은 추측을 할 수 있겠지만 원래 달신(Moon god)을 알라(Allah)라는 이름으로 섬기던 종족에서 태어난 무함마드가 자신의 종족신의 이름을 차용해서 유일신의 이름으로 그대로 사용했기 때문이라고 생각하는 것이 가장 자연스런 해석이라고 본다.[10]

---

10. Robert Morey, 『Islamic Invasion』, 51p.

SECTION 2

메카 체류 시기의
무함마드 계시

Why Muhammad's revelations are
changing repeatedly?

메카의 사회 정치적 상황

이슬람 학자들은 이슬람 이전의 시대를 '자힐리야' 시대라고 한다. 즉 무지의 시대라는 의미이다. 이는 넓은 의미로는 태고부터 이슬람 탄생까지를 말하는가하면 좁은 의미로는 이슬람이 탄생하기 전 150~200년 간의 시기를 말하기도 한다. 이때 아라비아 반도에서는 수많은 전쟁이 있었으며 사람들은 어떤 집단에 소속되지 않으면 생존하기 어려운 상황이었고, 오아시스나 수원지 혹은 초장들을 공유하는 개념이 보편적으로 퍼져 있었다. 이때는 무역권이나 대상로를 확보하기 위하여 전쟁이 비일비재했다.

특히 무함마드의 유년시절에 해당하는 575년부터 590년 사이에는 메카 지방의 부족들인 꾸라이시족과 하와진족 간의 네 차례의

유혈적 상권 쟁탈전이 이런 상황을 설명해 주는 좋은 예가 될 것이다.[1]
15~20개의 천막에 분산하여 수백 명의 군사를 거느리고 있을 정도의
세력으로는 생존하기 힘든 형편이 되므로 부족들 간의 연합이 보편
화 되었다. 그 대표적인 예로는 바로 메카를 중심으로 20개 씨족이
연합한 꾸라이시 부족 연맹이다. 이는 미래의 국가 탄생을 예견하게
하는 것으로 주변의 위협적인 사산조의 페르시아나 비잔틴과의 대
결을 피할 수 없는 상황이었기에 필연적으로 발생한 현상으로 볼 수
있을 것이다.[2] 이슬람 이전 시대는 성관계가 문란했고 아내의 수에
제한이 없었으며 여아들을 생매장하는 풍습도 있었다고 꾸란은 주
장한다.[3]

메카의 종교적 상황

무함마드가 태어났을 당시인 서기 570년 경 메카는 아라비아 일
대의 최대 도시로서 종교와 정치와 경제의 중심지였다.[4] 특히 주목
해야할 필요가 있는 부분은 메카의 카아바 신전이다. 카아바란 말은
입방체라는 의미의 아랍어다. 카아바 신전은 꾸란에 의하면 이브라

---

1. 정수일, 『이슬람 문명』, 42.
2. ibid.
3. 사피 아르라흐만 알쿠바라크푸리, 『인간 무함마드』 최영길 역, 71p.
4. 김용선, 『이슬람의 역사와 그 문화』 (서울: 명문당, 2002), 19~20p. 이슬람에서는 이 시대를 무지
   의 시대라고 하여 자힐리야(Jahiliyah) 시대라고 이름지어 부르고 있다. 이 시대에는 여아가 태
   어나면 모래 속에 묻어 살해하는 풍습이 있었으며 무지와 타락의 시대였다고 주장한다.
5. P. J. 스튜어트, 『펼쳐보는 이슬람』, 41p.

힘(아브라함)과 이스마일(이스마엘)이 건축했다고 한다.[5] 그 신전 안에는 주변 도시들이 섬기는 각종 우상들이 약 360여개가 안치되어 있었다.[6] 무함마드가 소속된 꾸라이시 족은 우상의 신전인 카아바 신전을 관리해 주는 것을 특권으로 생각하고 있었다. 왜냐하면 수백 킬로미터 정도 떨어진 도시의 우상들도 여기에 모아놓고 일 년에 하루씩 종족마다 제삿날을 정해 놓고 각 종족들이 메카신전에 와서 제사를 드리고 돌아가곤 했기 때문이었다.[7] 수백 킬로미터 사막 길을 걸어와서 제사만 드리고 바로 돌아가는 종족은 거의 없었다. 며칠 씩 쉬었다가 가면서 자연히 상권이 형성되었고 실크로드는 이곳을 지나가면서 아랍 최대의 시장이 되었고 경제의 중심지가 되었다. 그런데 카아바 신전에 있던 이 우상들 간에는 계급이 있었는데 그 중 최고의 위치를 점하는 지고신(至高神)은 알라(Allah)라고 부르는 신이었다.[8] 이는 무함마드가 소속된 꾸라이시(Quraish) 족속이 믿는 신이었다. 알라(Allah)가 꾸라이시족이 믿는 신이었다는 사실은 무함마드의 부친의 이름이 압둘라(Abdullah:알라의 종)였다는 사실을 봐도 확인할 수 있다.[9] 중동에서는 보편적으로 자신의 종족이 믿는 신의 이름을 자기 이름에 삽입하여 명명하곤 했다. 즉 성경의 다니엘(하나님은 나의 재판장이시다)이나 사무엘(하나님이 들으신다) 엘리야(하나님은 나의 하나님이다) 혹은

6. 유해석, 『이슬람이 다가오고 있다』 (서울: 쿰란출판사, 2005), 39p.
7. 레자 아슬란, 『알라 외에 다른 신은 없다』, 정규영 역(서울: 이론과 실천, 2006), 38~39p.
8. 김용선, 『이슬람의 역사와 그 문화』, 24p.
9. 김정위, 『이슬람 사전』, (서울: 학문사, 2002), 445p.

우상을 섬기는 자들도 아벳느고(느고의 종) 벨사살(벨이여 왕을 보호하소서) 등의 이름을 붙였던 것을 보면 알 수 있다. 그런데 무함마드의 부친 이름 압둘라(Abdullah)는 압드(abd: 종, 노예, 섬기는 자)라는 단어와 알라(Allah)라는 단어를 합쳐서 알라를 섬기는 자 혹은 알라의 종이라는 의미의 이름이다. 그의 부친이 태어났을 때 그 이름을 '압둘라' 라고 지었다는 것은 무함마드가 소속되었던 꾸라이시(Quraish)족이 무함마드 이전에도 알라(Allah)라는 신을 섬겨왔었다는 것을 증명해 준다.

무함마드 당시 메카의 우상숭배자들은 여러 가지 우상들을 섬기고 있었다. 그들 중 최고신이라고 일컬어지는 알라(Allah)라는 신은 이슬람이 창시되기 전에 아라비아에서 카아바 신전에 있는 360가지 우상 가운데 하나였으며 몇몇 부족들은 '달(Moon)의 신' 을 알라(Allah)라고 부르기도 했다.[10] 이는 지금도 이슬람 사원의 꼭대기에 초승달을 달아 놓은 것이라든지 이슬람 국가의 국기에 표기된 초승달 문양을 봐도 확인할 수 있는 부분이다.

그런데 그들이 섬기던 알라(Allah)에게는 세 딸이 있었다. 그들의 이름은 알 라트(Al-Lat) 알 우짜(Uzza) 알 마나트(Manat)였다(이하 라트, 우짜, 마나트라 한다 - 편집자 주).[11] 꾸란 53:19~20. 이는 꾸란에서도 확인이 된다. 이들은 알라(Allah)와 함께 이 세 여신들도 섬기고 있었다.

이제 너희는 라트와 우짜에 관하여 그리고 또 다른 여신인 마나트에 대하여 내게 이르라! 무엇이라 하느냐! 너희에게는 남성(아들)이

---

10. 마크 G, 『이슬람과 유대인 그 끝나지 않은 전쟁』, 132p.
11. -꾸란 53:19~23,

있고 알라에게는 여성(딸)이 있다 하느냐? 이는 실로 부당한 구별이
니라. 이것들은 너희들과 너희들의 조상들이 이름을 붙인 것에 지나지
않느니라. 알라께서는 이것들에게 아무런 권위도 내리지 않으셨느니
라."[12] —꾸란 53:19~23, 이슬람 국제출판국

무함마드는 꾸란의 여러 곳에서 알라(Allah)의 딸에 대해서 언급을
하고 있지만 알라의 딸들이 있다는 사실조차 근본적으로 부인하고
있다.[13] 그런데 여기서는 라트(Lat), 우짜(Uzza), 마나트(Manat)라는 세
여신들의 이름을 무함마드가 스스로 거론하면서 그 이름들은 그
당시 그의 설교를 듣고 있던 아랍인들뿐 아니라 그들의 조상들까지
도 알라의 딸들이라고 불러왔다는 사실을 꾸란을 통해서 인정하고
있는 것이다.

---

12. 최영길 번역 꾸란에는 "너희와 너희 선조들이 고안했던 이름들"이라고 번역했으며, 김용선 번
    역 꾸란에는 "그대들이나 그대들의 조상들이 부른 흔한 이름"이라고 번역했음.
13. 꾸란 16:57, 꾸란 6:100, 꾸란 37:149 등 여러 곳에서 알라에게 딸이 있다는 사실을 부인하고
    있다.

계시의 내용

무함마드가 메카에서 받은 계시의 내용은 대부분 평화로운 내용
이었지만 우상숭배자들이 받아들이기에는 힘든 것이었다. 그는 지
금까지 조상 대대로 믿어왔던 우상들의 권위를 무너뜨리고 알라를
유일신으로 선포한 것이었다. 그것이 간단한 일이 아님을 무함마드
도 알고 있었을 것이고 우상숭배자들의 반대와 핍박이 있을 것도
미리 예상하고 있었을 것이다. 그래서 그는 가능하면 핍박을 피하기
위해서 평화로운 내용의 구절들을 계시 받았다고 했다. 대표적인
구절들의 예를 들자면 아래와 같다.

"종교는 강제로 하지 말지니라"—구란 2: 256

"너희가 다 알라를 거부한다고 할지라도 알라는 너희의 도움을 필요로 하지 않는다."-꾸란 39: 7

"성경의 백성들을 인도함에 가장 좋은 방법으로 인도하되 논쟁하지 말라. 그러나 그들 중에 사악함으로 대적하는 자가 있다면 일러 가로되 우리는 우리에게 계시된 것과 너희에게 계시된 것을 믿노라. 우리의 신과 너희의 신은 같은 신이니 우리는 그분께 순종하노라."

-꾸란 29: 46

"진실로 믿음을 가진 사람들과 유대교인, 기독교인, 사비아교인, 누구든지 알라와 최후의 심판 날을 믿고 좋은 일을 행하는 자들은 그들의 신으로부터 보상을 받을 것이며, 두려움도 없고 슬픔도 없을 것이다."-꾸란 2: 62

위의 구절들을 보면 누구든지 심지어는 배신자들도 관용적인 태도로 대해주라는 것이며 강제로 종교를 전파하지 말라고 말하고 있다. 그리고 성경의 백성들(유대교인들이나 기독교인들)도 최후의 심판 날을 믿고 좋은 일을 행하면 구원을 받을 것이라는 말을 하고 있다.

또한 자신의 신분에 대해서 아래와 같이 이야기 하는 것을 보게 된다.

"내가 새로운 교리를 전하는 자가 아니며 내게 그리고 너희에게 어떤 일이 일을런지 내가 모르도다. 나는 다만 계시된 것을 따르는 자로 분명한 경고자에 불과하니라"-꾸란 46: 9

여기에 보면 자신을 특별한 사람으로 말하지 않는다. 다만 계시의 전달자에 불과하다는 태도가 분명하다.

또한 유대교인들과 기독교인들이 가지고 있던 신·구약 성경에 대해서도 그것이 진리라는 것을 아랍지역에 확증시켜 주기 위해서 꾸란이 내려진 것이라고 말하고 있는 것이다.

"이것 이전에 무싸(모세)의 성경이 안내서로써 그리고 은혜로 있었으며 아랍어로 된 이 성경이 그것을 확증하며 죄인들에게 경고하고 의로운 자들에게는 기쁨의 복음을 전하고 있노라."-꾸란 46:12

"알라가 그대에게 계시한 것에 그대가 의심한다면 그대 이전에 성경을 읽은 자들에게 물어보라. 실로 알라로부터 그대에게 진리가 이르렀나니 의심하지 말라."-꾸란 10: 94

"이 꾸란은 알라가 아닌 다른 것으로 인하여 있을 수 없으며 이전에 계시된 것을 확증하고 그 성경의 말씀을 설명하기 위해 계시되었으니 이는 만유의 알라로부터 온 것이 틀림없노라."-꾸란 10: 37

"그 성경은 우리 이전 두 백성(유대교 및 기독교인들)에게만 계시되었으니 우리는 실로 그들이 읽은 것이 무엇인지 알지 못하도다 라고 말하지 아니하도록 함이라."-꾸란 6:156

메카에서의 무함마드는 이슬람을 받아들이기를 거부하는 이교도들에 대한 태도가 전혀 위협적이지 않았으며 매우 부드러웠다.

말하라. 신앙 없는 자들이여. 너희들이 숭배하는 것을 나는 숭배하지 않는다. 내가 숭배하는 것을 너희들은 숭배하지 않는다. 나는 너희들이 숭배하는 것에 대한 숭배자가 아니다. 너희들은 내가 숭배하는 것에 대한 숭배자가 아니다. 너희들에게는 너희들의 종교가 있고 내게는 나의 종교가 있다. -꾸란 109:1-6, 김용선 역

지금도 전 세계의 어느 곳에서든지 이슬람 측에서 전도를 위해서 사용하는 구절들은 대부분이 위의 예문에 제시된 구절들처럼 메카에서 받았다고 하는 평화스런 구절들 중에서 취하여 사용하는 것을 볼 수 있을 것이다.

최초의 무슬림들

다신론적 상황에서 유일신을 선포한 무함마드의 소문을 들은 꾸라이시 족의 족장들은 무함마드를 불러 유일신을 주장하지 말라고 충고하였다. 아라비아 일대의 360 여개 종족의 우상들이 있는데 그들의 존재를 부인하면 종족간의 갈등이 유발될 여지가 있으며 우상숭배에 익숙한 그들에게 생소한 유일신 사상은 쉽게 받아들일 수가 없었다. 더구나 꾸라이시족이 받을 경제적인 타격도 무함마드의 유일신 주장을 반대하는 중요한 이유 중의 하나였다.[1] 그러나 무함마

---

1. 김용선, 『이슬람의 역사와 문화』, 27p.

드는 히라(Hira)동굴의 계시를 빙자하여 은밀히 알라(Allah)의 유일신 됨과 알라에게만 복종하라고 주장하고 다녔다. 제일 처음 그의 주장을 받아들인 것은 그의 아내 카디자(Khadija)였다.[2] 그리고 두 번째로 그의 조카 알리(Ali)[3]가 그의 주장을 믿었고 그 다음으로는 주어다 기른 노예 출신의 양자 자이드(Zaid)[4]와 아부 바크르(Abu Bakr)[5]가 뒤를 이었다.

핍박의 시작

무함마드는 우상숭배에 익숙해 있던 아라비아에서 유일신을 선포한다는 이유로 우상숭배자들에게 핍박을 당하게 되었다. 어찌 보면 당연한 현상이라고 보인다. 그들은 조상 대대로 섬겨오던 종족의 신

---

2. 카디자(Khadija)는 무함마드의 첫 번째 아내였다. 그가 25세 때 40세의 과부였던 그녀는 2~4번의 이혼 경력이 있었던 여인이었으며 낙타들을 거느리고 대상무역을 하는 부자였다. 그리고 그녀는 자신의 결정에 의해서 무함마드를 남편으로 맞아들였다. 이슬람 역사에서 거대한 대상 무역 상단을 경영했던 그녀에 대한 기록을 보면 이슬람 이전의 소위 무지의 시대(Jahilia)에 여아들이 태어나면 모래 속에 파묻어 죽이고 여성들을 노예나 짐승 취급하던 것을 무함마드가 이슬람을 가지고 온 후 여성들을 해방시켜 주었고 인권을 높여 주었다고 하는 주장에 설득력이 떨어진다.

3. 무함마드의 조카 알리는 무함마드의 딸 파티마 자흐라(Fatimah Zahra)와 결혼을 했고 아부 바크르(Abu Bakr), 우마르(Umar), 우스만(Uthman)에 이어 이슬람의 4대 칼리프(Khaliph)였으며 시아파의 창시자이며 초대 이맘(Iman)이었다. 그는 여러 가지로 모범적이었다고 하지만 무슬림 분파인 카리지(Khariji)파에 의해서 칼리프에 등극한지 5년 만인 서기 661년 이븐 물짐(Ibn Muljim)의 독 묻은 칼에 찔려 결국은 살해당하고 만다.

4. 유해석, 『이슬람이 다가오고 있다』, 52p.

5. 아부 바크르(Abu Bakr)는 무함마드가 죽은 후 그의 첫 번째 후계자(Khaliph)가 되었다.

들이 무시당하는 것을 참을 수 없었을 것이다. 메카의 주민들은 무함마드가 최초의 계시를 받을 때 보여준 심리적 불안과 종교적 이상체험을 간질병 환자의 발작이나 히스테리 환자의 망상증쯤으로 여겼다. 그래서 그를 지랄쟁이, 미친 놈, 마법사 등으로 매도하였다.[6]

그러나 무함마드는 자신의 사명을 확신하고 조심스럽게 측근들에게 포교활동을 하였다. 무함마드는 자신이 받은 계시가 과연 진리인지 아닌지에 대한 확신이 없어서 첫 계시를 받은 때부터 만 2년 동안은 고민과 갈등 속에서 침묵을 지켜왔지만 결심을 한 후에는 메카에서 공개적 포교활동에 나섰다.[7] 무함마드를 따르는 자들의 숫자가 늘어갈수록 그를 따르는 자들에게 가해지는 핍박의 강도는 더욱 심해져 갔다고 한다. 더구나 메카를 찾아오는 우상숭배자들의 순례를 통해서 경제적으로 많은 이익을 얻고 있는 꾸라이시족의 상류층들은, 무함마드의 유일신 주장이 자신들의 경제적 이익에 타격을 줄 것이 분명하기에, 메카의 살 길을 끊어 놓는 파괴분자로 보고 그에게 핍박을 가했던 것이다.[8]

---

6. 정수일, 『이슬람 문명』(서울: 창작과 비평사, 2002), 72p.
7. Ibid, 73p.
8. 김정위, 『이슬람 입문』, 한국 외국어대학교 출판부, 서울 1993, 38~39p.

타협

꾸라이시(Quraish) 족과의 타협

우상들이 난무하던 아라비아에서 유일신을 선포하기 시작한 무함마드는 처음부터 담대하게 우상숭배자들을 대적하며 나가기에는 역부족이었을 것이며 혼자서 감당하기는 무리였을 것이다. 그래서 많은 부분 우상숭배자들이나 그 당시의 기득권 세력과 타협이 이루어졌던 것을 역사를 통해서 살펴볼 수 있다. 무함마드의 종족인 꾸라이시족이 섬기던 신의 이름은 알라(Allah)였다.[1] 그는 유일신을 주

---

1. G. J. O. Moshay, Who is this Allah? (U. K. Dorchester House 1994), 138p.

장하면서도 그 유일신의 이름은 꾸라이시 족이 섬기던 종족신의 명
칭인 알라(Allah)를 그대로 가지고 왔다. 또한 그들이 섬기는 신의 제
사 제도라든가 제례 의식들을 그대로 모방했던 것이다.[2] 무함마드
는 그들이 사용하던 월력(Lunar Calender)을 그대로 사용하였다. 그리고
카아바 신전의 제사의식을 그대로 가져왔고, 카아바 신전을 돌면서
그들이 신성시하던 검은 돌에 입을 맞추는 행위도 메카의 꾸라이시
족의 환심을 사기 위해서 무함마드가 그대로 답습했던 것이다.[3] 또
한 메카의 카아바 신전을 향하여 기도하는 것도 그들의 풍습 중의
하나였다. 그러나 꾸라이시족의 섬기는 알라(Allah)는 달의 신(Moon
god)이었다고 한다.[4] 이 점에 대해서는 동의하지 않는 사람들도 있으나
많은 증거들이 이를 증명하고 있다.[5] 많은 인터넷의 자료들이 역사
적으로 고고학적으로 학문적으로 알라가 달의 신이었다는 것을 증
명해 주고 있다.[6] 그 당시 중동의 아랍권에서는 달의 신을 섬기는 풍
습들이 만연하였다. 뜨거운 사막 기후에서 견디기 힘들었던 그들에
게 달은 선선한 그늘을 제공해 주었고 달이 지나가고 나면 풀들이
이슬을 맺게 되고 그 이슬로 양들이 배를 채울 풀들이 자라며 그 양
의 고기와 젖을 먹고 사람들이 살 수 있는 것이다. 그래서 중동에서

---

2. Zwemer, Samuel Marinus, The Influence of Animism on Islam (London: Macmillan
   company, 1920), 148p.
3. Ibn Warraq, Why I am not a Muslim (U. S. A. New York : Prometheus Books, 2003), 36p.
4. G. J. O. Moshay, Who is this Allah?, 138p.
5. 인터넷으로 "Allah the moon god'을 검색해 보면 많은 자료를 볼 수 있다.
6. Robert A. Morey, Islamic Invasion (U. S. A. California: Chick Publications, 2000), 51p.

는 오래 전부터 여러 종족에서 달의 신을 각각 다른 이름으로 섬겨 왔다. 어떤 종족은 후발(Hubal)이라는 이름으로 어떤 종족은 일룸꾸 (Illumque)라는 이름으로 또 다른 종족은 씬(Sin)이라는 이름으로 달의 신을 섬겼지만 무함마드의 종족인 꾸라이시족은 알라(Allah)라는 이름으로 달의 신을 섬겨왔던 것이다.[7] 무함마드는 이슬람의 상징을 달의 신 형상으로 그대로 가지고 왔다. 그래서 오늘날도 이슬람 국가의 국기에 혹은 모스크의 꼭대기에 달의 신 형상을 걸어 놓게 된 것이다. 이는 유일신을 주장하는 무함마드가 자신의 종족신인 알라 (Allah)를 그대로 사용하고 그 신을 섬기던 대부분의 의식들을 그대로 모방함으로 아라비아 일대의 가장 강력한 종족인 꾸라이시족과의 충돌을 피하고자 함이었다고 보인다.[8]

알라(Allah)의 세 딸 숭배자들과의 타협

악마의 계시

무함마드는 핍박을 피하여 아비시니아로 도피한 사람들을 생각 하면서 그들이 더 이상 핍박을 받지 않고 다시 고향으로 돌아 와서

---

7. Syed Kamran Mirza, Was Allah The Moon God of Ancient Arab Pagan? 인터넷 사이트 참조: http://www.faithfreedom.org/Articles/skm30804.htm.
8. H.A.R Gibb,『이슬람』,이희수 최준식 공역, (서울: 도서출판 주류성, 1997), 84p. : 유목민들의 특징적인 종교 의식이나 공통의 성소(Common Sanctuary) 주위를 도는 순례 행진, 또 그 주위 에서 행하는 희생제의 축제를 보 존함으로 유일신으로의 전환을 쉽게 했다고 Gibb 은 말하고 있다.

살게 하기 위해서는 알라의 세 딸(알 라트, 알 우짜, 알 마나트- 이하 라트, 우짜, 마나트라 한다. - 편집자 주)인 여신들과 타협을 하고 그 여신들의 권위를 인정해 주는 것이 필요하다고 생각을 했다. 그러나 이것은 유일신 사상과는 모순되는 생각이었다. 알라(Allah)라는 이름으로 유일신의 이름을 정한 무함마드는 꾸라이시족들이 알라의 딸들이라고 생각하며 섬기고 있는 이 세 딸들의 권위도 인정을 해 주어야 하는가? 아니면 유일신 사상에 어긋나므로 버려야 하는가? 어느 쪽을 선택할까를 갈등했을 것이다. 사람들은 그가 어떤 태도를 취할 것인가를 궁금해 하며 기다렸을 것이다. 무함마드는 어떤 문제가 생길 때 그것을 계시라는 방법으로 해결하곤 했다.[9] 즉 알라(Allah)의 이름으로 계시를 받았다고 하면 그 말이 자신의 결정이라고 하는 것보다 훨씬 강력한 권위가 부여된다는 것을 알고 있었을 것이다.[10] 그 때의 상황과 계시라는 이름으로 내려온 해결책이 타바리(Tabari)의 하디스(Hadith)에 아래와 같이 기록되어 있다.

> 알라의 메신저는 자기를 따르는 자들이 편안한 삶을 살도록 해주는 일을 매우 좋아했다. 그래서 어떤 수단이던지 할 수만 있다면 그들과 화해하기를 원했다. 그는 그렇게 할 방법을 원했고 그 결과 아래와 같은 일이 발생했다. -타바리(Tabari)의『하디스』제 6권 107쪽.

---

9. Mark A. Gabriel, Culture Clash : Islam's war on the West (U. S. A.: Front Line A Strang Company, 2007), 39~42p. : 여기서 저자는 무함마드가 자기 양자 Zaid의 아내 Zainab 을 자신의 아내로 취하기 위해서 계시라는 방법을 사용한 것을 말하고 있다.
10. 돈 리처드슨,『코란의 비밀』, 95~97p. 저자는 무함마드와 알라 중 누가 상전인지 모르겠다고 한다.

이븐 후마이드(Ibn Humayd) - 쌀라마(Salamah)-이샥의 아들 무함마드(Muhammad b. Ishaq) - 마다니의 지야드의 아들 야지드(Yazid b. Ziyad al-Madani) -꾸라지의 카압의 아들 무함마드(Muhammad b. Ka'b al-Qurazi): 에 의하면

알라의 메신저는 어떻게 자신들의 종족이 자기에게 등을 돌렸는지를 보았다. 그가 알라로부터 받은 메시지를 그들이 거부하는 것을 보고 근심하면서 자신들의 종족과 화해할 수 있는 어떤 계시가 알라로부터 내려오기를 사모했다.

그는 자신의 종족을 사랑했으며 그들의 행복을 원하는 마음이 있었으므로 그들이 자신에 대해서 일으킨 어려움들이 부드럽게 해결되면 좋겠다고 생각하고 스스로 마음에 갈등하며 그 해결책을 간절히 사모했다. 그 때 알라의 계시가 내려왔다.

별을 걸어 맹세하기를 그것이 질 때에 그대들의 동지는 실수하지 않으며 그는 속지 않으며 자신이 원하는 대로 말하지 아니하며…. 그리고 그가 "너희는 라트와 우짜와 세 번째 마나트에 대해서 생각해 보았느냐?"라고 말하고 있었다.

바로 그 때 그의 마음속의 갈등과 그의 백성들에게 주고 싶은 것에 대한 열망 때문에 사탄은 그의 혀에 이런 말을 넣어 주었다.

"그들은 높이 나는 학과 같아서 그들의 중재는 열납 되느니라."11

꾸라이시족은 그가 자신들의 신들에 대해 하는 말들을 듣고 매우

---

11. P. J. 스튜어트, 『펼쳐보는 이슬람』, 83p.

기뻐하면서 그를 따르기 시작했고 무슬림들은 자신들의 메신저가 알라로부터 받은 메시지는 오류나 환각이나 실수가 없는 것이라고 완전히 믿었다. 그가 계시를 완성하기 위해서 부복했을 때 무슬림들도 자신들의 메신저를 따라했다. 꾸라이시족의 다신교도들과 다른 사람들은 자신들의 신들에 대해서 무함마드가 한 말을 듣고는 믿는 자나 안 믿는 자나 모두가 엎드려 함께 부복했다. 알 무기라(Al-Mughirah)의 아들 알 왈리드(Al-Walid)만은 예외였는데 그는 나이가 많아서 부복할 수가 없었기 때문에 계곡에서 흙을 한 줌 가져와 그 위에 경배했다. 그들은 모스크에서 흩어졌고 꾸라이시족들도 자신들의 신들에 대해서 이야기 하면서 "무함마드가 자신들의 신들에 대해서 '그들은 높이 나는 학들과 같아서 그들의 중재는 열납 되느니라'고 말하면서 최대의 찬사를 보냈다"고 말했다.

이것이 바로 그 유명한 '악마의 계시 구절(Satanic Verses)' 인 것이다.

악마의 계시를 취소하는 계시

무함마드가 악마의 계시를 통해서 알라(Allah)의 세 딸 여신들과 타협했던 사건으로 인하여 꾸라이시족이 무슬림이 되었다는 소문이 퍼지기 시작했다. 그래서 메카에서 핍박을 피해서 아비시니아에 도피해 있던 사람들에게 까지 이 소문이 전달되었다. 이들은 남자가 11명 여자가 4명이었다.[12] 무함마드가 꾸라이시족의 신 알라(Allah)와

---

12. 김용선, 『무함마드』, (서울: 명문당, 2003), 88~89p.

그 세 딸 신들인 라트(Lat), 우짜(Uzza) 그리고 마나트(Manat)와도 타협하여 알라를 절대 유일신으로 그리고 세 딸 여신들은 중재자로 인정을 해주며 타협을 한 것이다.[13] 이는 아직 세력이 작은 무함마드의 집단이 아라비아 일대의 최대의 종족인 꾸라이시족과 관련된 족속들을 정면으로 대적하기에는 무리였기 때문에 유일신 사상에 어긋나기는 하지만 핍박을 피하면서 세력이 커지기까지 시간을 벌자는 속셈이었을 수도 있다.

무함마드가 우상을 섬기는 다신교도들과 타협했던 이 기간이 얼마나 오래 지속되었는지는 정확한 자료가 없다. 그러나 이 기간이 결코 짧은 기간이 아니었음을 확인할 수 있는 증거가 있다.

전술한 바와 같이 무함마드를 따르던 무슬림들 중 일부는 다신교도들의 핍박을 피해서 아비씨니아(지금의 에티오피아)까지 도망가 있었는데 메카에서 지금의 아비시니아까지는 가장 가까운 지점끼리 직선으로 잇는다 하더라도 바닷길이 약 4백 킬로미터 육로로 약 3백 킬로미터 정도 되는 먼 거리이며 그들이 사우디아라비아와 가장 가까운 에티오피아의 변방으로 간 것이 아니라 국왕을 만났다[14]고 하는 것을 보면 에티오피아의 수도까지 갔다는 것을 의미하는데 이는 직선거리로 봐도 장장 1천 킬로미터가 넘는 매우 먼 거리다. 더구나

---

13. Al Tabari, Hadith, 6권 107 쪽.
14. 사피 아르라흐만 알무바라크푸리, 『인간 무함마드』, 최영길 역(서울: 도서출판 알림, 2006), 144~150p. : 에티오피아 왕 나자쉬는 무함마드의 추종자들을 우호적으로 환대하고 보호해 주었다고 한다.

그 때는 지금처럼 빠른 교통수단이 없는 때이고 전화나 인터넷처럼 신속한 통신 수단이 없는 시대였기 때문에 거기에 피난 가 있는 무함마드의 추종자들에게까지 꾸라이시 족속이 무슬림이 되었다는 소식이 전해졌다는 것은 결코 짧지 않은 시간동안 타협의 기간이 지속되었던 것으로 보인다. 이 점에 대해서는 이슬람의 학자 타바리(Tabari)는 그의 하디스에서 아래와 같이 진술하고 있다.

> 그 부복의 소식은 아비시니아에 있는 알라의 메신저의 동료들[15]에게 전달되었으며 부족들은 꾸라이시족이 이슬람을 영접했다고 말했다. 어떤 이들은 돌아가겠다고 일어났고 몇몇은 뒤에 남아 있었다.
>
> - Al Tabari, Hadith, 제 6권. 107.

언제나 다시 고향에 돌아갈 수 있을까를 지루하게 기대하던 아비시니아의 무슬림들은 얼마나 기뻤을까? 그들은 살림을 정리하고 돌아갈 준비를 하였다. 그리고 성급한 몇몇은 이미 출발하고 몇몇은 서두를 필요가 없다고 생각하여 천천히 짐을 정리하면서 돌아갈 준비를 하였다. 그러나 그들이 채 메카에 도착하기도 전에 충격적인 소식을 들었는데 즉 무함마드에게 다시 계시가 내려왔는데 알라의 세 여신들에게 중재자로서의 권위를 인정하는 그 계시를 취소하는 새로운 계시가 내려왔다는 것이다. 취소의 이유는 놀랍게도 "전에 계시는 사탄이 무함마드의 혀에 넣어 주었던 계시였기 때문" 이라고 하는 것이었다. 그 때의 상황을 타바리(Tabari)는 그의 하디스(Hadith)에서 아래와 같이 묘사하고 있다.

---

15. Ibid. 147p.

그 때 가브리엘(지브리일)이 알라의 메신저에게 와서 "무함마드여 무슨 일을 한 것이냐? 그대는 내가 알라로 부터 가져다주지 않은 것을 사람들에게 낭송했으며 내가 그대에게 말하지 않은 것을 말했느니라. 알라의 메신저는 매우 근심하며 알라를 두려워했는데 알라께서 계시를 내려 주셨다. 그분은 그에게 자비하셨으며 그를 위로하며 이전에는 그가 원하고 갈망하는 것처럼 사모하던 메신저나 예언자가 없었다고 하여 사태를 홀가분하게 해 주셨다. 그 후 알라께서는 사탄이 넣어준 계시들을 취소하셨고 그의 계시를 그에게 주시며 그가 다른 메신저나 예언자와 같다고 하셨다.

우리는 너희에게 메신저나 예언자를 보낸 일이 없으나 그가 (메시지를) 낭송할 때 사탄이 그가 낭송하는 구절 속에 말들을 삽입했다. 그러나 알라께서 사탄이 넣은 것을 취소하셨다. 알라께서는 그의 계시들을 세우셨다. 알라는 모든 것을 아시며 지혜로우시다.

그렇게 해서 알라께서는 무함마드의 슬픔을 제하시고 사탄이 주었다가 취소한 '그들의 신들은 높이 나는 학들과 같아서 그들의 중재는 열납 되느니라' 고하는 구절들로 인해 두려워하는 그를 다시 견고케 하셨다. - 알 타바리 하디스 위 부분 참조

그는 이제 다음 구절들을 계시하셨다.

"라트와 우짜와 세 번째 마나트에 대한 말씀이라." "너희들에게는 남성(아들)들이 있으며 그분에게는 여성(딸)들이 있다는 것이냐? 그것은 부당한 분배니라. 그것은 너희와 너희 조상들이 그렇게 불러왔을 뿐이니라." - 꾸란 53: 19~23

이 말은 그들의 신들의 중재가 알라에게 무슨 소용이 있겠느냐는 의미이다. 무함마드가 사탄이 자신의 혀에 넣어 준 것을 취소하는 계시를 받았을 때 꾸라이시 족속은 "무함마드가 알라 앞에서 너희 신들의 지위와 관련한 것을 돌이켰고 말을 바꿔 다른 것을 가져왔다"고 말했다. 무함마드의 혀에 사탄이 넣어준 그 두 구절로 화해하는 것처럼 보였던 그들의 관계는 후에 그 계시가 취소되자 무함마드와 그를 따르는 무슬림들에게 메카의 우상 숭배자들은 더욱 악의를 가지고 핍박을 강화하게 되었다.[16]

유대인 및 기독교인들과의 타협

여호와 하나님과 알라(Allah)의 동일신 주장

무함마드는 꾸라이시 족이 믿고 있던 알라(Allah)[17]와 그의 세 딸들과의 관계를 부인함과 동시에 알라를 유일신이라고 주장하면서 이미 유일신을 믿고 있는 유대교인들과 기독교인들을 이슬람으로 끌어들이기 위해서 기독교와 유대교의 하나님이 자신이 말하는 알라(Allah)와 같은 신이라는 계시를 받았다고 주장했다.

성경의 백성들(기독교인들 및 유대교인들)을 인도함에 가장 좋은 방법으로 인도하되 논쟁하지 말라. 그러나 그들 중에 사악함으로 대적하는

---

16. 알 타바리 하디스 위 부분 참조
17. 꾸라이시 족이 알라(Allah)를 믿던 종족이라는 것은 무함마드의 아버지 이름이 압둘라(알라의 종)라는 이름을 가진 것으로도 확인할 수 있다.

자가 있다면 일러 가로되, 우리는 우리에게 계시된 것과 **너희에게** 계시된 것을 믿노라. 우리의 신(알라)과 **너희의** 신(여호와 하나님)은 같은 신이시니 우리는 그분께 순종하노라. —꾸란29:46

무함마드는 유대교인들과 기독교인들의 하나님에 대해서 기독교인이었던 자신의 아내 카디자(Khadija)의 사촌 와라까(Waraqa)로부터 기독교의 하나님이나 성경에 대해서 들었을 것이다. 그리고 대상을 이끌고 장사를 하러 다니면서 기독교와 유대교의 하나님에 대한 정보를 많이 들었을 것이다. 그래서 기독교와 유대교의 하나님이 가지고 있는 여러 가지 속성들을 자신이 말하는 알라(Allah)가 가지고 있는 속성과 같다고 하는 계시를 받았다고 주장한다. 그는 알라가 창조주라고 말하는가 하면[18] 알라는 전능자[19]이며 알라는 심판 주[20]라는 계시를 받았다고 했다.

신·구약 성경이 진리라는 계시

무함마드가 신·구약 성경을 진리로 인정하는 것은 유대교인들과 기독교인들을 자신의 편으로 끌어들이기 위한 대단한 타협이었다. 그는 스스로 자신을 평범한 인간에 불과한 계시의 전달자라고 소개했다. 그리고 자신은 새로운 계시를 가지고 온 사람이 아니라 신·구

---

18. 꾸란 7:54.
19. 꾸란 35:1.
20. 꾸란 19:37.

약 성경이 진리임을 아랍인들에게 확증시켜주기 위해서 보냄을 받은 사람이라고 했다. 심지어는 자신의 계시에 의심이 간다면 이전의 경전 즉 신·구약 성경을 읽은 사람들에게 물어보라고까지 했다.

일러 가로되 내가 새로운 교리를 전하는 자가 아니며 내게 그리고 너희에게 어떤 일이 있을런지 내가 모르도다. 나는 다만 계시된 것을 따르는 자로 분명한 경고자에 불과하니라. —꾸란 46:9 최영길 역

이보다 이전에도 인도로써 자비로써 주어진 무싸(모세)의 경전이 있었다. 이 꾸란은 그것을 확증하는 것으로써 아랍어로 주신 것이니 의롭지 못한 자에게 경고하시며 선인에게는 복음을 전하는 것이니라.

—꾸란 46:12 김용선 역

이 꾸란은 알라가 아닌 다른 것으로 인하여 있을 수 없으며 이전에 계시된 것을 확증하고 그 성경의 말씀을 설명하기 위해 계시되었으니 이는 만유의 알라로부터 온 것이 틀림없노라. —꾸란10:37 최영길 역

알라께서 그대에게 계시한 것에 그대가 의심한다면 그대 이전에 성경을 읽은 자들(유대교 및 기독교인들)에게 물어보라[21] 실로 알라로부터 그대에게 진리가 이르렀나니 의심하지 말라. —꾸란 10:94 최영길 역

즉 무함마드는 성경이 진리임을 아랍지역에 확증시켜 주기 위해서 왔으며 새로운 계시를 전하기 위해서 온 사람이 아니라고 했다.[22] 그가 성경에 대한 지식이 불확실함에도 불구하고 이렇게 자신 있게

말할 수 있었던 이유에 대해서는 많은 추측이 가능하겠지만 확실한 증거가 없으므로 언급을 삼가는 것이 좋겠다. 그러나 그가 이렇게 성경을 진리로 인정한 것은 어떠한 수단을 써서라도 유대교인들과 기독교인들을 자신을 따르는 이슬람의 무리에 복속시키고자 했던 것이라고 보인다.

유대교인들과 기독교인들과의 우호적 관계

무함마드는 오래 전부터 이미 유일신을 믿고 있는 유대교인들과 기독교인들을 우호적으로 대하라는 계시를 받았다고 주장한다. 이는 무함마드의 세력 확장을 위해 그들을 자신의 공동체에 합류시키고자 만든 유인책이었던 것으로 보인다.[23] 그들의 경전을 진리로 인정하고 그들의 신을 같은 신으로 인정할 뿐 아니라 그들의 장래에 알라(Allah)께서 보상하실 것이라는 계시를 받았다는 것이다.

진실로 믿음을 가진 사람들과 유대교인, 기독교인, 사비아교인, 누구든지 알라(Allah)와 최후의 심판 날을 믿고 좋은 일을 행하는 자들은 그들의 신으로부터 보상을 받을 것이며, 두려움도 없고 슬픔도 없을 것이다. -꾸란 2:62 김용선 역

---

21. 이전의 성경을 읽어 본 사람들이란 그 당시의 아랍 지역에 사는 기독교인이나 유대교인들을 말하는 것으로 꾸란의 내용에 의심이 나면 신 · 구약 성경을 읽어본 유대교인들과 기독교인들에게 물어보라는 것으로 무함마드는 꾸란의 내용이 신 · 구약 성경의 내용과 같다고 생각했던 것 같다.
22. 꾸란 46:9.
23. 마크 A. G, 『이슬람과유대인 그 끝나지 않은 전쟁』, 117~121p.

배척

유대인들과 기독교인들

유대교인들과 기독교인들은 무함마드가 자신이 믿고 있는 알라 (Allah)가 유대교인들과 기독교인들이 믿고 있는 창조주 하나님과 같은 신이라고 주장할 때만해도 말도 안 되는 소리를 한다고 코웃음 치면서 일축하였다. 왜냐하면 자신들이 믿고 있는 신은 여호와라고 불리는 절대자요, 유일신이요, 천지를 창조하신 신이지만 무함마드가 말하는 신은 카아바 신전의 360개의 우상들 중의 최고신인 알라(Allah)인 것을 모두가 알고 있었기 때문이었다.

그런데 무함마드가 신·구약 성경의 권위를 인정해 주고 그것이 진리라고 말하는 것이었다. 그러자 유대교인들과 기독교인들은 그가 신·구약 성경이 진리임을 인정한다면 마냥 배척하기만 해서는 안 될 것 같은 생각이 들었을 것이다. 그리고 들리는 소문에 의하면 그가 자신들의 조상 아브라함에 대해서도 이야기 한다는 것이었다. 그리고 노아의 홍수와 모세와 예수에 대해서도 이야기 한다는 것이었다. 그래서 무함마드가 무슨 말을 하는가를 들어보기로 하였다. 그랬더니 정말로 창조주에 대해서 이야기하는가 하면, 6일 동안에 천지를 창조한 이야기[24]등을 하면서 그 창조주에게 복종하라고 하는 것이었다. 그렇다면 창조주가 둘일 수는 없는 것 아니겠는가?

---

24. 꾸란 11:7.

자신들이 여호와(Jehova)라고 부르는 그 창조주를 무함마드는 알라(Allah)라고 부르는 것이라고 생각하면서 그가 하는 말을 더 자세히 들어보기로 하고 따라다녔다.

그러다가 놀라운 사실을 발견했던 것이다. 그가 성경에 등장하는 사건이나 인물에 대해서 비슷하게 말하기는 하는데 실상은 성경과는 전혀 다른 소리를 하고 있는 것이었다. 예를 들면 예수의 모친 마리아(Mary)와 모세와 아론의 누이 미리암(Miryam)을 혼동하여 아론의 누이 마리암(Maryam)이 예수를 낳았다는 것이었다.[25] 이는 시대적으로 1,450여 년간 시대를 뛰어넘는 차이가 나는 전혀 다른 두 인물이었던 것이다. 마리아는 팔레스타인 지역에 거주했지만, 미리암은 애굽에 살던 사람이었다. 이렇게 역사적으로 지리적으로 혼동할 수 없는 전혀 다른 두 인물을 같은 사람으로 혼동한 이유는 무엇일까? 그것은 무함마드가 학문이 없는 문맹이었기 때문에 시대적인 감각이나 분별력이 없었다는 것을 이유로 들 수 있겠다. 또 한가지 분명하게 말할 수 있는 것은 서로 다른 두 종류의 계시를 내린 신은 결코 같은 신일 수 없다는 점이다. 다른 가능성을 찾아본다면 무함마드에게 신구약 성경에 대해서 정보를 제공해 준 사람이 성경을 잘 모르는 사람이었거나 또는 제대로 전달해 주었는데 무함마드의 기억력이 부족해서 혼동했을 가능성 등을 생각해 볼 수도 있겠으나 이들은 하늘로부터의 직통계시를 주장하는 무슬림들에게는 말도 안 되

---

25. 꾸란 19:28.

는 가설들일 뿐이다.

꾸란에 나오는 오류들을 다 지적하자면 지면이 부족할 것이기에 대표적인 오류들 중에 한 가지만 더 들어 본다면 출애굽기 1장에 보면 애굽 왕 바로가 이스라엘 백성들을 괴롭히기 위해서 국고성 비돔과 라암셋을 지으라고 명하는 장면이 나온다.[26] 그런데 그와 같은 사건이라고 생각되는 꾸란의 내용은 무싸(모세)의 신이 살고 있는 하늘까지 닿는 탑 즉 바벨탑을 쌓으라고 명령하고 있다. 더욱 놀라운 것은 파라오(바로)는 그 명령을 하만 장군에게 내렸다는 것이다.[27] 결론은 출애굽기 1장의 국고성을 짓는 사건과 창세기 11장의 바벨탑을 쌓는 사건과 에스더서의 하만 장군을 한 시대의 한 장소의 사건으로 말하고 있는 것이다.

그가 만일 참으로 성령의 계시를 받았다면 그런 오류가 없어야 할 것이나[28] 이렇게 심한 오류가 있었던 것은 그의 계시가 성령의 계시가 아닌 다른 영의 계시라는 것을 증명하는 유력한 증거가 되는 것이다. 그것은 무함마드가 글을 모르고 공부를 하지 못했기 때문에 역사와 지리에 대한 개념이 없었던 것으로 밖에는 설명할 길이 없다.[29] 무함마드가 글을 모르는 문맹이었다는 것은 꾸란에서 여러 차례 증명하

---

26. 출애굽기 1:11.
27. 꾸란 28:38.
28. 이사야서 34:16.
29. 최영길 번역 『성꾸란 의미의 한국어 번역』 서론에 보면 꾸란에서 말하는 역사는 세상의 역사가들이 말하는 역사와 다르며 꾸란에 나오는 과학은 세상의 과학자들이 말하는 것과 차이가 많다는 것을 인정하고 있다.

고 있는 것이다.[30]

메카의 우상숭배자들

무함마드가 메카 인근의 우상숭배자들과의 화해를 위해서 악마
의 계시를 받았다가 취소하는 사건이 생기자[31] 핍박은 더욱 심화 되
었다.

더구나 후에 메디나로 이름을 바꾸어 부르게 된 야스립(Yathrib)에
서 온 사람들이 카아바 신전에 제사 드리러 왔다가 무함마드를 만나
그의 이야기를 듣고는 몇 사람이 충성을 맹세하는 사건이 일어났다.
1년 후 다시 야스립에서 메카로 제사를 드리러 왔던 사람들 중 더
많은 사람들이 무함마드에게 충성을 맹세하게 되었다.[32]

그러자 무함마드에 대한 우상숭배자들의 핍박은 강화되었고,
무함마드는 자신을 따르는 사람들이 늘어나자 핍박이 더욱 심해진
것에 대한 압박을 받게 되었고, 이 일을 어떻게든 해결해야 할 기로
에 놓이게 되었다.

---

30. 꾸란 7:157: '즉 사도로서 문맹자인 메신저를 따르는 사람들이면 이 분의 일에 대해서는 그들이
    가지고 있는 율법이나 복음서에도 기록되어 있으니까 그것을 보면 알 수 있겠지만 그는 바른
    행실을 권하고 추한 행실을 금하고 좋은 것은 허락하고 나쁜 것은 금지하고 모두에게 지워진
    무거운 짐과 멍에를 벗겨 주신다. 그런고로 그를 믿고 그를 존중하며, 그를 돕고, 내리신 광명
    에 그와 함께 따르는 사람들이야말로 번영할 것이다.'
31. 사피 아르라흐만 알무바라크푸리, 『인간 무함마드』, 146p. : 여기서 저자는 완전한 오보에 의해서
    귀환했던 무슬림들은 다시 에티오피아로 돌아갔고 핍박은 더욱 심해졌다고 기록하고 있다.
32. 유해석, 『이슬람이 다가오고 있다』, 57~58p.

무함마드와 추종자들의 이주(히즈라 사건)

무함마드는 핍박이 심해짐에 따라 자신의 추종자들 중 아흔아홉 가정을 1~2차에 걸쳐 지금의 에티오피아인 아비시니아로 피난을 보냈다.[33] 그러자 메카의 족장들은 아비시니아의 왕 네구스에게 뇌물을 주면서 그들을 돌려보내달라고 요청하였다. 그러나 피신자들은 꾀를 내어 이싸(예수)를 찬양하는 꾸란 구절들을 읽어주었고, 이에 기독교인이었던 네구스 왕은 이슬람이 기독교와 한 뿌리에서 나온 것으로 생각하게 되어 오히려 그들을 감싸주고 보호해 주었다.[34] 이 때 무함마드는 감당하기 힘든 핍박을 모두 견디면서 조심스럽게 포교활동을 계속 해 나갔다. 그러나 어려운 일이 있을 때마다 그의 방패의 역할을 해 주던 그의 숙부 아부 탈립(Abu-Talib)[35]이 죽고 그의 아내 카디자(Khadija)마저 세상을 떠나 핍박을 막아 줄 방패막이가 갑자기 모두 사라져 버렸다. 이제 더 이상 무함마드는 메카에 머무를 수가 없게 되었다.[36] 무함마드는 메카에서 우상숭배자들의 핍박을 견디다 못해서 서기 622년에 자신을 따르는 추종자들과 함께 메카로부터 북쪽으로 약 250마일(약 4백 킬로미터) 정도 떨어진 메디나[37]로 이주

---

33. 정수일, 『이슬람문명』, 73p.

34. 최영길, 『이슬람 문화사』, 23p.
35. 무함마드의 숙부 아부 탈립은 무함마드가 8 살 때부터 무함마드를 길러주고 보호해 주었다.
36. Ibid. 38p.
37. 메디나의 원래 이름은 야스립(Yathrib)인데 무함마드가 득세한 후에 메신저의 도시(Madinat al- nabi)라고 하여 메디나로 그 이름을 바꾸어 부르게 되었다. (L. Esposito, John, The Oxford History of Islam, (New York: Oxford University press, 1999), 8p

하게 된다. 이를 '히즈라(Hijra 또는 혜지라)사건'이라고 하는데 히즈라 (Hijra)는 아랍어로 "이주(이민)한다, 이사한다, 이동한다."는 의미다. 이때 무함마드를 따르는 자들이 그와 함께 우상숭배의 도시 메카를 떠나서 메디나로 온 사건은 이슬람 역사에 있어서 매우 중요한 의미 가 있다. 왜냐하면 이제 무함마드의 공동체는 무함마드에게 내린 계 시를 절대 지침으로 움직이는 특별한 공동체인 움마(Umma)로 공식 출발한 것을 의미하기 때문에 이를 이슬람의 시작으로 보는 것이다. 무함마드와 함께 메카를 떠나서 메디나로 온 사람들을 무하지룬 (Muhajirun)이라고 하며 메디나에서 무함마드의 일행을 환영한 사람들 을 안사리(Ansari)라고 한다.[38]

---

38. L. Esposito, John, The Oxford History of Islam, (New York: Oxford University press, 1999), 9p

SECTION 3

메디나 체류 시기의 계시

Why Muhammad's revelations are
changing repeatedly?

메디나로 이주함

무함마드를 따르는 무리들이 메카에서 메디나로 떠날 수밖에 없었던 배경을 살펴보면 아래와 같다.

순례의 달이나 금식하는 달이 되면 폭력행사가 금지된다는 것을 알고 무함마드는 북쪽 4백 킬로미터 정도 떨어져 있었던 야스립(Yathrib: 메디나의 옛 이름)에서 온 사람들에게 조심스럽게 포교하였다. 그런데 뜻밖에도 그들은 흔쾌히 호응했다. 그들이 호응했던 이유는 그 당시 메디나에서는 아우스(Aus)족과 카즈라즈(Kazraz)족 간에 만성적인 분쟁을 겪고 있었기 때문에 오래된 소모적인 분쟁을 조정 해결해 줄 강력한 지도자가 필요했던 것이다. 그래서 그들은 621년 메카 근교의 아끄바(Aquba)에서 두 부족 대표 12명이 무함마드에게 제 1차 아끄바(Aquba) 충성서약을 하였다.[1] 그리고 이듬해 6월에는 12명을 포함한 75명이 제 2차 아끄바(Aquba)충성서약을 하였다. 메카의 박해

자들은 무함마드가 집에서 나오는 순간 급습할 계책을 세워놓고 있었는데 사촌 동생 알리(Ali)의 계략으로 무사히 빠져나와 메카 남쪽의 사우르 산 동굴에서 3일간 숨어 지내다가 70명의 추종자들과 함께 비밀리에 메카를 탈출하여 메디나 남쪽 3 킬로미터 지점의 꾸바 마을에 당도했는데 그 때가 서기 622년 7월 15일 이었다.[2]

무함마드가 메카에서 메디나로 활동 무대를 옮기게 된 것은 부족 내의 갈등과 분쟁을 조정·해결해 줄 강력한 지도자를 찾고 있었던 메디나 주민들의 필요와 메카에서의 핍박을 피해 떠날 수밖에 없어 다른 정착지가 필요했던 무함마드 일행들의 필요를 상호공동으로 충족시켜주는 사건이었다.

메디나에 와서 정착한 무함마드는 메디나 부근에 많은 유대인들이 살고 있음을 알고 그들을 자신의 편으로 끌어들이기 위해서는 좀 더 적극적인 방법을 강구해야할 필요를 느꼈을 것이다. 이제까지 메카에서 사용했던 방법들 즉 알라(Allah)는 그들이 믿는 여호와 하나님과 같은 신이라고 주장하는 것과 그들이 가지고 있는 신구약 성경을 진리라고 인정해 주는 방법 등은 그리 효과적이지 못했다. 왜냐하면 그들이 가지고 있는 신구약 성경의 내용과 자신이 계시라는 이름으로 말한 내용들이 도저히 같은 신이 내린 계시라고 인정할 수 없을 만큼 달랐기 때문에 그것들만 가지고는 새로 정착한 지역 인근에 있는 유대인들을 자신의 편으로 끌어들이는데 충분치 못하다고 생각하여 좀 더 효과 있는 다른 방법을 적용할 필요를 느꼈을 것이다.

---

1. 정수일, 『이슬람 문명』, 75. 어떤 자료에는 7명으로 기록하고 있음.
2. Ibid. 75.

메디나 계시의 내용

초기 계시

예루살렘을 향한 기도

메디나에 도착한 무함마드를 따르는 이슬람 공동체는 메카에서 함께 떠나온 사람들과 메디나에서 그를 환영한 무리들뿐만 아니라 아비시니아(에티오피아)에 도피했던 무리들까지 합류하자 이미 무시할 수 없는 규모의 세력이 되었다. 그런데 이제까지 메카의 카아바 신전을 향하여 기도해 오던 무함마드가 자신을 따르는 이슬람 공동체 앞에서 예루살렘을 향하여 기도하는 것이었다. 360개의 우상들을 카아바 신전에 모아놓고 메카 중심으로 신앙생활을 하던 사람들에게는 매우 충격적인 사건이었다. 그러나 무함마드는 자신의 종교가 이미 유일신 종교로 오랫동안 자리 잡은 유대교와 기독교의 뿌리와 같은 것이라는 것을 설득하기 위한 효과적인 방법으로, 자신을 따르는 무리들에게 기도할 때에는 예루살렘 성전을 향하여 기도하라고 하였다.[1] 이것은 바로 무함마드가 유대교인들과 기독교인들을 자신의 추종자들로 끌어들이기 위한 또 하나의 강력한 유인책이었다.

유대교인들과 기독교인들에게는 예루살렘 성전이 신앙의 고향이요, 평화의 터전이었다. 유대인들의 조상들이 바벨론에 포로로 잡혀갔을 때에도 그들은 강변에 수금을 걸어놓고 예루살렘 노래를 부르면서 목을 놓아 울었다고 시편 기자는 노래하고 있다(시편 137:1). 바벨론에 포로로 잡혀갔던 다니엘은 누구든지 바벨론의 왕 외에 어느 신에게나 사람에게 무엇을 구하면 사자 굴에 던져 넣기로 한 조서에 어인(御印)이 찍힌 것을 알고도 예루살렘으로 향하여 열린 창에서 전에 행하던 대로 하루 세 번씩 무릎을 꿇고 기도했다고 한다(다니엘 6:7~10). 다윗의 뒤를 이어 이스라엘 임금이 된 솔로몬은 예루살렘에 성전을 지어 놓고 낙성식을 할 때 예루살렘 성전을 향하여 기도하는 자의 기도를 응답해달라고 기도하면서 이방인이라도 이 전을 향하여 기도하면 응답해 달라고 하나님께 간구하였다(열왕기상 8:38, 42~43, 48~49). 따라서 예루살렘을 향한 유대교인들과 기독교인들의 마음은 그야말로 눈물겹도록 애틋하고 간절한 것이었다.

---

1. 김용선, 『이슬람의 역사와 그 문화』, 31p. : 여기서 저자는 "예루살렘을 향하여 기도하던 무함마드가 기도 방향을 메카의 카아바로 바꾼 이유는 '카아바는 알라의 집이며 아브라함이 건설한 것으로서 아브라함의 종교로 돌아가자는 의미에서 기도의 방향을 바꾼 것'이며 우상숭배자들과 타협하기 위해서 바꾼 것은 아니라"고 주장하고 있다.

무함마드는 바로 이 점을 이용한 것이다. 자신을 따르는 추종자들에게 예루살렘 성전을 향하여 기도하라고 명한 것은 꾸란(Quran)에 기록되어 있지 않다. 그러나 하디스(Hadith)에 보면 메디나로 이동하고 나서 초기에 무함마드는 유대인들이 금식하는 것을 보고 아슈라(Ashura)[2] 금식을 명했으며[3] 또한 메디나에 도착한지 16~17개월 동안 예루살렘을 향하여 기도한 것으로 알려졌다.[4] 유대인의 금식이나 기도방향을 모방한 것은 그들과의 동질성을 부각시켜 그들을 자신의 편으로 끌어들이기 위한 과감한 시도였다고 보인다.

유대인들의 금식 모방

무함마드는 메디나에 와서 성경의 백성들을 자신의 편으로 끌어들이기 위해서 유대인들의 금식을 따라 하라고 명령했다. 이는 유대인들이 섬기는 여호와 하나님이 자신들이 믿는 알라(Allah)와 같은 신이라는 것을 믿게 하기위한 전략 중 가장 과감한 타협[5]이었다. 이에 무함마드는 자신의 동료들에게 "너희(무슬림)들은 저희보다 무싸(모세)의 승리를 더 경축할 권리가 있다. 그러므로 이날 금식하라."라고 명했다.

---

2. 이슬람력으로 Muharram 달의 제 10일을 의미함.
3. Sahih al-Bukhari, Volume 6, Book 60, No. 202.
4. 최영길, 『성꾸란 의미의 한국어 번역』, 꾸란 2:142 각주 참조, 39p.
5. 이스라엘 백성들은 1년에 하루 7월 10일 속죄일에 금식을 한다. 이는 모세가 애굽왕 바로에게 승리한 사건과는 관계가 없다. 그러나 무함마드는 유대인들의 입으로 "모세가 승리한 것을 경축하기 위해서 금식하는 절기"라고 말하고 있는 것이다.

그러므로 무함마드는 메디나에 도착한 초기에 원래 유대인들이 무하람달 10일에 금식하는 것을 보고 자신을 따르는 무리(무슬림)들에게도 그와 같이 하라고 명했던 것[6]을 알 수 있다. 이는 무싸(모세)와의 관련성을 주장하기 위한 하나의 도구에 불과 했던 것이다.

메디나 통치권 장악 후의 계시

무함마드가 메카의 핍박을 피하여 메디나[7]로 이주하여 메디나 전체의 통치권을 잡기까지는 약 1년 반 정도의 시간이 소요되었다고 한다. 무함마드와 그의 일행이 메디나로 오기 전까지 그곳의 주민들은 매우 무질서한 편싸움으로 어지러운 도시였다고 한다. 무함마드는 여기서 특정 부족에만 의존하던 종래의 집단 개념을 바꾸어 부족의 한계를 뛰어 넘는 새로운 집단 개념인 움마(Umma: 이슬람 공동체)를

6. 성경 레위기 16:29 이스라엘 백성들은 1년에 하루 속죄일을 정하여 백성들을 위해서 속죄 행사를 행했는데 이 날은 금식을 했다. 이는 유대인들의 달력으로 7월 10일 이었으나 무함마드는 이를 무하람 달 10일이라고 한 것을 보면 그 당시 아라비아에 살던 유대인들이 이슬람력으로 무하람 달 10일을 지켰거나 혹은 무함마드가 유대교력 7월 10일은 이슬람력 무하람 10일로 잘못 알았던 것으로 보인다.

7. 이 도시의 원래의 이름은 야스립(Yathrib)이었는데 후에 이슬람의 세력이 커지고 무함마드가 메신저라는 이름으로 알려지게 되자 메신저의 도시라는 이름의 아랍어 Madinat al Nabi 라는 이름으로 부르게 되는데 이를 줄여서 마다나 혹은 메디나라고 부르게 되었다

8. 유해석, 『이슬람이 다가오고 있다』, 60p.

9. 사피 아르라흐만 알무바라크푸리, 『인간 무함마드』 최영길 역, 250p.

건설하며[8] 소위 메디나 헌장을 반포하였다.[9] 이 메디나 헌장은 부족들 간의 상잔(相殘)을 금지하고 모든 분쟁은 알라(Allah)와 그가 파견한 메신저 무함마드가 중재한다고 규정하였다. 이는 무함마드가 메카에서 메디나로 신변의 위협을 느껴 도피해 온 일개 난민이 아니라 움마(Umma, 이슬람 공동체)라는 새로운 집단에서 행정, 사법권을 행사할 수 있는 권한이 인정되었음을 의미하는 것이다. 또한 이 헌장에 보면 무함마드의 지휘에 따라 단합하여 그의 대적과 공동 투쟁할 것을 천명함으로서 군사동맹의 성격도 띄고 있었다.[10] 거기에는 자유 거래 보장, 채무 상환 등 공동체의 경제 질서와 생활 규범도 명시하였다.[11] 이렇게 해서 점차적으로 영향력을 강화하기 시작한 무함마드는 드디어 메디나의 최고 통치자로 등극하게 되었다. 그가 메디나의 최고 통치자가 되고 난 후에 첫 해인 서기 624년부터 그의 계시의 내용은 완전히 바뀌게 된다.[12]

카아바(Kaaba) 신전을 향한 기도

유대교인들과 기독교인들을 자신의 편으로 끌어들이기 위해서 예루살렘을 향하여 기도하라고 말하던 무함마드는 그들이 도저히 자신의 메신저 됨과 자신의 계시의 정통성을 인정하지 않자 그들을

---

10. Ibid. 251p.
11. 정수일, 『이슬람 문명』, (서울: 창작과 비평, 2002), 77p.
12. 마크 G., 『이슬람과유대인 그 끝나지 않은 전쟁』, 168~170p.

배척하기로 작정했다.[13] 지금까지는 유대교인들과 기독교인들이 무함마드의 계시를 거짓이라고 해도[14] 그들을 징계할만한 힘이 없어서 평화와 관용으로 위장하여 포교하였지만, 이제 메디나로 와서 통치권을 잡고 난 후에는, 그들을 징계할 만한 충분한 힘이 생겼기 때문에 더 이상 묵과할 수 없었던 것이다. 물론 이 조치는 메디나에서 최고 통치자로서 공식 출발하고 난 뒤 첫 새해를 맞이하는 서기 624년부터 시작되었다.[15] 기도의 방향을 아랍어로 끼블라(Qiblah)라고 하는데 무함마드는 유대교인들과 기독교인들을 유인하기 위해서 그들의 기도방향인 예루살렘을 향하여 메디나에 도착한 지 16~17개월 동안 기도했으나 그들이 자신을 메신저로 인정하지 않고 배척하자 기도의 방향을 이전의 방향으로 바꾸어 버리는데 그 내용이 꾸란에는 아래와 같이 기록되어 있다.

어리석은 백성이 말하도다. 그들이 예배하던 예배의 방향을 무엇이 바꾸었느뇨, 일러 가로되 동서가 알라 안에 있으며 그분께서는 믿음이 진실한 자들을 옳은 길로 인도하시니라 그리하여 알라는 너희들에게 중용의 한 공동체를 선정했나니 너희는 그 공동체의 증인이 될 것이며 그 메신저가 너희들에게 한 증인이 되리라 또한 '너희가 그 전에 행했던 기도의 방향'을 지정했나니 이는 메신저를 따르는 자와 따

---

13. 프랜시스 로빈슨, 『케임브리지 이슬람사』, 손주영 역 (서울: 시공사, 2006), 37p.
14. 꾸란 10:17: 알라께 거짓을 날조하고 또 알라의 계시를 부정하는 자만큼 더 나쁜 자가 있겠는가? 죄를 범한 자들이 번성한 일은 없다 (김용선 번역 한글 꾸란).
15. 마크 G., Ibid. 151~153p.

르지 않는 자를 구별코자 함이라 그것은 알라의 인도를 받지 못한 자
들에게는 커다란 시험이나 알라께서 너희의 믿음을 좌절시키지 아니
했으니 알라는 실로 온 인류에게 사랑과 자비로 충만한 분이시라···
진실로 알라는 모든 일에 전지전능하시니라.

-꾸란 2: 142~143, 148 최영길 역

처음에 왜 예루살렘으로 기도방향을 정했는지는 꾸란에 명기되어
있지는 않으나 혹자는 그것도 알라의 계시에 의해서 정해졌던 것이
며[16] 후에 그 방향을 바꿀 때도 알라의 명령에 의해서 바꾸었는데 왜
기도의 방향을 바꿔야 하는지는 꾸란의 여러 절을 통하여 장황하게
설명하고 있다. 즉 알라는 동에도 계시고, 서에도 계시니까 방향을
바꿀 수 있다[17]는 것이며 둘째는 지금 무함마드를 따르고 있는 자들
이 진짜 무슬림인지 가짜 무슬림인지 확인하기 위해서 바꾼 것[18]이며
셋째는 알라가 전능하신 분이니까[19] 무슨 일이든지 할 수 있으며 전
능하신 알라께서 바꾸시면 무슬림들은 오직 순종하기만 하면 된다
는 것이다. 여기서 한 가지 중요한 점을 지적하고 싶은 것은 무함마
드가 계시를 받았다고 말하면서 예루살렘을 향하여 기도하던 무슬
림들에게 그 전에 행하던 기도 방향으로 바꾸라고 명하는 것을 볼

---

16. Dashti, A Study of the Prophetic Career of Mohammad, translated from Persian by
    F.R.C. Bagley (U.S.A. CA: Mazda Publishers, 1994), 92p.
17. 꾸란 2:142.
18. 꾸란 2:143.
19. 꾸란 2:148.

수 있다. 그 전에 행하던 기도방향이라는 것은 물론 메카 방향을 말하는 것이다. 그렇다면 무슬림들이 이전에 메카를 향해서 기도하는 풍습을 가지고 있었다는 것을 무함마드가 꾸란에서 인정을 하고 있는 것이다.[20] 그러므로 메카를 향해서 기도하는 무슬림들의 풍습은 이슬람 이전에 그들이 우상을 섬길 때부터 전해내려 오던 풍습인 것이다.

아슈라(Ashura) 금식을 라마단으로 대체

무함마드는 유대인들이 자신의 권위를 인정하지 않자 그들을 따라하던 아슈라(Ashura) 금식을 점차로 약화시키다가 나중에는 완전히 폐기하고 라마단 한 달 동안의 금식으로 대체함으로써 그들과의 결별을 선언한 것이다. 아래의 하디스를 보자

아이샤(Aisha)가 말하기를
사람들은 라마단(Ramadan) 달에 금식이 의무화되기 전까지는 무하람 달의 10일인 아슈라(Ashura) 날에 금식을 하였다. 그 날에 카아바 신전은 덮여 있곤 했다. 알라(Allah)께서 라마단 달의 금식을 의무화했을 때 알라의 메신저는 "누구든지 아슈라(Ashura) 날에 금식을 하고 싶은 사람은 해도 좋고 하고 싶지 않은 사람은 하지 않아도 좋다"고 말했다.

-Sahih al-Bukhari, Volume 2, Book 26, Number 662

---

20. 꾸란 2:143.

이븐 우마르(Ibn Umar)가 말하기를

메신저(무함마드)는 무하람 달 10일 아슈라(Ashura)날 금식을 준수했고, (무슬림들에게) 그날 금식할 것을 명했으나 라마단(Ramadan)달 금식이 정해졌을 때 아슈라(Ashura)의 금식은 폐기되었다.[21]

이를 보면 무함마드는 메디나 초기에는 유대인들의 환심을 얻기 위해서 그들이 지키는 금식을 같이 지켰으나 그들이 좀처럼 무함마드의 메신저 됨을 인정하지 않자 자신과 자신을 따르는 무슬림들이 유대인들보다 더 신실한 신앙인이라는 것을 보이기 위해서 라마단 달 한 달 동안 금식을 명한 것이라는 것을 부카리(Bukhari)의 하디스(Hadith)를 통해서 확인할 수 있는 것이다. 이는 유대인들과의 유사성을 추구하던 상황화 전략으로부터 그들과 분리를 선언하는 차별화의 시작을 의미하는 상징적인 행위라고 볼 수 있다.

기독교인들을 핍박할 명분 설정

무함마드는 그동안 유대교인들과 기독교인들이 믿는 여호와 하나님은 자신이 믿으라고 주장하는 알라(Allah)와 같은 신이라고 했다.

---

21. 유대인들의 금식을 모방하던 것을 폐기한 무함마드의 행동은 유대인들과의 차별화를 위한 조치로 보인다. 이는 금식에 국한된 것이 아니라 이제부터 모든 면에서 차별화 정책을 택한 것을 보여주는 상징적인 행위인 것이다. Sahih al- Bukhari. Volume 3. Book 3. Book 31. Number 116.

그리고 그들이 가지고 있는 경전인 신·구약 성경이 진리라고 말했다. 자신은 새로운 계시를 가지고 온 메신저가 아니라 신·구약 성경이 진리라는 것을 아랍 지역에 확증시켜 주기 위해서 보냄을 받은 메신저라고 자신을 소개했다. 심지어는 자신이 가지고 온 계시에서 의심나는 것이 있으면 이미 성경을 가지고 있는 유대인들과 기독교인들에게 물어보라고 까지 하였다.[22] 그리고 신·구약 성경을 믿는 유대교인들과 기독교인들은 알라(Allah)의 은총을 입을 것이라고 말했다.[23] 그러나 유대교인들과 기독교인들은 무함마드의 계시가 거짓임을 알았다. 왜냐하면 자신의 조상들이 수천 년 동안 하나님의 말씀으로 알고 믿어왔던 성경의 내용과 그의 계시는 너무나 달랐기 때문이었다.[24] 그래서 그들은 무함마드가 알라(Allah)의 계시를 받았다고 하면서 성경과 비슷한 내용을 이야기 할 때 즉각 반발하곤 했다. 그것은 계시가 아니라 거짓말이라는 것을 분별할 수 있는 사람들은 유대교인들과 기독교인들 외에는 없었다. 우상 숭배자들은 성경의 내용들을 모르기 때문에 무함마드의 계시의 진위를 분별할 능력이 없었을 것이다. 이에 무함마드는 자신을 배척하는 기독교인들과 유대교인들에게 진노하였으나 메카에서 부터 메디나 초기까지는 그

---

22. 꾸란 10:94, 알라께서 그대에게 계시한 것을 그대가 의심한다면 그대 이전에 성경을 읽은 자들에게 물어보라 실로 주님으로부터 그대에게 진리가 이르렀나니 의심하지 말라(최영길 역 한글 꾸란).

23. 꾸란 2:62, 진실로 믿음을 가진 사람들과 유대교인, 기독교인, 사비아교인, 누구든지 알라와 최후의 심판 날을 믿고 좋은 일을 행하는 자들은 그들의 주로부터 보상을 받을 것이며 두려움도 없고 슬픔도 없을 것이다(김용선 역 한글 꾸란).

24. 마크 G., 『이슬람과유대인 그 끝나지 않은 전쟁』, 126~127p.

들을 징계할 만한 힘이 없었으므로 참으면서 평화적 계시를 발표할 수 밖에 없었다. 이들이 가장 즐겨 사용하는 평화적 계시는

'종교에는 강요가 없나니 진리는 암흑 속으로부터 구별되느니라. 사탄을 버리고 알라(Allah)를 믿는 자 끊어지지 않는 단단한 동아줄을 잡았노라. 알라는 모든 것을 들으시며 모든 것을 알고 계시니라.'

- 꾸란 2:256 최영길 번역

하지만 서기 624년 무함마드가 메디나에서 최고 통치자의 자리에 오르고 나니 경제적으로 정치적·군사적으로 힘이 생겼다. 그는 자신의 메신저 됨을 인정하지 않는 유대교인들과 기독교인들을 징계하고 싶었을 것이다. 그러나 이제까지 그들은 무슬림들이 믿는 알라(Allah)와 같은 신을 믿고 있으며 그들의 경전은 진리라고 말해왔던 그가 그들을 징계하려면 사람들이 납득할만한 명분이 필요했다.[25] 무함마드가 유대교인들과 기독교인들을 징계해야한다고 내세운 명분은 과연 무엇이었을까?

성경 변질론에 대한 계시

메카에서 힘이 없을 때 무함마드는 기독교인들이 가지고 있는 성경은 진리라고 말했다. 그가 이렇게 말한 데는 몇 가지 이유가 있었

---

25. Ibid, 144~145p

을 것이다. 첫째로 생각해 볼 수 있는 것은 무함마드가 자신이 받은 계시를 유대교인들과 기독교인들이 믿고 있는 창조주로 부터 내려온 계시와 동일한 종류의 것이라는 것을 인정받고 싶었을 것이다. 그래서 그는 자신의 계시를 말하면서 이 꾸란이 이전에 있었던 성경을 확증하는 것이라고 말했다.

> 이것 이전에 모세(무ㅆ)의 성경이 안내서로서 그리고 은혜로 있었으며 아랍어로 된 '경전인 꾸란이 그것을 확증하며' 죄인들에게 경고하고 의로운 자들에게는 기쁨의 복음을 전하고 있노라. -꾸란 46:12 최영길 역

꾸란의 구절을 보면 무함마드는 처음 소수의 추종자들을 이끌며 메카에 있을 때는 신·구약성경과 같은 내용의 계시[26]들을 아랍 지역에 경고하기 위해서 선택받은 사람이라는 자의식이 있었던 것으로 보인다.[27] 아랍어를 사용하는 아랍 지역의 사람들에게 경고하는 것이 자신의 사명이라고 생각했던 것이다.

> 이와 같이 우리가 그대에게 아랍어로 꾸란을 계시한 것은 그대가 '어머니의 도시(메카)와 그 주변에 사는 주민에게' 경고하고 아무 의심될 것도 없는 소집의 날을 알려주기 위해서다. 일부는 천국 안으로 들어가고 다른 나머지는 지옥의 불 속으로 들어가는 바로 그 날을

---

26. 꾸란 3:3, 알라는 구약과 신약을 내리셨고 앞서 온 것을 진리로 확증하면서 그대에게 그 책을 계시하노라(최영길 역).
27. 꾸란 6:156, 그 성경(꾸란을 계시한 이유)는 우리 이전 두 백성(유대교인들과 기독교인들)에게만 계시되었으니 우리는 실로 그들이 읽은 것이 무엇인지 알지 못 하도다 라고 말하지 아니하도록 함이라(최영길 역).

-꾸란 42:7 김용선 역

알라는 그것을 '아랍어로 계시하였으니' 이로 하여 너희가 이해
하고 배우도록 함이라. - 꾸란 43:3 최영길 역

위의 두 구절을 보면 아라비아의 메카와 그 주변에 사는 주민
들이 이해할 수 있도록 아랍어로 꾸란을 계시했다고 말하고 있다.
이 두 구절 외에도 꾸란의 계시는 아랍인들을 위한 것이라고 말하는
구절들이 많이 있다.[28] 이를 볼 때 메카에 있을 때 무함마드는 이슬
람이 세계적인 종교가 되리라고는 상상을 못했으며 다만 유대교인
들과 기독교인들이 믿고 있는 하나님의 계시를 아랍지역에 전달
하는 자로 자처하면서 그 경전을 아랍 사람들이 잘 읽고 이해할 수
있도록 아랍어로 계시했다고 말했던 것이다. 그러나 꾸란을 한국어
로 번역한 최영길 교수는 이를 "어머니 도시의 주민들과 그 주변의
모든 백성들에게" 라고 번역해 놓고 이 구절에 각주를 달아 "전 세계
의 모든 백성들에게" 라고 설명하고 있다.[29] 오히려 메카에 있을 때
무함마드는 성경의 백성들이 자신의 계시의 근원을 의심하지 않을
까를 염려하여[30] 꾸란이 옛날에 내렸던 성경과 같은 것이라고 강조했

---

28. 무함마드는 꾸란 20:113, 꾸란 26:195, 꾸란 39:28, 꾸란 41:3, 꾸란 41:44, 꾸란 46:12, 꾸란 16:103
   등 매우 여러 차례 아랍 사람들이 명백히 이해할 수 있도록 아랍어로 꾸란을 계시한 것이라고
   설명하고 있다.
29. 최영길, 『성꾸란 의미의 한국어 번역』, 42:7 주석 참조, 914p.

었다. 그리고는 자신의 계시를 의심하는 자들은 강력한 심판을 받을 것 이라는 경고도 잊지 않았는데 이는 아래 구절을 보면 확인할 수 있다.

그는 '우리의 계시가 무엇인지를 알자 곧 비웃어 버렸다. 이런 무 리에게는 수치스런 업벌이 가해지리라.' 그들 뒤에서 기다리고 있는 것은 지옥이다. 그들이 벌어들인 것도 알라를 제외하고 그들이 선택 한 보호자도 아무런 도움이 되지 않았다. 그들에게는 오직 큰 징벌이 가해질 뿐인 것이다. 이거야말로 인도이시다. '주의 계시를 믿지 않 는 자들에게는 등을 돌려 가혹한 형벌이 가해지리라??

-꾸란 45:9~11 김용선 역

무함마드가 이런 수고와 노력을 했음에도 불구하고 "성경의 백 성들" (이는 무함마드가 유대교인들과 기독교인들을 지칭하는 꾸란의 관용어임)은 그의 메신저 됨을 인정하려 들지 않았다. 그가 이렇게까지 한 것은 힘이 없던 무함마드가 성경의 백성들을 무슬림으로 유인하기 위해서 그랬던 것이었다.[31]

그런데 메디나로 와서 아라비아 반도의 제2의 도시인 메디나의 최고 통치자로 등극하고 힘이 생기자 유대교인들과 기독교인들이 가지고 있는 성경은 변질되고 위조되었다고 말을 바꾸었다. 아래 구 절을 보라.

---

30. 꾸란 26:196~197, 그것은 선조들의 성경에서도 언급이 되었거늘 이스라엘 자손들의 학자들이 그것이 사실임을 알고 있는 것만으로도 예증이 되지 않느뇨? (최영길 역).

31. Mark G. , 『Islam & Jews The unfinished battle 』(Fl. U.S.A : FrontLine, 2003), 94p.

그들이 성약을 깨뜨림으로 말미암아 알라는 그들을 저주하였고 그들의 마음을 거칠게 하였노라 '그들은 말씀을 위조하고' 그들에게 계시된 진실의 말씀을 망각하고 있나니 너희는 그들 가운데 소수를 제외하고는 '모든 것이 위조됨을 발견하리라'. -꾸란 5: 13 上최영길 역

너희들은 그들이 너희와 더불어 믿음을 같이 하기를 바라느뇨. 그들의 무리가 알라의 말씀을 듣고 이해하면서도 그 말씀을 왜곡하도다. -꾸란 2:75 최영길 역

그렇다면 성경의 백성들이 가지고 있는 말씀이 언제 어떤 내용이 바뀌었다는 말인가?

무슬림들은 꾸란에 기록되어 있는 대로 유대교인들과 기독교인들이 가지고 있는 신·구약 성경이 변질되었다고 말한다. 그러나 그들은 성경이 언제 변질되었는지를 물으면 답변이 불가능한 딜레마에 빠지게 된다. 왜냐하면 무함마드가 메카에 있을 때는 신·구약 성경이 진리라는 것을 확증시켜주기 위해서[32] 자신이 온 것이라고 말해 왔었다. 그러나 메디나에 와서 최고 통치자가 된 후 정치적·군사적·경제적으로 힘이 생기자 성경이 변질되었다고 하니 그러

---

32. 꾸란 10:37, 이 꾸란은 알라를 물리어 놓고 날조되는 그런 것이 아니라, 이전에 내리신 것을 확인하는 것이고, 만유의 주께서 의심할 여지도 없는 인간을 위한 성전을 상세히 설명하는 것이다 (김용선 역).

면 언제 변질되었단 말인가?

보통 무슬림들은 언제라고 정확하게 말할 수는 없지만 무함마드가 태어나기 훨씬 이전에 변질되었다고 말한다.[33] 그러나 이렇게 말할 때 그들은 꾸란에 자체 모순이 있다는 것을 시인하고 있는 것이다. 왜냐하면 무함마드가 메카에 있을 때는 분명히 성경의 백성들이 가지고 있는 경전은 진리라고 말했기 때문이다.

> 모세(무ﷺ)에게 성경을 주었으나 바른 일을 행하는 이들을 위해 나의 은혜를 완성하고자 했으며 모든 것을 설명하여 주고자 함이며 복음과 은혜로서 믿음을 가진 자들이 그의 주님을 영접하도록 함이라 이것은 알라의 축복으로 계시한 성경이거늘 이것을 따르라 그리고 공경하라 그리하면 너희가 은혜를 받으리라. '그 성경은 우리 이전 두 백성(유대교인들과 기독교인들을 의미함)에게만 계시되었으니 우리는 실로 그들이 읽은 것이 무엇인지 알지 못하도다 라고 말하지 아니하도록 함이라'
>
> —꾸란 6:154~156 최영길 역

이 부분을 주석한 최영길 박사의 각주를 보면 "심판의 날 '우리에게는 성경이 계시되지 아니했고 유대교인과 기독교인 두 백성에게만 계시되었기 때문에 우리는 그 성경 안에 있는 내용을 알지 못하도다' 라고 말하지 못하도록 이 꾸란이 최후의 메신저 무함마드를 통해서 계시된 것으로 해석된다." 고 주석하고 있다.[34] 한국의 권위

---

33. Ibid. 130p.
34. 최영길,『성 꾸란 의미의 한국어 번역』, 245.

있는 이슬람 학자인 최영길 박사가 분명하게 이 두 백성은 즉 유대 교인들과 기독교인들을 의미하는 것이라고 주석하고 있고 꾸란은 그들에게 계시된 것과 같은 내용의 계시라고 주장을 했던 사실은 아무도 부인할 수 없는 꾸란의 구절이 증명하고 있는 것이다. 메카에 있을 때는 알라의 계시에 의해서 진리라고 선포되었던 신·구약 성경! 그것의 아랍어 판이 "꾸란" 이라고 무함마드가 말하고 있었다는 데 이의를 제기할 사람은 없는 것이다.

그런데 메디나에 와서 그것이 변질되었다고 말한다면 언제 변질되었다는 말인가? 신·구약 성경이 무함마드 이전에 변질되었다는 것은 위의 구절을 볼 때 논리가 맞지 않는다. 무함마드 이후에 변질되었다는 것은 상상할 수도 없는 가정이다. 왜냐하면 무함마드가 살아 있을 때 메디나에서 통치자로 등극하고는 성경이 변질되었다고 말했기 때문이다.

논리적으로 성경이 변질된 시기가 무함마드 이전도 아니고 무함마드 이후도 아니라면 무함마드 당시에 변질되었다고 밖에는 다르게 선택할 여지가 없다.

그런데 신·구약 성경이 형성된 과정을 보면 구약 39권은 서기 90년 얌니아(Yamnia) 종교회의에서 정경으로 확정 선포했고, 신약 27권은 서기 397년에 카르타고(Carthage) 종교회의에서 정경으로 확정 선포함으로 66권의 신·구약 성경이 완성된 것이다.[35] 그래서 4세기

---

35. Patrick A, O. 'Boyle, D.D. , New Catholic Encyclopedia (U.S.A :Washington. 1967), 160p.

말에 신·구약 성경은 정경으로 온 세계에 공포된 것이다. 그 후에는 **아무도 성경에 한 구절도 더하거나 뺄 사람이 없다. "내가 이 책의 예언의 말씀을 듣는 각인에게 증거하노니 만일 누구든지 이것들 외에 더하면 하나님이 이 책에 기록된 재앙들을 그에게 더하실 터이요, 만일 누구든지 이 책의 예언의 말씀에서 제하여 버리면 하나님이 이 책에 기록된 생명나무와 및 거룩한 성에 참여함을 제하여 버리시리라"**(요한 계시록 22: 18-19)고 선언했는데 누가 감히 성경 말씀을 변경할 수 있겠는가?

놀라운 것은 1947~1948년에 이스라엘의 어느 양치기 소년에 의해서 사해 부근의 쿰란 동굴에서 기원전 2세기부터 기원 후 1세기 사이에 기록된 성경의 고대 사본이 발견된 것이다.[36] 온 세계가 놀랄만한 이 사건을 통해서 분명히 밝혀진 중요한 사실 중 하나는 오늘날 우리가 사용하는 성경의 내용이 기원전부터 전혀 변질되지 않은 상태로 오늘날 우리 손에 까지 전달되어 각 나라 언어로 읽히고 있다는 것이 과학적으로 입증된 것이다.

그러므로 무함마드가 7세기 초 메카 지역에서 활동하다가 메디나로 이주하여 초기에 세력을 잡지 못했던 시기인 610년부터 623년까지는 성경이 진리라고 주장하다가 메디나 최고 통치자로서 권력을 잡게 된 624년부터 그가 죽은 632년까지는 성경이 변질되었다고 주장한 것은 사실 성경이 변질된 것이 아니라 기독교인에 대한 무함

---

36. E. M. Blaiklock, The Zondervan Pictorial Bible Atlas (Michigan U.S.A. Zondervan Publishing House, 1981), 412~413p.

마드 자신의 입장이 변화된 것이라는 것을 역사적·과학적으로 입증할 수 있는 것이다.

무엇이 변질되었다는 것인가?

성경이 언제 변질되었는가를 묻는다면 답변이 궁색한 무슬림들도 무엇이 변질되었느냐고 물으면 참조할만한 꾸란의 구절들이 많이 있다.

왜냐하면 무함마드는 처음부터 자신의 계시가 성경의 백성들이 가지고 있는 신·구약 성경과 내용상의 차이가 너무 많이 있었기 때문에 어차피 입장 정리를 해야 할 필요가 있음을 알았을 것이다. 그가 택할 수 있었던 태도는 두 가지 중의 한 가지였을 것이다. 첫째는 자신이 성경에 대해서 무지해서 실수가 많았는데 너그러이 보아 용서해 달라고 하는 겸손한 태도를 취하는 방법이 있었을 것이다. 둘째는 내가 받은 계시가 진짜이고, 너희 것은 잘못된 혹은 변질된 계시라고 하는 오만한 태도를 취할 수도 있었을 것이다. 그러나 전자의 입장을 취하는 데는 많은 무리가 따랐을 것이다. 왜냐하면 지금까지 자신의 계시는 누구에게 배운 것도 아니고 하늘에서 천사를 통해서 직접 받았다고 하는 직통 계시를 주장해 왔었는데,[37] 이제 와

---

37. 무함마드는 자신이 글을 모르는 문맹 메신저(Ummi Prophet)이기 때문에 이는 사람에게서 배운 것이 아니고 하늘의 원본을 그대로 계시 받은 것이기에 누구도 이와 비슷한 것을 만들어 낼 수 없다고 한다(최영길 번역 꾸란 2:23 및 43:4 각주 참조).

서 사전 정보 수집이 잘못 되었다거나 자료가 부정확했다거나 하는 말은 이제까지 자신이 세운 알라의 메신저로서의 권위를 한꺼번에 무너뜨리는 것이 되기 때문에 함부로 취할 수 있는 태도는 아니었을 것이다. 그래서 그는 후자를 선택할 수밖에 없었던 것이다. 즉 너희들이 가지고 있는 성경은 변질된 것이고 내가 가지고 온 꾸란이 참 진리라고 주장하는 태도를 취하게 되었던 것이다.

그렇다면 무엇이 변질되었다는 말인가? 쉽게 말하면 성경과 꾸란과 내용상의 차이가 나는 모든 부분은 성경이 변질되었기 때문이라고 주장했던 것이다.[38]

성경의 어느 부분이 변질되었는가에 대한 이슬람 측의 자료에 의하면 제일 먼저 강하게 제시하는 부분이 무함마드에 관한 부분이다. 즉 무함마드가 장차 예언자로 등장할 것을 신·구약 성경에 많이 예언해 놓았는데[39] 유대교인들과 기독교인들이 그것들을 변질 시켜서 무함마드와 관련된 구절들을 모두 없애 버렸다는 것이다.

신약에서 변질되었다고 주장하는 내용

한편 이슬람 측의 주장을 들어보면 기독교인들이 무함마드의 출현에 관해 예언된 성경 구절들을 모두 없애 버리고자 했는데, 아직도 변질되지 않고 보존된 성경구절들이 조금은 남아 있다는 것이다.

---

38. 마크 G., 『이슬람과 유대인 그 끝나지 않은 전쟁』, 144~145p.
39. 꾸란 7:157, 꾸란 61:6.

아래 꾸란의 구절을 살펴보자.

　　그들은 메신저이며 무학자 메신저를 따르는 이들이라 그들은 '그
　　들의 기록서인 구약과 신약에서 그를 발견하리라' 그분은 그들에게
　　옳은 것을 명령하였고 그릇된 것을 금기하였으며 또 그들에게 성결한
　　것을 허락하시고 그들의 무거운 짐과 그들의 멍에들을 벗겨 주시니
　　그분을 믿고 그분을 존경하며 그분을 도와 그분에게 계시된 빛을 따
　　르는 이들은 번성하리라. _꾸란 7:157 최영길 역

　　그러면 구약과 신약의 어디에 무함마드에 관한 기록이 남아 있다
는 것인가?

　　이슬람 신학자들의 주장에 의하면 신약성경에도 무함마드가
장차 올 것이라고 예언된 구절들이 간혹 남아 있다고 한다. 그 대표
적인 것이 바로 "보혜사"라는 것이다. 신약성경 요한복음 14장부터
16장까지 예수께서 장차 오실 것이라고 말씀하시던 "보혜사"가
바로 무함마드라는 것이다.[40] 신약성경은 원본이 헬라어로 기록되
었는데 헬라어 원문에 보면 보혜사를 파라클레토스(Παρ?κλητο?)라
고 기록하고 있으나 원래는 페리클레토스(Περικλητο?) 즉 "빛나는 자,
칭찬받는 자"라는 뜻이었는데 복사하는 사람들이 실수로 혹은 고의
로 이것을 잘못 기재했다는 것이다. 그런데 아랍어로 칭찬받는 자,
혹은 빛나는 자라는 말은 "아흐마드(Ahmad) 혹은 무함마드(Muhammad)"

---

40. 공일주, 『이싸냐 예수냐』(서울: 죠이선교회 출판부, 1997), 115p.

라는 것이다. 놀라운 것은 꾸란에 보면 예수께서 직접 나는 아흐맏(무함마드)이 장차 올 것을 너희에게 알려주기 위해서 왔다고 선포했다고 기록되어 있다는 점이다.

마리암의 아들 이싸(예수)가 이스라엘 자손들이여 실로 나는 너희에게 보내어진 메신저로써 내 앞에 온 구약과 '내 후에 올 아흐맏(Ahmad)이란 이름을 가진 한 메신저의 복음을 확증하노라' 그러나 그가 분명한 예증으로 그들에게 임하였을 때 이것은 분명한 마술이라 하였더라. -꾸란 61:6 최영길 역

그러나 성경의 예수는 보혜사를 설명하시면서 **"하나님께서는 그가 영원토록 너희와 함께 있게 하실 것이다"**(요한복음 14:16), 또 **"보혜사는 진리의 성령이시며 그가 예수의 가르침을 생각나게 할 것이다"**(요한복음 14:26), 또 **"보혜사란 진리의 성령을 말하는 것이며 그가 예수를 증거할 것이다"**(요한복음 15:26), 라고 말씀하고 있다. 그러므로 보혜사란 인간을 말하는 것이 아니라 성령을 말하는 것이고 영원히 교인들과 함께 하셔서 예수를 증거 하시고, 예수의 가르침을 생각나게 하실 분이라는 것이 성경의 가르침인 것이다. 그런데 이슬람에서는 요한복음 16:7에 예수께서 "내가 가면 보혜사를 너희에게 보내리라"고 하신 말씀만을 발췌하여 이것이 무함마드를 의미하는 것이라고 주장하고 있으면서 예수께서 하신 말씀과 가르침을 생각나게 하는 것이 아니라 전혀 다른 말들을 알라(Allah)의 이름으로 말하고 있는 것이다.

구약에서 변질되었다고 주장하는 내용

또한 구약에 신명기 18:15에 본다면 모세의 설교에 "네 하나님 여호와께서 너의 중 네 형제 중에서 '나와 같은 선지자' 하나를 너를 위하여 일으키시리니 너희는 그를 들을찌니라."라고 말한 그 모세와 같은 선지자가 곧 무함마드를 말한다는 것이 이슬람 측의 주장이다. 이는 분명한 메시아 예언 구절 중의 하나이다. 성경을 주석한 어떤 학자의 주석을 봐도 예외 없이 이는 메시아이신 예수 그리스도를 예언하고 있다고 해석하고 있다. 그러나 이슬람 학자들은 이 구절이야말로 무함마드가 올 것을 예언하는 구절이라고 주장한다. 그들의 주장을 들어보면

- ▶ 무싸(모세)와 무함마드는 결혼[41]을 했다. 그러나 이싸(예수)는 안 했다.
- ▶ 무싸(모세)와 무함마드는 자녀를 두었다. 그러나 이싸(예수)는 아니다.
- ▶ 무싸(모세)와 무함마드는 전쟁[42]을 했다. 그러나 이싸(예수)는

---

41. 무함마드의 결혼 횟수는 어디까지를 결혼으로 보느냐하는 관점에 따라 최소한 13명과 결혼했다는 사람(최영길, 『무함마드와 이슬람』, 84p.)으로부터 15명이라는 사람(유해석, 『이슬람이 다가오고 있다』, 82p.)및 그 외에도 견해가 다양하다. 그가 25세 때 결혼한 카디자(Khadija)가 죽을 때까지는 다른 아내를 얻지 않았으나 그가 죽자 그는 여러 명의 아내를 두기 시작했다. 다른 무슬림들에게는 4명까지의 아내를 허용(꾸란 4:3)한 그는 정식 결혼한 여자들 뿐 아니라 전쟁포로나 노예들, 고모나 고모부의 딸들, 이모나 이모부의 딸들, 메카에서 함께 나온 여인들, 스스로 몸을 바치는 여인들, 중 누구나 취하거나 버릴 수 있는 권세를 알라로부터 부여받았다고 한다 (꾸란 33:50~51).

아니다.

▶ 무싸(모세)와 무함마드는 사람[43] 을 죽였다. 그러나 이싸(예수)
는 아니다.

▶ 무싸(모세)와 무함마드는 세상에서 나라를[44] 세웠다. 그러나
이싸(예수)는 아니다.

위와 같은 몇 가지 점을 비교해 볼 때 무싸(모세)가 말하던 "나와 같
은 선지자" 라는 예언 구절은 절대로 이싸(예수)가 아니라 무함마드를
의미하는 것이 옳다는 것이다.

그러나 우리가 알아야 할 것은 두 인물이 아무리 공통점이 많아
도 핵심적인 부분 한 두 가지가 다르다면 전혀 다른 인물일 수 밖에
없다는 것을 알아야 한다. 아무리 얼굴도 비슷하고 몸무게도 비슷하
고 신장도 비슷하고 걸음걸이, 말투… 등 수십 가지 특징이 비슷하
더라도 부모가 다르다든지 생년월일 혹은 이름 등 핵심적인 것 한~두
가지가 다르다면 이는 전혀 다른 인물임을 간단하게 확인할 수 있는
것이다. 매우 중요한 핵심적인 것 몇 가지만 비교해 본다면

  * 모세와 예수는 기적을 행했다. 그러나 무함마드는 아니다. 하
나님께서 자신이 보내신 선지자라는 것을 확인시켜 주시기 위해서

---

42. 유해석,『이슬람이 다가오고 있다』, 74p. : 여기서 저자는 무함마드가 메디나에서 10년 동안 70
    여 차례의 전쟁을 치렀으며 이 중 무함마드가 직접 진두지휘한 전쟁이 27회라고 한다.
43. 무함마드는 그가 죽인 사람 수를 정확하게 알 수 있는 사람이 없을 정도로 많은 사람을 죽였다
    는 것을 부인할 사람은 없을 것이다.
44. 이슬람 학자들의 주장하는 무함마드의 잔혹성에 대한 변명은, 그가 "국가를 세운 메신저" 이기
    때문에 국가의 정의구현을 위해서 악한 자들을 죽일 수밖에 없었다는 것이다.

모세를 통해서 여러 가지 기적을 행했던 것을 성경을 통해서 볼 수 있는데 무함마드는 한 가지 기적도 행하지 못했고, 더구나 꾸란에 보면 유대인들이 무함마드에게 네가 정말 하나님께서 보내신 메신 저라면 기적을 행해 보라[45]고 했을 때 무함마드는 아무 기적도 행할 수 없었고, 다만 꾸란이 기적이라고 말했다는 것이다.[46]

＊ 모세와 예수는 학문과 지식이 충만했다. 그러나 무함마드는 문맹이었다. 무함마드가 문맹이라는 것은 꾸란에 명시되어 있는 것 이다.[47] 모세는 애굽의 궁궐에서 40년 동안 최고의 학문과 재주를 익 혔으며 예수께서는 하늘과 땅의 모든 지식을 알고 계셨으나 무함마 드는 문맹이기에 모세와 같은 선지자가 무함마드라고 주장하는 것 은 무모한 일이다.

＊ 또한 모세가 말했던 "나와 같은 선지자" 란 의미는 본문을 자세 히 읽어 보면 "너의 형제 중에서" 라는 단서가 붙은 것이다. 너의 형 제 중에서란 말은 "이스라엘 혈통에서 태어난 사람들 중에서" 라는 말이다. 예수께서는 분명히 이스라엘 혈통을 타고 유다 지파에서 태

---

45. Mark G. , 『The Unfinished Battle Islam & the Jews』, 86~87p.
46. 꾸란 29:50~51, 어째서 그이에게는 주로부터 직접적인 증표가 주어지지 못했는가고 그들은 말 한다. 그러나 참으로 여러 증표는 알라에게만 있는 것, 나는 공공연한 경고자에 불과하다고 말 해 주어라. 알라가 그대에게 경전을 내리고 그가 그것을 모든 사람에게 읽어 주는 것으로 충분 하지 않는가. 그 자체만으로 믿음이 깊은 이들에게는 더 없는 자비와 교훈이다(김용선 역).
47. 꾸란 7:158, 말하라, 모든 자들, 나는 너희들 모두에게 보내진 알라의 메신저이다. 알라께서는 하늘과 땅을 통치하시는 분, 따로 여하한 신도 없으며, 살리기도 하시고 죽이기도 하시는 분이 시다. 그러므로 알라와 문맹인 메신저를 믿으라. 또 알라와 그 말씀을 믿고, 그를 따르라. 그러 면 너희들은 반드시 바르게 인도될 것이다(김용선 역).

어나셨지만 무함마드는 이스라엘 혈통이 아니라 아라비아 반도의 꾸라이시(Quraish)족의 하심(Hashim)가에서 태어났다. 그러므로 모세가 말하던 "나와 같은 선지자" 란 절대로 무함마드가 될 수가 없는 것이다.

이렇게 분명한 증거가 있음에도 불구하고 많은 무슬림들은 구약성경에 예언된 무싸(모세)와 같은 선지자가 바로 무함마드를 의미하는 것이라고 귀에 못이 박히도록 교육을 받고 있는 것이다.

성경이 변질되었다고 주장하는 근거

그렇다면 무함마드가 성경의 백성들이 가지고 있는 신·구약 성경이 변질되었다고 주장하는 근거는 무엇인가? 그것은 무함마드가 계시 받았다고 하는 꾸란이 그 근거의 전부다.

성경이 진리라는 증거는 수 없이 많이 있다. 역사적으로 고고학적으로 수많은 학자들이 성경의 진리 됨을 확인하여 왔다.[48] 그리고 1,600년 동안에 걸쳐서 40여명의 성경 저자들이 성경이 진리라는 것을 상호 보완적으로 증명해 왔다.

너희는 여호와의 책을 자세히 읽어 보라, 이것들이 하나도 빠진 것이 없고 하나도 그 짝이 없는 것이 없으리니 이는 여호와의 입이 이를

---

48. 성경의 진리됨을 밝히기 위해서 성경고고학 혹은 성경 비평학자들이 성경의 역사성과 문화적 사회적 정황을 학문적으로 살펴 성경의 진리임을 밝히고 있으나 꾸란 고고학이나 꾸란 비평학은 존재하지 않는다. 만일 어떤 무슬림 학자가 그런 것을 연구한다고 하면 크게 불이익을 받을 것이다. 이는 꾸란의 계시가 의심이나 질문을 허용하지 않을 뿐 아니라(꾸란 5:101) 꾸란의 내용 중 6하 원칙에 의해서 기록되어 있지 않기 때문에 연구 자체가 불가능하기 때문이기도 하다.

명하셨고 그의 신이 이것들을 모으셨음이라. -이사야 34:16

너무나 분명하게 하나님의 신이 그 책들을 친히 명하셨고 친히 모으셨다고 말씀하고 있기에 성경을 자세히 살펴보면 다 짝이 있고 근거가 있고 하나님께서 성령을 통해서 직접 명하셨다는 것을 확인할 수 있는 역사적·고고학적·학문적인 증거가 있는 것이다. 어떤 두 사람이 1백년 5백년 혹은 천년을 사이에 두고 받은 계시라도 그계시의 근원이 성령이라면 그 두 사람의 계시는 상호 보완적이고 서로 진리 됨을 증명해 주는 것이다.

그러나 꾸란은 전혀 다르다. 성경이 변질되었다고 주장하지만 성경이 변질되었다는 증거를 과학적·고고학적·학문적으로 입증할 수 있는 근거도 없고 증인도 없는 것이다. 유일한 증인이 있다면 꾸란을 계시 받았다고 하는 무함마드가 단독으로 증인이 되는 것이다. 이슬람의 교리는 꾸란을 완벽하게 해석하는 일이 불가능하기에 반드시 아랍어로 읽어야 한다고 하며 이는 절대로 변질되지 않은 순수한 알라의 원서(Original Book of Allah)라고 주장한다.[49]

무함마드의 기독교인들에 대한 미움

위의 이유들 즉 성경이 변질되었다든지 삼위일체를 부인한다든

---

49. 최영길『이슬람 문화』, (서울: 도서출판 알림, 2004), 98p.

지 하는 이유는 무함마드가 기독교인들을 핍박하기 위한 명분으로 내세운 것이지만 그것은 사실에 근거한 것이 아니었다는 것이 앞 장의 설명에 의해서 증명이 되었다고 본다.

이슬람 측의 주장을 들어보면 무슬림들이 기독교인들을 미워할 수 밖에 없는 이유를 역사적인 측면에서 설명하려고 한다. 즉 한국 사람들은 35년간(1910-1945) 일본의 침략으로 고생했기 때문에 반세 기가 지났음에도 불구하고 일본에 대한 감정이 좋지 못한 것이 사실 이지 않은가? 그러나 십자군 전쟁은 기독교인들이 성지탈환이라는 명목으로 이슬람 지역에 들어와 200여년간(1096-1291) 괴롭힌 사건이 역사적으로 부인할 수 없는 사실이기 때문에 기독교인들을 생각하 면 십자군의 잔인한 역사를 기억하게 되어 미워하는 것이 당연한 것이 아니겠느냐며 반문한다.

그러나 그것은 사실이 아니다. 십자군 전쟁이 역사적 사실이 아 니라는 말이 아니다. 무슬림들이 십자군 전쟁 때문에 기독교인들을 미워하는 것이 아니라는 것이다. 무슨 근거로 그렇게 주장할 수 있 는가? 상식적으로 생각해봐도 11세기 말에 발생한 십자군 전쟁 때 문에 7세기 초부터 무함마드를 비롯한 무슬림들이 기독교인들을 미 워했다는 것이 설득력이 있다고 보는가? 실제로 중동지역에 가보면 11세기에서 13세기까지 있었던 십자군 전쟁을 기억하며 살아가는 서민들을 거의 만나볼 수 없을 것이다. 정치하는 사람들이 자주 주 장하기 때문에 "그런 일이 있었나보다"라고 생각하는 것이다.

그렇다면 7세기부터 무함마드가 기독교인들을 미워하게 되고 핍 박하게 된 진정한 이유는 무엇인가?

무함마드의 계시 비판

　　무함마드가 기독교인들을 미워하게 되었던 가장 중요한 실제적
동기는 그가 계시를 받았다고 하면서 신·구약 성경에 기록되어
있는 구절들과 비슷한 꾸란의 구절들을 말할 때마다 유대교인들과
기독교인들 즉 성경의 백성들은 그것이 사실이 아니라는 사실을
즉각 분별할 수 있었기 때문에"그것은 계시가 아니라 거짓이라"고
폭로했을 것이다.[50] 왜냐하면 유대인들은 성경을 거의 외우다시피
하면서 일점일획이라도 소중히 여기며,[51] 존중하였고 기독교인들도
성경 말씀을 주야로 묵상하면서[52] 오랫동안 신앙생활을 해 왔기 때
문에 성경의 인물들이나 사건들에 대한 내용은 일단 듣는 순간에 그
것이 성경의 내용과 일치하는지 아닌지를 분별할 수가 있었던 것이다.
그런데 무함마드가 알라(Allah)의 계시라고 말하는 내용들은 그들이
지금까지 소중히 여기며 묵상해왔던 신·구약 성경과는 너무나 많은
차이가 나는 것이었다.[53] 그래서 그들은 무함마드가 받았다고 하는
계시를 듣는 순간 즉각 "저것은 계시가 아니라 거짓말이다."라고 배
척했을 것이다. 그러나 우상을 숭배하는 사람들은 무함마드의 말이
사실인지 아닌지 분별할 수 있는 능력이 전혀 없었다. 유독 성경의

---

50. William Montgomery Watt, Muslim-Christian encounters (London: Routledge,1991), 24p.
51. 신약성경 마태복음 5:18.
52. 구약성경 시편 1편 2.
53. 진원숙, 『충돌의 역사』(서울: 신서원,2002), 251p.

백성들만이 무함마드의 계시가 자신들이 섬기는 창조주 하나님의 영에 의한 계시가 아니라는 것을 분별할 수 있었고 그래서 그를 배척했던 것이었다. 많은 사람들 앞에서 계시를 받았다고 하면서 중요한 선포를 하던 무함마드에게 성경의 백성들의 배척은 매우 난감한 문제였을 것이다.

결국 무함마드는 기독교인들이 가지고 있는 성경이 변질되었다고 주장하면서 자신의 계시를 거짓이라고 하는 자들에게 저주를 선언하고 기독교인들을 미워하기 시작했던 것이었다.

> 대체로 알라에게 '터무니없는 거짓된 날조로, 진리가 나타나도 이를 거짓말이라 이르는 자처럼 악한 자가 더 있을까?' 지옥 속에는 믿지 않는 자들을 위한 거주지가 마련되어 있지 않다는 말인가?
>
> —꾸란 29:68 김용선 역

> 알라께 거짓을 날조하고 또 '알라의 계시를 부정하는 자만큼 더 나쁜 자가 있겠는가?' 죄를 범한 자들이 번성한 일은 없다.
>
> —꾸란 10:7 김용선 역

이런 구절들 외에도 꾸란은 수시로 알라의 계시를 부정하는 사람들에게 심판과 저주를 선언한다(꾸란 7:146, 꾸란 7:176, 꾸란 7:177, 꾸란 7:182, 꾸란 8:54, 꾸란 10:39, 꾸란 23:44 꾸란 23:49, 꾸란 26:117, 꾸란 26:160…).

무함마드는 성경의 백성들의 배척을 처음에는 모든 선지자들을 배척한 역사적인 사건들을 들어 일반화 시키고자 한다. 즉 노아(누흐)의 시대에 살던 사람들은 홍수가 날 것을 미리 경고한 노아(누흐)의 계시를 믿지 않다가 결국은 멸망을 당한 사건이라든지 모세(무싸)의 경고를 듣지 않고 멸망을 당한 애굽의 바로왕의 경우 등을 예를 들면서 일반적으로 선지자들은 배척을 당했었으며, 선지자의 계시는 항상 무시를 당해 왔다는 것을 주장하면서 자신이 계시가 무시당하는 것을 참아 왔다. 그러나 그의 인내는 메디나에 와서 무너지게 되는데 막강한 통치권을 잡으면서 더 이상 참을 이유가 없어진 것이다.[54]

영이 다르기 때문이다.

무함마드가 기독교인들을 미워하게 된 실제적인 동기는 자신의 계시를 인정하지 않기 때문이라고 한다면 영적인 동기는 무함마드에게 계시를 내려준 영은 성령이 아니기 때문이라는 것이다. 그렇다면 그 영은 어떤 영일까?

예수 그리스도의 신성을 부인하는 영

무함마드가 기독교인들을 핍박해야하는 명분으로 내세운 것은 예수는 여러 사도 중의 한 사람에 불과한데 기독교인들이 예수를 신의 아들로 받들고 있다는 것이다.[55] 그래서 기독교인들을 다신교도

---

54. 무함마드가 메디나의 통치자로 등극하고 처음 새해를 맞는 서기 624년 초부터 성경의 백성들에 대한 그의 평화로운 계시는 사라지고 기독교인들은 세 신(神)을 믿는 다신교도로 유대교인들은 변질된 성경을 가지고 있는 알라의 저주를 받은 자들로 계시의 내용이 바뀌었다.

로 몰아 부치며 핍박을 했던 것이었다. 아랍어로 다신교를 표현하는 단어는 무쉬리쿤(Mushrikun)이라고 한다. 그런데 이 단어의 어원은 쉬르크(Shirk)에서 나온 것이다. 쉬르크란 말은 "함께한다, 공유한다, 나눠 가진다."는 의미이다. 즉 알라(Allah)외에는 신이 없다고 하는 것이 무함마드의 주장인데 기독교인들은 예수 그리스도를 하나님의 아들 즉 성자 하나님으로 부르니 이는 알라의 신성을 나눠가지는 또 하나의 다른 신으로 보는 것이다. 그래서 기독교인들을 핍박하는 것이다.

　　그러나 여기서 우리는 무함마드의 계시의 배후에 숨어있는 영의 정체를 밝히고 넘어가야 할 필요를 느낀다. 무함마드가 예수의 신성을 부인하는 이유는 무엇이며 이는 무엇을 의미하는 것인가?

**　　그러므로 내가 너희에게 알게 하노니 하나님의 영으로 말하는 자는 누구든지 예수를 저주할 자라 하지 않고 또 '성령으로 아니하고는 누구든지 예수를 주시라 할 수 없느니라.' -고린도전서 12:3**

　　성경은 분명히 "사랑하는 자들아 영을 다 믿지 말고 오직 영들이 하나님께 속하였나 시험하라 많은 거짓 선지자가 세상에 나왔음이니라(요한일서 4:1)라고 말씀하고 계시다. 그런데 성령으로 아니하고는 누구든지 예수를 주시라 할 수 없다고 말씀하고 계신 것이다. 그러므로 예수의 동정녀 탄생이라든지, 예수의 기적이라든지 하는 것들은 이슬람의 꾸란에서도 인정을 하는 것이지만[56] 그 계시를 내

55. 김종빈, 『갈등의 핵 유대인』(경기: 효형출판사, 2007), 9p.

린 배후의 영이 성령인가 아닌가 하는 것은 예수 그리스도의 신성을 인정하느냐 아니냐에 달려 있는 것이다. 예수 그리스도의 신성을 부인하는 영은 성령이 아니라는 점을 분명히 알아야 한다. 따라서 이 성경 말씀에 의하면 이슬람의 영은 성령이 아니라는 증거가 되는 것이다.

삼위일체를 부인하는 영

무함마드는 기독교인들을 핍박할 수 있는 명분을 만들기 위해서 기독교인들이 믿고 있는 삼위일체를 정죄하고 나섰다. 이슬람은 단일신론을 신봉하기 때문에 다른 죄는 용서받을 수 있으나 다신교도는 절대 용납할 수 없는 것이다.[57] 그래서 기독교인들을 핍박하기 위한 명분으로는 기독교인들을 다신교도들로 정죄했던 것이다. 그렇게 해서 삼위일체론을 거론하면서 기독교인들은 세 신을 섬기는 잡신교인들로 몰아세운 것이다. 아래 구절을 보면 꾸란에 기록된 삼위일체를 정죄하는 내용들을 볼 수 있을 것이다.

'신은 즉 마리암(마리아)의 아들 구세주이시다'라고 하는 자는 이미 믿지 않는 자이다. 그러나 구세주(메시아)는 말하고 있지 않는가? '이스라엘 자손들아, 내 주이시며 너희들의 주이신 알라를 숭배하라' 알라와 나란히 다른 어떤 것을 숭배하는 자에게 알라께선 천국으로 들어

---

56. 꾸란은 이싸(예수)의 동정녀 탄생이나 기적들을 인정한다. 그러나 그의 신성은 부인한다.
57. 김성철, 『종교학 대사전』(서울: 한국 사전연구사, 1998), 1038p.

가는 것을 금하셨다. 그가 살 곳은 지옥의 불이다. 불의의 무리에게는 아무도 도울 자가 없다. '참으로 알라는 세 분 중의 한 분이시다'라고 하는 자는 이미 믿지 않는 자이다. '한 분의 알라 이외에 딴 신은 없다. 그런 말을 그만 두지 않는다면 믿음을 배반하는 이런 자에게는 반드시 고통스러운 벌이 내리게 될 것이다' ─구란 5:72-73

또 알라께서 이렇게 물었을 때의 일, "마리암(마리아)의 아들 이싸(예수)여, 너는 사람들에게 '알라가 아니라 나와 나의 어머니를 신으로 숭배하라'라고 말하였는가? 이싸(예수)는 대답하기를 '당신에게 영광 있으라. 말할 권리도 없는 제가 어떻게 말할 수 있겠습니까? 만일 제가 그런 말을 하였다면, 당신은 이미 알고 계실 것입니다. 당신은 내 마음 속에 있는 것을 이미 알고 계시지 않습니까? 그런데 저는 당신의 마음속을 모릅니다. 참으로 당신은 보이지 않는 것을 모두 알고 계십니다. 저는 당신이 명령하신 것, 내 주이면서 당신의 주이신 알라를 숭배하라는 이외는 아무 것도 그들에게 말하지 않았습니다…

─구란 5:116-117 上 김용선 역

무함마드가 말하던 삼위일체라는 것은 기독교인들이 말하는 삼위일체와 같은 의미가 아니다. 기독교인들은 성부와 성자와 성령을 삼위일체라고 말하지만, 꾸란에서 말하는 삼위일체는 위의 구절에서 보듯이 알라(Allah)와 마리암(Mariam:마리아)과 이싸(Isa:예수)를 말하는 것이다. 즉 알라께서 마리암(마리아)과 관계를 해서 이싸(예수)를 낳았는데[58] 기독교인들이 이싸(예수)를 신으로 믿는다면 그 모친은 여신으로 믿어야 하지 않겠는가?[59] 결국 기독교인들은 이 셋을 신으로 믿고 있다고 주장하는 것이다. 세상의 기독교인들 중에 삼위일체를 이렇게 말하거나 가르치는 성직자나 학자는 없다. 그러나 무함마드는 기독교인들을 핍박할 구실을 만들기 위해서 소위 꾸란의 계시를 통해서 이렇게 무리한 억지 주장을 하고 있는 것이다.

십자가를 부인하는 영

무함마드는 알라(Allah)의 계시를 받았다고 하면서 예수 그리스도가 십자가에 못 박혀 돌아가셨다는 사실을 부인하고 있다. 다음 꾸란 구절에 의하면

그 뿐인가 '우리들은 구세주, 신의 사도, 마리암(마리아)의 아들 이싸(예수)를 죽였다.'고 말하고 있다. 어째서 잡혀 죽었겠는가? '어찌하여 십자가에 매달렸겠는가? 단지 그와 같이 보였을 뿐이다.' 본래 이 점에 대해 논쟁을 벌이고 있는 사람들은 그에 대해 의문을 갖고 있다. 이에 관해서 그들에게 어떠한 확실한 지식이 있는 것도 아니고 단지 '제 나름대로의 억측에 불과하다.' 아니 그들은 절대로 이싸(예수)를 죽이지 않은 것이 확실하다. —꾸란 4:157 김용선 역

무함마드는 예수가 십자가에 못 박혀 죽지 않았다고 말하고 있는

---

58. 돈 리처드슨, 『꾸란의 비밀』, 이희민 역(서울: 쿰란출판사, 2008), 27p.
59. 요하힘 그닐카, 『성경과 꾸란 무엇이 같으며 무엇이 다른가』, 154p.

것이다. 단지 그와 같이 보였을 뿐이라고 꾸란은 말하고 있다. 그러면 이슬람의 교리에 의하면 예수의 십자가는 도대체 어떻게 설명하고 있는 것인가?

그들의 설명에 의하면 이렇다. 이싸(예수)가 제자들과 함께 저녁식사를 하고 나서 잠자리에 들었는데 제자들 중의 한 사람이 이싸(예수)를 팔기 위해서 어둠속을 달려 나갔다고 한다. 그런데 자비로운 알라께서 다락방에서 제자들과 잠자고 있는 이싸(예수)의 얼굴과 달려가는 제자의 얼굴을 바꿔치기 하셨다는 것이다. 그래서 서기관들과 바리새인들에게 이싸(예수)를 넘겨주면 얼마를 주겠느냐고 물을 때 그들이 이싸(예수)의 얼굴을 알아보고 그 자리에서 체포해 십자가에 매달아 죽게 했다는 것이다. 그리고 진짜 이싸(예수)는 다른 사람의 얼굴을 하고 살다가 죽음을 보지 않고 승천했다는 것이다. 위의 꾸란 구절은 이 이야기를 뒷받침하고 있는 것이다.[60]

그러면 무함마드는 왜 이싸(예수)의 동정녀 탄생도 인정하고 기적들도 인정하면서 십자가만을 부인하고 있는 것인가?

그 이유는 성경을 통해서 확인할 수 있는 것이다. 하나님께서 죄에 빠져서 죽을 수밖에 없는 인류를 구원하시기 위해서 선택하신 유일한 방법이 바로 십자가인 것이다.[61] 죄가 없으신 예수께서 죄인들을

---

60. 꾸란 4:157. (최영길 역), 여기서 최영길 박사는 "바르나바의 복음서"를 인용하여 이싸 대신에 다른 사람이 대신하여 살해당했다는 이론을 제시하고 있다.

61. 사도행전 2:36, 그런즉 이스라엘 온 집이 정녕 알지나 너희가 십자가에 못 박은 이 예수를 하나님이 주와 그리스도가 되게 하셨느니라 하니라.

구원하시기 위해서 숨겨놓으셨던 비밀이 바로 십자가였던 것이다. 메시아가 태어나면 택한 백성들을 죄에서 해방시켜 주실 것이라고 성경에서 여러 차례 예언해 놓고 계신다. 예수 그리스도는 근본 하나님의 본체시나 육체를 입으시고 우리 가운데 거하시면서 고통당하시다가 결국은 우리 죄를 대신 갚아 주시기 위해서 십자가에서 돌아가신 것이다. 천하 인간에게 구원을 얻을만한 다른 이름을 주신 일이 없는데 하나님께서 그 인류를 구원하시기 위해서 택하신 유일한 방법이 바로 십자가인 것이다.

그런데 마귀 혹은 적그리스도는 인류가 구원받는 것을 시기하는 영이다. 이들은 택한 백성이라도 한 사람이라도 더 미혹하여 지옥으로 끌고 가고자 최선을 다하며 우는 사자와 같이 삼킬 자를 찾아다니고 있는 것이다.[62] 그런데 그 마귀 혹은 적그리스도가 인류를 멸망시키기 위해서 사용하는 방법은 바로 십자가를 부인하는 방법이다.

초대교회에 영지주의(그노시스)라는 이단이 있었다. 이 이단은 예수께서 육체로 오셨다는 사실을 부인했다.

"하나님의 영은 이것으로 알지니 곧 '예수 그리스도께서 육체로 오신 것을 시인하는 영마다 하나님께 속한 것이요, 예수를 시인하지 아니하는 영마다 하나님께 속한 것이 아니니 이것이 곧 적그리스도의 영이니라.'오리라 한 말을 너희가 들었거니와 이제 벌써 세상에 있느니라." -요한일서 4:2-3

---

62. 베드로 전서 5:8, 근신하라 깨어라 너희 대적 마귀가 우는 사자같이 두루 다니며 삼킬 자를 찾나니

이 영지주의 이단의 배후에 적그리스도의 영이 있다고 성경은 말씀하고 계신다. 그 때 영지주의 이단의 배후에 숨어서 인류의 구원을 방해하며 역사하던 영인 적그리스도의 영은 예수께서 육체로 임하심을 부인하였다고 하는데 그 이유는 무엇일까? 이는 예수께서 육체로 임하심을 부인하면 십자가는 자동으로 부인되기 때문에 인류 구원의 길은 원천적으로 봉쇄되는 것이다.

그런데 이슬람의 영은 예수께서 육체로 임하심을 부인하지는 않는다. 오히려 육체로 임하신 예수의 거의 모든 부분을 인정하고 있다. 그렇지만 십자가만은 부인한다. 즉 초대교회 때에 영지주의라는 이단의 배후에 숨어서 인류 구원을 방해하던 적그리스도가 이제는 더욱 교묘한 방법으로 예수 그리스도의 모든 면을 인정하면서 십자가만 부인하는 방법으로 인류 구원을 원천적으로 봉쇄하려는 방법을 사용하고 있는 것이다.[63]

십자가를 부인하는 영은 적그리스도의 영이요, 인류 구원을 방해하는 영이요, 하나님의 인류구원 계획을 대적하는 영인 것이다. 그러므로 예수 그리스도께서 십자가에 못 박혀 돌아가셨다는 사실을 부인하는 이슬람의 영은 인류 구원을 위해 갖은 고초를 겪으시고 우리를 구원하기 위해서 피 흘려 돌아가신 예수 그리스도의 고귀한 희

---

63. 기독교의 상징은 십자가다. 예수 그리스도의 십자가는 그의 많은 사역들 중의 하나가 아니라 가장 중요한 핵심이며 그것이 없으면 기독교는 무의미한 종교가 되는 것이다. 그래서 교회의 제일 높은 곳에는 십자가를 달며 이것을 부인하는 것은 기독교 전체를 멸망시키려는 사탄의 계략이다.

생과 사랑을 조롱하는 것이며 기독교의 핵심을 부인하는 것이기에 적그리스도의 영이라는 것이 명백히 증명된다.

예수의 부활을 부인하는 영

초대교회 전도자들의 핵심적인 내용은 부활이었다. 십자가에 돌아가신 사건은 그 당시 예루살렘에 사는 많은 사람들이 목격하였으므로 더 이상 부인할 수 없는 사실이기에 예수 그리스도의 메시아 되심을 증명할 수 있는 유력한 도구는 부활의 메시지였던 것이다. 그래서 초대교회 사도들은 전도할 때 자신들을 "부활의 증인"으로 묘사했다.

이 예수를 하나님이 '살리신지라 우리가 다 이 일에 증인이로다.'

-사도행전 2:32

너희가 거룩하고 의로운 자를 부인하고 도리어 살인한 사람을 놓아 주기를 구하여 생명의 주를 죽였도다. 그러나 하나님이 죽은 자 가운데서 '살리셨으니 우리가 이 일에 증인이로다.' -사도행전 3:14~15

너희가 나무에 달아 죽인 예수를 우리 조상의 '하나님이 살리시고' 이스라엘로 회개케 하사 죄 사함을 얻게 하시려고 그를 오른손으로 높이사 임금과 구주를 삼으셨느니라. '우리는 이 일에 증인이요' 하나님이 자기를 순종하는 사람들에게 주신 성령도 그러하니라 하더라.

-사도행전 5:30~32

초대교회의 사도들이 전도[64]할 때 스스로를 부활의 증인으로 소개했다는 점은 매우 중요한 것이다. 예수 그리스도의 부활 사건은 그분의 신성과 메시아 되심을 증명하는 사건이며 예수 그리스도께서 지상에서 전하신 말씀이 모두 진리라는 것을 확인하는 중요한 의미가 있는 것이다. 왜냐하면 예수께서는 살아계실 때 여러 번 제자들에게 자신이 고난 받을 것과 다시 살아나실 것을 말씀하셨기 때문에 이 사실은 예루살렘에 사는 모든 믿지 않는 자들까지 다 알고 있었고, 심지어는 예수를 대적하는 무리들까지 알고 있었다.

그 이튿날은 예비일 다음 날이라 대제사장들과 바리새인들이 함께 빌라도에게 모여 가로되 주여 '저 유혹하던 자가 살았을 때에 말하되 내가 사흘 후에 다시 살아나리라 한 것을 우리가 기억하노니 그러므로 분부하여 그 무덤을 굳게 지키게 하소서' 그의 제자들이 와서 시체를 도적질하여 가고 백성에게 말하되 그가 죽은 자 가운데서 살아났다 하면 후에 유혹이 전보다 더 될까 하나이다 하니 빌라도가 가로되 너희에게 파수꾼이 있으니 가서 힘대로 굳게 하라 하거늘 저희가 파수꾼과 함께 가서 돌을 인봉하고 무덤을 굳게 하니라. -마태복음 27:62-66

대제사장들과 바리새인들은 예수를 십자가에 죽이는데 가장 중요한 역할을 했던 사람들이었다. 그들까지도 예수께서 살아계실 때에 "내가 죽은 지 사흘 후에 다시 살아날 것이다"고 예언하셨던 것을

---

64. 초대교회 교인들의 전도할 때 두 가지 핵심 주제는 예수께서 그 조상들이 수천 년 동안 기다려 오던 바로 그 메시아라는 것과 그가 죽은 자 가운데서 다시 살아났다는 부활의 메시지였다.

알고 있었다. 그런데 만일 부활 사건이 일어나지 않았다면 예수 그리스도께서 지상에서 하셨던 모든 말씀은 믿을 수 없는 거짓말이 되고 마는 것이다.[65] 그래서 예수께서 부활하신 후 천사는 무덤을 찾아온 여인들에게 "그가 여기 계시지 않고 말씀하시던 대로 살아 나셨느니라 와서 그의 누우셨던 곳을 보라."(마태복음 28:6)고 말씀하셨던 것이다.

부활 사건은 그러므로 기독교의 가장 중요하고 큰 기둥 중의 하나이다. 인류의 구원이 십자가 위에서 예수께서 "다 이루었다"[66]고 말씀하심으로 완성되었다면, 예수께서 지상에서 가르치시고 명하신 모든 말씀들이 진리임을 확인하고 보증하는 사건은 바로 부활 사건이었던 것이다.

그런데 적그리스도의 영은 이슬람의 옷을 입고 와서 예수의 부활을 부인함으로서 진리를 거짓으로 만들고자 하며 하나님의 인류 구원 계획을 조롱거리로 만들고자 하는 것이다.

그들은 절대로 그(이싸)를 '죽이지 않은 것이 확실하다. 알라께서 그를 자기 곁으로 끌어들인 것'이다. 알라께서는 위력 있고 총명하신 분이시다. -구란 4:157 下-158 김용선 역

이슬람에서는 예수(이싸)가 십자가에서 죽었다는 사실을 부인하

---

65. 기독교의 인류구원의 진리는 십자가에서 완성되었지만 부활 사건으로 확증된 것이다. 그리스도의 부활이 없었다면 겁쟁이 제자들은 흩어져 버리고 복음은 초대교회에 이미 소멸되었을 것이다.
66. 요한복음 28:30.

니까 부활은 자동적으로 부정되는 것이다. 죽지 않았다고 하면서 어찌 다시 살아났다고 할 수 있겠는가? 그래서 그들은 죽지 않고 승천했다는 교리를 주장하는 것이다. 이는 기독교의 많은 교리들 중에 한 가지를 부정하는 것이 아니라 기독교에서 가장 핵심적인 부분인 십자가와 부활을 부정함으로 인류 구원의 길을 원천적으로 봉쇄하고자 하는 것이다.

이런 면으로 볼 때 무함마드가 받았다고 하는 이슬람의 계시는 절대로 성령의 역사가 아니라는 것을 확인할 수 있는 것이다.[67]

기독교를 대적하는 영

근본적으로 무함마드가 기독교인들을 핍박하던 원래의 이유는 기독교와 이슬람의 영은 서로 다른 영이기 때문이다. 성령과 적그리스도의 영은 서로 평화롭게 공존할 수가 없는 것이다. 진리와 거짓은 아무리 비슷하게 꾸민다 할지라도 언젠가는 정체가 드러나게 되는 것이다.

근신하라 깨어라 너희 대적 마귀가 우는 사자같이 두루 다니며
삼킬 자를 찾나니 -베드로 전서 5:8

무함마드가 기독교인들을 핍박했던 일은 이슬람 측에서 아무리

---

67. 하르트무트 보브친,『무함마드는 이렇게 말했다』염정용 역(서울: 들녘, 2005), 27p.

그것을 부인하려고 해도 도저히 부인할 수 없는 역사적 사실이며 그 근본적 이유는 영이 다르기 때문이라는 것이다.

믿는 자들이여 유대인과 '기독교인들을 친구로 그리고 보호자로써 택하지 말라' 그들은 서로가 친구들이라 그들에게로 향하는 너희가 있다면 그는 그 무리의 일원이거늘 알라는 이 우매한 백성들을 인도하지 아니하시니라. –꾸란 5:51 최영길 역

유대교인이나 '기독교인은 당신이 그들의 종교를 추종하지 않는 한 만족치 않을 것이다.' 말하라. "알라의 인도만이 진실한 인도이다"라고. 만약 당신이 지식을 얻은 다음에도 그들의 욕망에 따른다면 알라로부터 떨어져 당신을 보호할 자도 도울 자도 없다.

–꾸란 2:120 김용선 역

'알라의 종교는 이슬람뿐이며' 이전에 성경을 받은 자(기독교인, 유대교인)들도 달리하지 아니하였으나 그 후 그들에게 그른 지식이 도래하였더라. 알라의 말씀을 불신하는 자 알라의 심판을 곧 받으리라.

–꾸란 3:19 최영길 역

'이슬람 외에 다른 종교를 추구하는 자 결코 수락되지 않을 것이니' 내세에서 패망자 가운데 있게 되리라. –꾸란 3:85 최영길 역

이슬람에서는 하루에 메카를 향해서[68] 다섯 번씩 기도하고 있다는 사실을 모르는 사람은 거의 없을 것이다. 그런데 그들은 무슨 기도

를 할까를 질문해 본 일이 있는가? 그 기도의 내용은 매일 상황에 따라 바뀌는 것이 아니다. 천주교처럼 매주 교황청에서 보내주는 내용을 기도하는 가변적인 것이 아니다. 이미 무함마드 시대에 확정된 기도문인 일곱 절로 된 꾸란 1장 개경 장(Opening Chapter)을 외우는 것이다. 이는 7세기부터 지금까지 전혀 바뀌지 않았으며 앞으로도 이슬람이 존재하는 한 절대로 바뀌지 않을 것이다. 이 기도문은 각자 자신들의 모국어로 외우는 것이 아니다. 꾸란의 언어인 7세기에 무함마드가 사용하던 문어체 아랍어로 외어야 한다. 그래서 무슬림일지라도 그 내용이 무엇을 의미하는지 모르고 무조건 외우는 사람들이 많을 것이다. 왜냐하면 그들은 아랍어를 모르지만 하루 5번씩 하는 기도는 이슬람의 규정 상 반드시 아랍어로 외워야하기 때문이다.[69] 그러나 우리가 그 내용을 살펴보면 그 영의 정체를 알 수가 있는 것이다.

그렇다면 지구상의 모든 무슬림들이 하루에 다섯 번씩 의무적으로 외워야 하는 영원불변하는 이슬람의 기도문인 꾸란의 개경 장[70]에는 무슨 내용이 기록되어 있을까?

1절: 자비롭고 자애로우신 알라의 이름으로

---

68. 무함마드는 메디나로 이주한 후 유대인들의 환심을 사기 위해서 예루살렘을 향하여 16~17개월간 기도했으나 그들이 계속 배척하자 메카 방향을 향해 기도하는 것으로 바꿨다.
69. 최영길, 『무함마드와 이슬람』, 156~157p.
70. 이슬람의 기도는 하루 메카를 향하여 5회씩 시간을 맞춰 하는데 개경장을 외우는 것은 의무적으로 17회(아침:2회, 점심: 4회, 오후: 4회, 저녁: 3회, 밤: 4회 총 17회)이지만 마지막 7절까지 외우는 것은 하루에 최소한 5회이다.

2절: 온 우주의 주님이신 알라께 찬미를 드리나이다.

3절: 그 분은 자애로우시고 자비로우시며

4절: 심판의 날을 주관 하시도다.

5절: 우리는 당신만을 경배하오며 당신에게만 구원을 비노니

6절: 저희를 바른 길로 인도하여 주시옵소서.

7절: 그 길은 당신께서 축복을 내리신 길이며 '노여움을 받은 자나 방황하는 자들' 이 걷지 않는 가장 올바른 길이옵니다. -최영길 역

여기서 7절에 나오는 노여움을 받은 자는 누구며 방황하는 자들은 누구를 말하는 것인가? 꾸란의 어느 주석을 읽어봐도 노여움을 받은 자들은 유대인들을 말하는 것이며 방황하는 자들이란 기독교인들을 말하는 것이라고 해석하고 있다.[71] 어떤 이슬람 학자들도 이를 다른 의미로 해석하지 않는다. 이 얼마나 무서운 일인가? 전 세계 인구의 20퍼센트 정도를 차지하고 있는 무슬림들이 매일 하루 다섯 번씩이나 기독교인들은 방황하는 자들이라고 선포하고 있는 것이다. 그들은 왜 이렇게 지나칠 정도로 기독교를 대적하는 일들을 제도화시켜서 강제로 매일 확인 고백하게 하는 것일까? 이는 이슬람의 영이 기독교의 성령을 대적하는 적그리스도의 영이라는 것을 분명하고도 쉽게 확인할 수 있는 근거가 되는 것이다.

---

71. 인터넷 꾸란 사이트인 http://thequran.com에 들어가 보면 꾸란 영문 번역본 4개가 나오는데 그 중 Al-Hilali 번역에 보면 괄호를 열고 노여움을 받은 자는 유대인들이고 방황하는 자는 기독교인이라고 본문에 설명을 포함시켜 놓고 있다.

유대인들을 핍박할 명분 설정

무함마드는 메카에 있을 때 유대인들을 성경의 백성들 및 같은 신을 섬기는 사람들이라고 하며 그들을 자신의 휘하에 끌어들이려고 하다가 그들이 배척하자 힘이 없어서 참고 있었는데 메디나에 와서 통치자의 자리에 올라 힘이 생기자 유대인들을 핍박하기 시작했다. 그런데 그동안 좋은 사람들이라고 하던 유대인들을 핍박하기 위해서는 명분이 필요했다.

무함마드는 과연 유대인들을 왜 핍박해야 하는지에 대한 명분을 무엇이라고 내세웠을까?

성경을 변질시켰다는 주장

무함마드는 유대인들이 모세(무싸)의 성경을 변질시켰다고 주장했다. 물론 이는 유대인들을 핍박할 명분을 만들기 위한 것이었다. 이미 언급했던 대로 무함마드가 살던 시대는 66권의 신·구약 성경이 확정 공포되고 나서 3세기 째로 접어들던 시대였다. 신·구약 성경은 4세기 말에 공인되었고 무함마드는 7세기 초에 계시를 받았다고 했다. 그 때는 신·구약 성경이 있었으나 이것이 아직 아랍어로 번역되지는 않았다고 한다. 어떤 자료에 보면 무함마드 당시에는 구약 성경은 아랍어로 번역되지 않았고, 신약성경은 마태복음 정도가 일부 번역되었을 것[72]이라고 추측한다.

이를 보면 무함마드는 신약성경과 구약성경이 존재한다는 것을 알고 있었다. 복음서와 모세(무쌔)의 율법을 구분해서 언급하고 있는 것을 꾸란에서 자주 볼 수 있다.

> 알라는 '구약과 신약을 내리셨고' 앞서 온 것을 진리로 확증하면서 그대에게 그 책을 계시하노라 -꾸란 3:3 최영길 역

그렇지만 무함마드는 신·구약 성경이 왜곡되었다고 주장했다. 이것은 자신의 계시인 꾸란과 신·구약 성경 간의 내용상의 극심한 차이를 합리화하기 위해서 불가피한 조치였다고 보인다.

> 또 그들 가운데는 '성전을 왜곡하여 성전의 문구처럼 너희들에게 생각케 하는 자가 있다.' 그리고 그것이 알라께서 내리신 것이 아닌데도 알라께서 받은 것이라고 말한다. 그들은 알면서 '알라께 대해 거짓말을 하고 있다.' -꾸란 3:78 김용선 역

성경을 왜곡한 죄는 정죄 받아서 마땅하다는 논리가 적용되면서 유대인들은 무함마드에게 가혹한 징계를 받게 된다.

> 믿는 자들이여 너희 종교를 조롱과 오락으로 하는 자들을 친구로 삼지 말라 '이들은 너희 이전에 성경을 받은 자들로 믿음을 배반했노라' 너희가 믿는 자라면 알라만을 두려워하라. 예배의 부름에 그들은 그것을 조롱과 오락으로 간주했으니 그들은 지혜가 없는 백성이었노라 성경의 백성들에게 일러 가로되 우리가 알라와 우리에게 계시된 것과

---

72. 마크 G., 『이슬람과 유대인 그 끝나지 않은 전쟁』, 113~114p.

이전에 계시된 것을 믿는다하여 우리를 배반하느뇨. 너희 대다수는
거역자들이라. 일러 가로되 내가 너희에게 그것보다 사악한 것을 일
러주사 알라로부터 벌이 있으리라 알라의 저주와 분노를 초래하는 그
들과 그들 가운데 '일부가 원숭이나 돼지로 형상화' 된 그들과 우상을
숭배하는 그들이니라. 이들은 가장 나쁜 곳에서 올바른 길을 벗어나
방황하리라. -꾸란 5: 57~60 최영길 역

한글로 번역된 꾸란은 문맥이 맞지 않아 이해할 수 없이 표현되
어 있으나 원문의 의미는 "그들(유대인들)이 알라의 저주를 받아 원숭
이와 돼지로 만들어 졌다" 는 의미이다.[73] 지금도 무슬림들 중 지하
드 운동을 하는 사람들이나 원리주의자들 특히 팔레스타인 지역에
서는 어린이부터 노인들까지 모든 무슬림들은 유대인들이란 알라
께서 원숭이나 돼지로 만든 족속들이라고 가르치며 죽여야 할 백해
무익한 존재들로 가르치고 있다.[74] 이는 기르트 월더스(Mr. Geert Wilders)
라는 이름을 가진 네덜란드 국회의원이 이슬람의 위험성을 알리는
피트나(Fitna:이슬람을 대항하는 투쟁을 지칭하는 아랍어)라는 16분 짜리 동영상
에서도 확인할 수 있다. 그중 3분 51초부터 4분 17초까지 나오는 대
화 내용을 보면 선생님의 질문에 3살짜리 유치원 여자 아기가 대답
하는 형식으로 영상이 잡혔는데 그 예쁘게 생긴 '바쉬밀라' 라는 이
름의 유치원 아이는 유대인이 무엇이냐고 묻는 선생님의 질문에 "알

---

73. 꾸란 5:60. (Hilali역, Palmer역, Shakir역 영문 참조)
74. http://kr.youtube.com/watch?v=0AxKT_taS0s 인터넷 동영상 참조.

라께서 원숭이와 돼지로 만든 자들"이라고 꾸란에 쓰여 있다고 대답하는 장면을 담고 있다. 또한 이슬람 성직자의 아랍어 설교 내용 중 유대인들은 한 사람도 남김없이 죽여야 한다고 칼을 빼들고 설교하는 한 설교자의 동영상도 담고 있다.[75] 이를 보건대 7세기에 무함마드가 유대인들을 미워한 그 모델을 본받아 21세기의 무슬림들은 유대인들과 아무런 원한이 없는 사람들임에도 불구하고 자신들의 경전인 꾸란에 그렇게 명령하고 있고 또한 자신들이 본받아야 할 무함마드의 역할과 모범이 그렇게 가르치고 있기 때문에 유대인들을 미워하게 되는 것이다.[76]

유대인들이 메시아를 죽였다는 주장

유대인들을 핍박하기 위한 명분을 얻기 위해서 구실을 찾던 무함마드는 유대인들이 "우리가 메시아를 죽였다"고 주장한다고 말했다.

'마리암(마리아)의 아들이며 알라의 선지자 알마씨 이싸(예수 그리스도를 의미함)를 우리가 살해하였다라고 그들(유대인들)이 주장하더라.'그러나 그들은 그를 살해하지 아니하였고, 십자가에 못 박지 아니했으며,

---

75. Geert Wilders, 『fitna』, http:// kr.youtube.com 동영상 프로그램으로 들어가서 "fitna"를 검색하면 볼 수 있다. (http://kr.youtube.com/watch?v=bL9XoM1rbG8)
76. 김용선, 『한역 꾸란(이슬람 경전)』(서울, 어학사), 715p. 여기서 김용선 박사는 꾸란 98:6(진리를 거부한 계전의 백성이나 다신교도들은 지옥의 불 속에 떨어져 그 속에서 영원히 살리라. 이는 중생들 중에 가장 나쁜 자이다)의 각주를 통해서 '기독교인과 유대교인의 경전은 최후의 위대한 예언자의 출현을 위한 준비인데 신·구약 성경에 예언된 메신저 무함마드가 왔음에도 불구하고 진리를 구하려 하지 않고 이를 거부하고 그들 자체의 기호와 욕망을 따를 뿐이기에 그들은 최악의 인간들이라'고 설명하고 있다.

그와 같은 형상을 만들었을 뿐이라. 이에 의견을 달리하는 자들은 의심이며 그들이 알지 못하고 그렇게 추측을 할 뿐 그를 살해하지 아니했노라. 알라께서 그를 오르게 하셨으니 알라는 권능과 지혜로 충만하심이라. -꾸란 4:157~158

예수 그리스도를 아랍어로 알마씨 이싸(Al-Masih Isa)라고 한다. 위의 꾸란 구절은 분명히 유대인들이 알마씨 이싸를 살해하였다고 주장한다고 무함마드가 알라의 계시라고 하면서 제시한 것이다. 그러나 유대인들은 예수를 그리스도 즉 메시아[77]로 인정하지도 않으며 아직도 메시아가 오지 않았다고 하며 메시아를 기다리고 있는 민족임을 우리가 익히 알고 있는 것이다. 그러나 무함마드는 유대인들이 예수를 메시아로 인정하면서 우리가 메시아를 죽였다고 주장한다고 말하고 있는 것이다. 이는 전혀 근거가 없는 말이며 만일 이것이 알라의 계시라면 그 계시는 거짓임이 자명한 것이다. 성령께서는 이런 계시를 내리실 수 없는 분이시다.

에즈라(에스라)를 알라의 아들이라고 함

자신이 계시를 받았다고 하면 이는 계시가 아니라 거짓이라고 배척하는 유대인들을 생각할 때마다 무함마드는 유대인들을 정죄하고

---

77. 그리스도는 헬라어이며 메시아는 히브리어로 "기름부음을 받은 자"라는 같은 의미인데 이를 아랍어로 마씨(Masih) 혹은 정관사 알(Al)을 붙여서 알 마씨(Al-Masih)라고 한다.

싶었을 것이다. 그래서 죄목을 만들었는데 유대인들이 에즈라(성경의 에스라를 의미하는 듯함)를 알라의 아들이라고 주장한다는 것이다.

'유대인이 이르길 에즈라(에스라)가 알라(Allah)의 아들이라고 말하고'기독교인들은 이싸(예수)가 알라(Allah)의 아들이라 하니 이것이 그들의 입으로 주장하는 말이라. 이는 이전에 불신한 자들의 말과 유사하니 알라(Allah)가 그들을 욕되게 하사 그들은 진실에서 멀리 현혹되어 있더라. -꾸란 9:30 최영길 역

유대인들은 특정 선지자를 "알라의 아들" 이라고 부르지는 않는다. 이는 무함마드가 지어낸 말인 것 같다. 아니면 어떤 이들로부터 들은 정보인데 그것이 올바른 정보가 아니었던 것이라고 볼 수 있다. 왜냐하면 지금까지도 유대인들은 에스라(에즈라)가 알라의 아들이라고 주장하는 사람이 없기 때문이다. 그러나 무슬림들은 꾸란의 계시는 알라로부터 직접 받은 계시이기 때문에 누구에게 들은 말이 아니라고 주장하니 그렇다면 그 알라(Allah)는 바르지 못한 정보를 계시하는 신(神)으로서 성령과는 다른 영이라는 것을 확인할 수 있다.

성직자들을 신격화하여 섬긴다

무함마드는 계속해서 유대인들을 핍박하고 정죄할 명분을 찾으나 그 명분들이 사실은 전혀 근거가 없는 명분들이었다. 그 중의 하나는 유대인들이 성직자들을 신격화하여 섬기고 있다는 것이다. 그 주장을 보면 아래와 같다.

그들(유대인들과 기독교인들)은 '알라 외에 아흐바르와 루흐반[78] 그리고 마리암(마리아)의 아들 이싸(예수)를 그들의 주님으로 경배하나 알라 외에는 경배하지 말라 그분 외에는 신이 없노라.' 그들이 더불어 섬기는 것 위에서 알라여 홀로 영광을 받으소서. -꾸란 9:31 최영길 역

우리가 주지하고 있는 사실은 유대인들은 천지를 지으신 여호와 하나님 외에 어떤 인간이나 사물도 신으로 숭배하는 일을 하지는 않는다. 그러나 본문은 알라 외에 유대인과 기독교인들이 섬기는 신이라고 주장하면서 아흐바르와 루흐반[79] 그리고 이싸를 거론하고 있는 것이 보인다. 그러나 이것은 조금만 상식이 있는 사람이라면 인정할 수가 없는 전혀 근거 없는 주장이다. 그러므로 무함마드가 거론한 위의 이유들은 사실상 유대인들이 저지르지 않은 죄를 억지로 누명 씌우려는 것으로 볼 수밖에 없다.

스스로 알라의 아들로 자처함

무함마드는 유대인들에게 죄목을 만들어 핍박하기 위해서 유대

---

78. 최영길, 『성꾸란 의미의 한국어 번역』, 꾸란 9:31 주석 참조 (아흐바르란 율법학자 성직자 목사 사제 및 학자 등의 뜻이며 루흐반은 수사, 염세주의자, 은둔자 및 세상을 단념한 자라는 의미로 본문에서의 아흐바르는 유대인 율법학자 및 성직자를 , 루흐반은 기독교의 율법학자 및 성직자로 이해된다고 최영길 번역 꾸란은 328쪽에서 주석하고 있다).
79. 이슬람의 시아파에서는 이맘(Imam) 숭배 사상이 있다. 이맘은 절대로 죄를 지을 수 없다는 이맘 무오무죄설도 교리로 만들어 가르치고 있다.

인들이 스스로 알라의 아들이라고 주장한다는 것이었다.

　'유대인과 기독교인들이 이르되 우리는 알라의 아들이요 그 분의 사랑받는 자들이라 하니'일러 가로되 그렇다면 왜 그분께서는 너희의 죄악에 대해 벌을 내리겠느뇨. 너희도 그분이 창조한 인간이거늘 그분의 뜻이 있을 때 관용을 베푸시며 그분의 뜻이 있을 때 벌을 주시니라 천지의 모든 것이 알라께 있으며 그 사이의 삼라만상이 그분의 것이거늘 모든 것이 그분에게로 귀의하노라. ―구란 5:18 최영길 역

　유대인들은 스스로 알라의 아들이라고 말하지 않는다. 그런데도 무함마드는 유대인들이 자칭 알라(Allah)의 아들이요 그분의 사랑받는 자들이라고 한다는 계시가 내려왔다는 것이다. 유대인들은 여호와 하나님 외에 다른 신을 절대로 섬기지 않는 사람들이다.[80] 그런데 스스로 알라(Allah)라는 신의 아들이라고 여기는 유대인이 누가 있었을까?[81] 이는 누가 보더라도 억지로 만들어낸 죄목이라고 밖에 해석할 수가 없는 것이다.

---

80. 구약성경 출애굽기 3:14~15.
81. 살레 H. 알아이드,『이슬람국가에서의 비무슬림의 권리』, 최영길 역(서울: 도서출판 알림, 2006). 24p. 역자 최영길 박사는 이 책의 모든 Allah라는 이름을 "알라 하나님"으로 번역하고 있다. 이는 속성 상 '알라 하나님'과 '여호와 하나님'과의 차이를 인정하는 것이라고 볼 수 있다.

무함마드의 유대인들에 대한 미움

유대인들은 기독교인들과 같이 성경을 가지고 있는 백성들이었다. 그들은 조상 대대로 유일신 창조주 하나님만을 섬기고 있었다. 그들은 모세를 통해서 주신 하나님의 율법을 지키는 것을 생명처럼 소중히 여기고 있었다.[82] 심지어 신·구약 중간사(中間史)를 보면 로마 군인들이 공격해 왔는데도 안식일에 일하지 말라는 율법을 지키기 위해서 무기를 들지 않아 목숨을 버린 사람들도 있을 정도로 율법에 철저한 사람들이었다.[83] 그런데 무함마드는 유대인들이 생명처럼 소중히 여기는 율법과 전혀 다른 내용의 말들을 알라(Allah)라는 신의 이름으로 계시를 받았다고 하는데 놀라운 것은 그 알라가 자신들이 믿는 여호와 하나님과 같은 신이라고 주장하는 것이었다. 유대인들은 이것을 참을 수가 없었던 것이었다. 그들은 무함마드가 귀신 들렸거나 제정신이 아닌 것으로 여겼다.[84]

우리는 지금까지의 종교에서 이런 말을 들어본 적이 없었으니 이것은 꾸며낸 우화에 불과 하노라. -꾸란 38:7 최영길 역

그들에게 한 경고자가 왔을 때 불신자들은 놀라며 그를 거짓말쟁이 마술라라 부르더라. -꾸란 38:4 최영길 역

---

82. 최창모, 『이스라엘사』(서울: 대한교과서주식회사, 2007), 196~199p.
83. W. 푀르스터, 『신·구약 중간사』, 문회석 옮김(서울: 컨콜디아사, 1979), 65p.
84. 꾸란 37:36.

128 무함마드의 계시는 왜 자꾸만 바뀔까?
Why Muhammad's revelations are changing repeatedly?

거짓말하는 사람이 가장 싫어하는 것은 자신이 거짓말하고 있다는 것을 폭로하는 사람이다.[85] 유대인들은 무함마드의 계시를 믿을 수가 없었다. 성경과 비교해 보면 거짓이라는 것이 분명하기에 그들은 무함마드가 거짓을 말하면서 계시를 받았다고 주장한다고 말했다. 따라서 무함마드는 유대인들을 가장 미워했던 것이다. 그래서 무함마드는 꾸란의 계시를 통해서 유대인들을 친구로 삼지도 말 것이며 그들은 가장 악한 자들이라고 정죄하고 있는 것이다.

그대는 믿는 자에 대해'더 심한 적의를 가진 것이 유대교인'과 다신교도라는 것을 알고 있을 것이다. -꾸란 5:82 上 최영길 역

그러나 믿음을 배반하고'우리들의 증언을 거짓이라고 한 자들은 지옥 불 속에서 살비 될 것이다.' -꾸란 5:86

성전을 받고 있는 사람들아, 우리가 특히 너희들의 손 앞에 있는 것을 확증하고자 내려준 것을 믿어라. 우리가'뒤 흔적도 볼 수 없을 정도로 얼굴을 짓밟히고'때로는 안식일을 지키지 못한 자들이 저주를 받기 전에. 알라의 명령은 완전히 단행되는 것으로 알라.

-꾸란 4:47 김용선 역

위에 인용된 꾸란 4:47은 원래 이렇게 번역되어야 바른 것이다.

---

85. 엘리어트 애런슨 & 캐럴 태브리스,『거짓말의 진화』, 박웅희 역 (서울: 추수밭, 2007), 289p.

"오 성경의 백성들(유대인들과 기독교인들)아! 우리가 (무함마드에게)내린 계시를, 곧 너희가 알고 있는 바를 확고히 해주는 그 계시를 믿으라. 그렇지 않으면 '우리는 너희 얼굴을 눈, 코, 입이 없는 뒷목처럼 만들어 버리거나, 우리가 안식일을 어긴 자들을 저주한 것과 동일한 방식으로 저주할 것이다.[86] 알라의 명령은 때를 가리지 않고 집행된다.'고 번역해야 할 것이다. 이는 이집트 출신으로 카이로에 있는 알 아즈하르(Al Azhar) 이슬람 신학대학에서 이슬람 역사와 문화 연구로 박사학위(Ph. D.)를 받고 교수를 역임하다가 기독교로 개종하고 미국으로 가서 기독교 교육학으로 박사학위(Ph. D.)를 취득한 마크 G.박사가 영문으로 번역한 것을 한글로 다시 번역한 것이다.

무함마드의 유대인 징계

무함마드가 언젠가 유대인들이 사는 나이디르(Naydir) 부족을 방문했다. 그때 한 유대인 남자가 무함마드에게 돌을 던지며 공격을 해왔다. 무함마드는 아무 상처도 없이 메디나로 돌아와서 그 사내의 행동에 대해서 계시를 받았다고 하며 지하드를 준비하라고 명령했다. 서기 625년 그들은 6일 동안 나이디르(Naydir)를 포위하여 그들의 농산품의 주생산물인 대추야자 나무를 모두 베어 불태워버리며 집들

---

86. 마크 G., 『이슬람과 유대인 그 끝나지 않은 전쟁』, 151~152p.

을 파괴했다. 결국은 항복을 받아냈고 그들의 돈을 모두 빼앗은 뒤 추방시켜 버렸다(꾸란 59:2). 그들은 휴대할 수 있는 생필품을 가지고 그 마을을 떠나 가까이 있는 카이바르에 있는 유대인 마을로 갔다. 꾸란 59장에 보면 이때의 일을 상세히 기록하고 있는데 무함마드는 그 고을 백성들의 것을 빼앗아 무슬림들에게 준 알라를 찬양하라고 말하고 있다. - 꾸란59:6-7 김용선 역

나이디르족들의 이웃에 살고 있던 다른 유대인 족속인 꾸라이자 (Quraizah)족은 언젠가 무함마드가 자신들도 공격할 것이라고 생각 하고 메카지역의 사람들과 힘을 합쳐 무함마드를 타도하고자 했다. 서기 627년 무함마드는 그 마을을 25일 동안 포위하여 결국은 항복 을 받아냈고, 그 고을의 8백~9백 명 되는 모든 유대인 남자들을 메디 나로 끌고 가서 죽이고 파 놓은 구덩이에 생매장해 묻어버렸고, 여자들과 아이들은 전리품과 함께 군인들에게 나누어 주었다.[87]

메디나 주위에 살던 3유대인 족속들 중 나이디르족과 꾸라이자 족이 무함마드가 이끄는 무슬림들에게 전멸을 당하고 이제 남은 것은 카이바르(Kaybar)족뿐이었다. 무함마드는 이들을 마저 전멸시키기로 작정하고 628년 자신의 사촌인 알리(Ali)를 장군으로 세우고 카이바 르(Kaybar)로 진군하여 그들 중 남자들은 모두 죽이고 여자들 중 가장 아름다운 여인을 자신의 노예로 택한 다음 나머지 여인들은 전리품 으로 나누어 주었다. 그들 중 유대인 여인의 이름은 레이하나(Reihana)

---

87. 마크 G., 『이슬람과유대인 그 끝나지 않은 전쟁』, 164~165p.

였으며, 이슬람으로 개종하면 노예 신분에서 해방시켜 주고, 무함마드의 아내로 삼겠다고 제의했으나, 그 제의를 보기 좋게 거절했기에 무함마드의 아내의 반열에는 들지 못했으나 평생을 무함마드 집에서 성노예로 살았다고 역사가들은 증언하고 있다.[88] 무함마드는 유대인들과 그들의 종교를 아라비아 반도에서 없애 버리겠다고 선언했으며 그의 말은 그대로 이루어졌다.[89]

무함마드가 유대인들을 미워하여 아라비아 반도에서 죽이고 몰아낸 것은 명목상으로는 유대인 남자가 돌을 던져 죽이려 했다든지[90] 혹은 유대인 여인이 무함마드를 독살하려 했다든지[91] 등의 명분을 이야기하고는 있지만 사실은 자신이 계속 메신저로 인정을 받으려면 신·구약 성경의 내용을 알고 있는 유대인의 존재는 가장 큰 장애가 되었으므로 그들이 변질된 성경을 가지고 있다고 정죄하면서 그들을 제거하려했던 것으로 보인다.[92]

---

88. 최영길, 『무함마드와 이슬람』, 103p.
89. 마크 G., 『이슬람과유대인 그 끝나지 않은 전쟁』, 165~166p.
90. Ibid, 157p.
91. 김정위, 『이슬람 입문』, 42p.
92. 꾸란 59:15~17: 그들 이전의 자들(멸망당한 나이디르 족)처럼 이들도 사악한 결과를 맛보리니 고통스러운 웅벌이 있으리라. 그들은 사탄과 같나니 사탄은 인간에게 불신하라 하여 불신하면 그는 나는 너희가 관계가 없으며 나는 만유의 주님이신 알라를 두려워 하도다 라고 말하니라. 그리하여 이들의 말로는 불지옥이 되어 그곳에서 영주하니 그것이 사악한 자들을 위한 보상이라(최영길 역).

계시 상호간의 모순 처리를 위한 계시

질문 금지령

무함마드가 메카 시대의 소규모 집단으로 이슬람을 시작했을 때 힘이 없었기 때문에 어려움과 핍박을 견디면서 살아야 했다. 그 때는 더 많은 사람들에게 호감을 가지게 하고 무함마드를 대적하며 핍박하는 자들에게 자극을 주지 않기 위해서 평화로운 계시를 말할 수밖에 없는 입장이었다.

그러나 무함마드가 메디나로 이주하여 그 도시의 통치자로 등극하게 되자 갑자기 신분의 변화가 일어나면서 자신을 대적하는 자들을 도리어 핍박하는데 있어서 아무런 장애도 느끼지 않게 되었다. 그래서 그는 성경이 변질되었다든지 알라(Allah)에게 자식이 있다고 말한다든지 삼신을 믿는 종교라는 등의 명분을 붙여서 알라(Allah)의 이름으로 강력한 징계를 명하였다.

무함마드를 따라서 메카에서 메디나로 이주한 무하지룬(Muhajirun) 들은 그의 입에서 나오는 메카 계시도 들었고 메디나 계시도 들었다. 그래서 두 계시간의 모순된 점들 간의 갈등과 의문이 일게 되었다. 예를 들면 기독교인들을 어떤 시각으로 보느냐는 문제를 보면 메카에 있을 때는 "경전의 백성들"이요, 같은 신을 믿는 사람들이요 등 매우 우호적으로 말을 해 왔으나, 메디나에 와서 입장이 달라지고 나서는 기독교인들을 친구로 삼지도 말라[1]는 등 그들은 알라(Allah)와 동반자를 둔 다신교도들로 취급하고 있는데 도대체 철저히 순종을 하고자 해도 어느 쪽에 비중을 두어야할지를 분간할 수가 없었을 것이다. 그 뿐 아니라 기독교인들이 믿는 성경은 진리이며 신·구약 성경이 진리라는 것을 확증하는 것이 바로 꾸란이라고[2]했다가 성경은 변질된 것이라고[3] 말을 바꾸니 그럼 꾸란은 변질된 것을 확증하는 것이란 말인가? 또한 종교를 강요하지 말라고[4] 계시하고 나중에는 이슬람을 믿지 않는 자는 죽이라고[5] 하니 어찌 혼동이 없겠는가?

그래서 그들은 질문을 쏟아내기 시작했던 것이다. 두 가지가 다 옳을 수는 없었다. 어느 한 쪽을 취해하만 하는 상황이었다. 그러나

---

1. 꾸란 5:51.
2. 꾸란 3:3.
3. 꾸란 5:13.
4. 꾸란 2:256.
5. 꾸란 8:12, 꾸란 9:5.

알라의 계시는 아무도 취소할 수 없다고 하니 매우 난감한 일이었다.

　　그대의 주님의 말씀이 진리와 정의로 완전함이니 그분의 말씀을 변경할 자 아무도 없노라. 그분은 모든 것을 들으심과 아심으로 충만 하시기 때문이라. -꾸란 6:115 최영길 역

　　알라께서 실로 그 메시지를 계시했으니 알라께서 그것을 보호하 리라. -꾸란 15:9 최영길역

이러한 사례가 한두 건이 발생한 것이 아니라 계시 전반적인 흐 름이 메카의 것과 메디나의 것은 확연히 달랐다. 따라서 무함마드를 따르는 무슬림들이 혼돈과 질문이 생기는 것은 당연한 현상이었다. 그래서 무함마드는 이 문제에 대해서 입장을 정리해야 할 필요를 느꼈을 것이다. 그 때 다음과 같은 계시가 내렸다는 것이다.

　　믿는 사람들이여. 여러 가지의 일을 물어서는 안 된다. 너무 분명히 알고 보면 오히려 해가 될 것도 있다. -꾸란 5:101 上 김용선 역

　　믿는 자들이여 분명한 것은 묻지 말라 했으니 그것이 오히려 해롭 게 하느니라. 또한 꾸란이 계시되는 것을 묻는다면 이는 더욱 너희들 에게 해악이라. -꾸란 5:101 上 최영길 역

질문을 허락하지 않겠다는 것이다. 지금도 이슬람권에서는 학생 들에게 종교적인 질문을 용납하지 않는다. 심지어는 신학교에서 조 차 질문을 허락하지 않는다고 한다.[6] 무함마드가 질문을 허락하지

않는 이유가 있는데 이는 그렇게 질문을 하다보면 자꾸 의심이 생겨서 결국은 불신자들이 된다는 것이다. 이전에도 어떤 사람들이 그러한 질문을 하다가 불신자들이 되었다는 것이다.[7] 이것이 소위 말하는 이슬람의 "질문 금지령" 인 것이다.

취소(Mansukh) 교리

질문 금지령이 내렸으나 사람들의 의문은 풀리지를 않았다. 어떻게 알라(Allah)께서 상호 모순되는 두 가지 계시를 내리실 수가 있는가? 왜 그랬을까? 알라(Allah)께서도 상황에 따라 뜻이 달라질 수가 있는 건가? 이런 질문들이 쏟아져 나오는 것을 수습할 사람은 계시의 전달자를 자처하는 무함마드 밖에는 없었다. 그러나 무함마드 자신도 변명이 매우 궁색한 상황이었다. 그럴 때마다 그는 알라(Allah)의 이름으로 계시를 받는 방법을 통해서 해결을 하곤 했다. 그래서 그는 다시 알라의 이름으로 다음과 같은 계시를 내렸다는 것이다.

인간은 누구도 알라의 계시를 변경하거나 취소할 수 없지만 그 계시를 내리신 알라께서는 전능하시기 때문에 이전에 내린 계시를 취소할 수도 있고 변경할 수도 있고 다른 것으로 대치시킬 수도 있

---

6. youtube.com/mark gabriel 이집트의 신학교 이슬람 문화와 역사 교수였던 그가 개종하여 간증한 내용이 인터넷 동영상에 떠 있는데 그 4개중 첫 번째 간증 동영상에서 언급된 내용이다.
7. 꾸란 5:102 최영길 역.

다는 것이다.[8]

우리가 이전에 계시한 문구를 취소하였거나 혹은 일부러 망각하게 했을 경우에, 그 이상 또는 그와 동등한 것을 주려하고 있다. 알라가 전지전능하시다는 것을 당신은 모르느냐? 하늘과 땅의 주권이 알라게 있고 알라 이외에는 보호자나 원조자가 없다는 것을 모르느냐?

—꾸란 2:106~107 김용선 역

어떤 말씀도 폐기하지 아니하며 망각케 하지 아니하되 보다 나은 혹은 그와 동등한 말씀으로 대체하시나니 알라는 모든 일에 전지전능하심을 모르느뇨. 천지가 알라게 있음을 너희는 알지 않느뇨, 그분 외에는 보호자도 원조자도 없노라. —꾸란 2:106~107 최영길 역

최영길 역에 보면 위 구절의 첫 번째 부분인 "이전에 계시한 문구를 취소하였거나 혹은 일부러 망각하게 했을 경우에"라는 말을 "어떤 말씀도 폐기하지 아니하며 망각케 하지 아니하되"라고 번역하여 정반대의 의미를 보여주고 있다. 그러나 그 뒤에 나오는 부분을 보면 "그와 동등한 말씀으로 대체 하신다"고 하니 의미상으로는 대체한다는 말이나 먼저 것을 폐기하고 새것을 세운다는 말이나 같은 표현이기는 하지만 혐오스러움을 약화시키기 위하여 고의로 반대로

---

8. 진리라는 것은 취소할 수도 없고 취소할 필요도 없이 영원한 것이어야 한다는 것을 전제로 할 때 꾸란의 구절을 취소한다는 것은 이것이 진리가 아니라는 자체증거로 볼 수 있다.

번역한 것으로 보인다.

이는 꾸란의 "처음 계시와 나중 계시가 상호모순이 될 경우에는 나중 계시에 의해서 이전 계시는 자동으로 취소된다."는 교리다.(꾸란 2:106, 꾸란 5:15, 꾸란13:39) 이것을 이슬람의 만수크(Mansukh)교리라고 한다. 이 만수크 교리에 의해서 "종교는 강제로 하지 말지니라." (꾸란 2:256)는 꾸란의 평화스런 메카 계시의 대표적 구절은 "이교도를 죽이라." (꾸란 9:5)는 메디나 계시의 구절에 의해서 취소된 것이다.

Nasikh(대체) 교리

보편적으로 진리라는 것은 상황과 조건에 따라서 변하지 않는다는 특성이 있다. 그러나 이슬람의 경전이라고 하는 무함마드의 계시인 꾸란은 상황에 따라서 그리고 시대에 따라서 진보되고 새것으로 대체된다는 특성이 있다. 이는 진리는 절대 불변이라는 원리와 위배되는 것이지만 이슬람에서는 이를 자연스러운 것으로 받아들이고 있는 것이다.

즉 모세에게 내린 계시는 모세 시대의 상황에 필요한 말씀을 주셨던 것이며 예수 그리스도는 그 당시의 상황에 필요한 말씀을 주셨다고 주장한다. 그리고 메카 시절의 계시는 메카의 상황에 맞는 계시였으며 메디나 시대에 비로소 온 인류가 영원토록 지켜야 하는 최후의 메시지라는 주장인 것이다. 그들은 이를 나시크(Nasikh) 즉 "대체" 교리라고 한다. 이는 '취소' 만수크(Mansukh)교리의 또 다른 표현으로 보인다.[9] 즉 A가 B에 의해서 취소(만수크)되었다면 B는 A를 대체(나씨크)한 것이다.

이슬람에서는 이 나시크(대체) 교리에 의해서 모세의 율법인 토라는 복음서인 인질(Injil)에 의해서 폐기 혹은 대체되었으며, 인질은 꾸란에 의해서 폐기되었다고 적용하는 것이다. 그것은 완전 폐기된 것이 아니라 어느 것을 폐기할 것인지 혹은 어느 것을 보존해야 할 것인지를 꾸란에 의해서 평가한다는 것이다.[10]

이전의 사람들을 위한 복음이라 그리고 '옳고 그름의 지침서'를 내렸노라 알라의 말씀들을 배반하는 자 그들에게는 엄한 벌이 있을 것이라 알라는 강하사 그들을 패배하게 하시니라. 천지에 있는 어떤 것도 알라께는 은폐될 수 없노라. -꾸란 3:4~5 최영길 역

인간들을 인도하기 위해서 정사(正邪)를 구별하는 기준'을 내리시었다. 알라의 계시에 불신하는 자는 엄한 벌을 받을 것이다. 알라께서는 전능하시며 악에 보답하신다. 알라께는 땅 위에 있는 것이나 하늘에 있는 것이나 모두 숨길 수 없다. -꾸란 3:4~5 김용선 역

즉 신·구약 성경의 내용 중에서 꾸란의 내용과 일치되는 것은 진리이므로 보존해야 하는 것이며 꾸란의 내용과 차이가 나는 것은

---

9. 취소 교리로 인하여 이슬람 학자들 간의 견해 차이가 있다. 어떤 학자는 취소 불가를 이야기 하지만 서로 모순되는 구절들은 그 중 하나를 취소하지 않으면 스스로의 모순을 해명할 방법이 없는 것이다.
10. 처음에는 신·구약 성경을 확증하는 것이 꾸란 이라고 했다가 나중에는 꾸란이 신·구약 성경의 옳고 그름을 가리는 지침서라고 주장하는 것이다.

꾸란에 의해서 폐기되어야 한다는 것이다. 이 논리에 의해서 신·구약 성경은 꾸란에 의해서 자동적으로 폐기되었다는 주장이 도출되는 것이다. 물론 이슬람 학자들은 신구약 성경을 꾸란과 함께 진리로 인정한다고 주장하지만 서로 둘 다 진리라고 하기에는 내용상의 차이가 많기 때문에 지금 기독교인들이 가지고 있는 성경은 변질된 것이므로 변질되지 않은 원래의 신구약 성경을 꾸란과 함께 진리로 인정한다고 주장한다.

이슬람 세력 확장을 위한 계시

서기 622년 메카 지역의 핍박을 피하여 무하지룬(Muhajirun)들과 함께 메디나로 온 무함마드는 자신을 추종하는 안사리(Ansari)들의 협력을 얻으며 세력을 키워 나가다가 서기 623년 말경 메디나의 최고 통치자로 등극하게 되는데, 통치권을 쥐고 난 후 첫 해인 624년부터는 기도 방향을 예루살렘에서 메카로 바꾸었다.[11] 평화적 태도에서 전투적 태도로 바꾸어 군사적 힘을 길러 주변의 유대교인들과 기독교인들을 평정하면서 자신의 조상들인 꾸라이시 족속들과 전쟁을 하다가 628년 메카의 다신교도들과 10년 불가침 평화 조약인 후다이비아 조약을 맺었다.[12] 그러나 무함마드는 스스로 이끌었던 27회의

---

11. 꾸란 2:142에 대한 최영길 각주 참조: 무함마드가 서기 622년 메디나로 와서 16~17개월간은 예루살렘을 향해 기도하였으나 그 후 메카방향으로 바꿨다고 한다. 그러므로 624년부터 바꾼 것이 옳다.
12. 정수일, 『이슬람문명』, 79p.
13. 유해석, 『이슬람이 다가오고 있다』, 74p.

전쟁을 통해서 강인한 전투력을 길렀다.[13] 이슬람 세력 확장을 위하여 싸우는 전쟁을 지하드라고 명하며 이 전쟁에 참여하는 일에 불만을 품은 사람들은 위선자(꾸란 9:81)라고 하며 정복 전쟁을 시작했다. 서기 630년 그는 1만 명의 군대를 이끌고 후다이비아에서 10년 불가침 조약을 맺은지 18개월 만에 메카를 공격했는데, 전세가 일방적으로 불리하다는 것을 판단한 메카 진영은 싸우지도 않고 무조건 항복을 함으로서 무함마드가 이끄는 이슬람 군은 메카에 무혈 입성하여 알라의 군대의 위대함을 다시 한 번 과시하게 되었다.[14] 그리하여 그는 꿈에도 그리던 아라비아 최강 종족인 메카의 꾸라이시(Quraish) 종족을 점령하고 아라비아 반도를 무슬림들의 통치하에 두게 되었다. 그러면서 그의 꿈은 다시 더 넓은 세계로 향하여 커지게 되었다. 그는 세계를 이슬람으로 점령하기 위해서 자신을 따르는 무슬림들에게 '성스러운 전투'를 명했는데 이것이 지하드인 것이며 이는 모든 무슬림들의 의무인 것이다.[15] 그러나 무슬림들이 강한 자들에게 포로로 잡혔거나 비 무슬림 지역에서 이슬람 종교 때문에 핍박을 받을 우려가 있을 때는 위장(타끼야:Taqya)을 전략적으로 허용하고 있다.[16]

지하드(Jihad)의 계시

---

14. 이슬람 역사에서는 메디나의 무슬림 군대가 메카를 무혈입성으로 점령한 것을 매우 자랑스런 역사로 기술하고 있으나 이는 10년 평화조역을 18개월 만에 파기하고 얻은 승리인 것이다.
15. 꾸란 2:216.
16. 혹자는 타끼야(위장:Taqya) 교리를 시아(Shiah) 무슬림만의 특징으로 말하고 있지만 이는 꾸란에 계시된 아무도 부인할 수 없는 모든 무슬림들이 실천하는 이슬람의 교리다(꾸란 2:225 참조).

지하드의 정의

지하드(Jihad)라는 개념은 아랍어의 '싸움' '투쟁' 혹은 '분투 (struggle)' '노력' '발버둥 치다' 등의 뜻을 가지고 있는 단어다. 처음에는 이슬람을 확산시키기 위하여 전쟁을 하는 뜻으로만 쓰이던 이 단어가 시간이 흐르면서 점차적으로 이슬람을 확산시키기 위해 사용되는 모든 수단과 방법을 의미하게 되었다. 흔히 이슬람의 지하드에는 대지하드(大 Jihad)와 소지하드(小 Jihad)가 있다고 배운 사람들이 있을 줄 안다. 그러나 이런 개념은 무함마드 당시에는 없었던 개념들이며, 무함마드가 죽은 지 450년 정도 지난 후에 이슬람을 평화적인 모습으로 보이고자 하는 무슬림들이 만든 개념이다.[17]

우리가 잘 아는 현대 이슬람 지하드의 아버지라 불리는 이집트의 싸이드 꾸틉(Sayyid Qutb)[18]은 지하드의 발전을 4단계로 분류했다.

1단계 : (서기 610-622년)무슬림 초기에 메카에서 메디나로 이주하기 전에는 알라 (Allah)께서 지하드를 용납하지 않으셨다(꾸란 2:256). 즉 평화의 단계다.

2단계 : (서기 622-624년) 핍박 받는 자들을 위해서 지하드를 해도 좋다는 알라(Allah)의 허락이 주어졌다. 즉 방어의 단계다.[19]

---

17. William Montgomery Watt, Islam : Short history (Oxford : One World Publishing, 2002), 86p.
18. 싸이드 꾸틉(1906~1965)은 이집트의 교육자 출신으로 정부 장학금으로 미국에 유학하여 공부를 마치고 귀국하여 이집트 이슬람 원리주의 지하드 운동의 아버지가 되어 현대 지하드 운동의 모델이 된 사람이다.

3단계 : (서기 624-630년) 알라(Allah)께서 무슬림들을 대항해서 싸우고
　　　　자 하는 자들과는 지하드를 명령하셨다(꾸란 2:216). 즉 투쟁
　　　　의 단계다.

4단계 : (서기 630-632년) 알라(Allah)께서 모든 다신교도 및 우상 숭배
　　　　하는 자들과 전쟁을 하여 지하드(Jihad)를 통해 정복하라고
　　　　명하셨다(꾸란 9:5, 꾸란8:39). 즉 정복의 단계다

　　그는 이 단계들은 각기 다음 단계에 의해서 대치되는데 4단계는
영원한 것이라고 하였다.[20]

　　소동이 없어질 때까지 그리고 종교가 모두 알라(Allah)께로 귀일할
때까지 그들과 싸움을 계속하라. ─꾸란 8:39 김용선 역

　　알라와 내세를 믿지 아니하며 알라와 메신저가 금기한 것을 지키
지 아니하고 진리의 종교를 따르지 아니한 자들에게 비록 그들이 성
경의 백성들(기독교인과 유대교인들)이라 하더라도 항복하여 인두세
(Zizya)[21] 를 지불할 때까지 지하드 하라. 그들은 스스로 저주스러움을
느끼리라. ─꾸란 9:29 최영길 역

---

19. 김용선,『코란의 지혜와 신비』, 39p. : 저자는 '방어의 목적으로 싸우는 전쟁만이 성전이며 먼저
　　공격하면 성전이 아니라' 고 함.
20. Sayyid Qutb, Milestones, Revised Edition, Chapter 4 "Jihad in the cause of Allah".
　　internet site research: http://www.answering-islam.org/Hahn/jihad.htm#fn7
21. 이슬람으로 개종하지 않은 성서의 백성들이 이슬람의 통치를 받을 때 납부해야하는 세금

이슬람에서는 인류를 둘로 나누는데 즉 이슬람을 받아들인 '평화의 집(dar-al-salam)' 혹은 '이슬람의 집(dar-al-islam)'에 사는 사람들과 이슬람을 받아들이지 않은 '전쟁의 집(dar-al-harb)'에 사는 사람들로 구분한다. 물론 기독교에서도 교인과 불신자들로 나누는 구분이 있지만 그들이 기독교를 믿지 않으면 그들과 전쟁을 하여 죽이라는 가르침은 없다. 그러나 무슬림이 아닌 모든 인류는 무슬림들의 전쟁의 대상이며, 이들은 전쟁의 집에 살고 있다는 것이다.[22] 이를 위해 '칼의 구절'인 꾸란 9장 5절 "금지된 달이 지났음에도 이슬람을 받아들이지 않은 이교도들이 눈에 띄면 보이는 대로 잡아 죽이라"는 구절이 계시되었다는 것이다.

이슬람 측에서 주장하는 바에 의하면 지하드(Jihad)란 불가피한 상황에서 생존을 위해 무기를 들어야 할 필요가 있을 때 무슬림들이 행하는 방어전쟁을 말한다고 주장한다. 그러나 사실 지하드란 무함마드가 가장 중요하게 여기던 정복수단이며 이슬람화의 수단이며 모든 무슬림들의 의무이다. 이슬람의 핍박이 무서워서 자신들의 우상을 버리고 무함마드가 유일신이라고 주장하는 알라(Allah)를 받아들여 무슬림이 되었던 사람들이 이교도들을 죽이라는 지하드에 참여하는 것을 거부하는 일이 발생되었을 때 무함마드는 이런 계시를 받았다고 한다.

너희의 손들을 자제하라. 그리고 이슬람 세를 지불하라는 말을 들

---

22. L. Esposito, John, UNHOLY WAR: Terror in the Name of Islam (U.K.: Oxford University Press, 2002), 35p.

었던 그들에게 지하드(Jihad)에 임하라는 명령이 내려지니 그들 중의 한 무리는 알라를 경외하는 것처럼 하니 알라를 두려워해야 할 그들이 사람들을 두려워하는 자들을 보지 않았느뇨. 주여 당신은 왜 우리로 하여금 전투에 임하도록 하나이까? 우리 생명의 기한을 다소나마 유예하여 주소서 라고 말하매 그들에게 이르되 현세의 쾌락은 순간이나 영원한 내세는 알라를 공경하는 이들에 더 복이 되니라. 또한 업적은 불평등한 대우를 받지 않노라. ─구란 4:77 최영길 역

그러므로 위의 구절에 의하면 지하드는 선택의 여지가 없는 모든 무슬림들의 의무라는 것이다.

전쟁을 좋아하는 사람이 어디에 있겠는가? 특히 재산이 많고 생활이 풍족한 사람들은 전쟁에 참여하기를 원하지 않고 잔류(殘留)하기를 원했다. 그뿐 아니라 여러 가지 이유를 만들어 전쟁에 참여하지 않으려는 자들이 있었다. 그들에 관하여 무함마드에게 알라로부터 이런 계시가 내려왔다는 것이다.

알라를 믿고 사도와 함께 싸워라는 천계의 1장이 내렸을 때 그들 중의 부자들은 그대에게 허가를 청하기를 "우리들을 잔류자들과 함께 남게 해주시오"라고 말했다. 그들은 부녀자와 함께 있는 것을 기뻐한다. 그들의 마음은 봉인되어 있기 때문에 모르고 있다. 그러나 사도 및 그와 함께 믿는 사람들은 생명과 재산을 내던지고 싸웠다. 이들 사람들에게는 좋은 일이 있다. 이런 자들이야 말로 영광이 있는 자들이다. 유목부족 중에 구실을 만들어 허가를 받기 위해 온 자가 있다. 또 알라의 그 사도에게 거짓말을 하여 남아있는 자도 있다. 신앙이 없는 그

들에게는 통렬한 징벌이 내릴 것이다. —꾸란 9:86~90 김용선 역

그러므로 지하드가 방어 전쟁이라는 말은 터무니없는 주장이다. 만일 적들이 공격하여 방어를 해야 할 입장이라면 부자들은 자신들의 재산을 지키기 위해서라도 더욱 적극적으로 전쟁을 도왔을 것이다. 그러나 꾸란의 분위기는 전혀 그렇지 않다는 것을 확인할 수 있는 것이다.

지하드의 상급

무함마드는 이 지하드를 명령하면서 다음과 같은 꾸란 구절들을 계시 받았다고 하였다.

현세를 버리고 후세를 바라보고자 하는 자는 남을 위해 자기를 희생하고 알라의 길을 위해 싸우는 자(지하드 하는 자)는 누구든지 전사하든지 또는 개선하든지 알라로부터 큰 상[23]을 받게 될 것이다.

—꾸란 4:74 김용선 역

꾸란에 준하는 이슬람의 경전인 하디스에 보면 알라(Allah)를 위해 지하드를 하다가 순교한 사람은 6가지 상을 받는다고 하는데
첫째 : 순교자는 피를 흘리자마자 죄를 사함 받고
둘째 : 지옥의 징계를 면제 받는 대신 천국에 거하게 되며

---

23. 하르트무트 보브친, 『무함마드는 이렇게 말했다』, 염정용 역 (서울: 들녘, 2005), 158p.

셋째 : 더 큰 테러로부터 보호를 받으며

넷째 : 세상과 그에 속한 모든 것을 합한 것보다 더 좋은 홍옥(Ruby) 왕관을 머리에 쓰게 될 것이며

다섯째 : 72명의 처녀들과 결혼을 하게 될 것이며

여섯째 : 70명의 친척들의 중보자의 자격을 갖게 될 것이다.[24]라는 것이다.

꾸란에 의하면 진실한 무슬림이라는 것은 생명과 재산을 바쳐 지하드 하는 자를 말한다고 정의하고 있으며 이런 자들에게는 천국에서 아름다운 처녀들이 은 술잔을 받쳐 들고 비단 침대에서 기다리고 있다는 것이다.

믿는 자란 알라와 그 메신저를 믿어 결코 의심을 품지 않으며 재산과 생명을 걸고 알라의 길에서 싸우는(지하드 하는)자 이리라. 이런 자야말로 진실한 자이니라. ─꾸란 49:15 김용선 역

착한 행위의 보수는 착한 것이 아니겠는가?⋯ 그곳에는 아름다운 처녀들이 있다⋯ 이제까지 인간이나 진도 다 같이 그녀들에게 손댄일은 없다. ─꾸란 55:60~74 김용선 역

비단 침대위에 마주보고 기댄다⋯ 술잔과 주전자와⋯ 두통도 없고 취하는 일도 없다. 그들은 기호에 따라 과일을 고르고 짐승이나

---

24. Tirmidhi and Ibn Maiah, ishkat al-Masabih, Vol. 1:814.

새의 고기도 원하는 대로 얻을 수 있다. 눈이 크고 빛깔이 흰 처녀도 있다. 그녀들은 마치 감추어진 진주와 같다. 이것이 그들이 행한 일에 대한 보상으로 주어진 것이다. -꾸란 56:15~24 김용선 역

위선자와 배신자들의 저주 계시
무함마드는 알라의 계시에 의해서 이슬람에 해악을 끼치는 사람들을 네 종류로 분류했다.
첫째 위선자들
둘째 배신자들
셋째 모든 이교도들을 포함한 불신자들
넷째 성경의 백성들 즉 유대교인들과 기독교인들

이슬람의 경전인 꾸란에서는 이들을 어떻게 정의하고 있는지를 살펴보자.
무함마드는 위선자를 세 가지로 나눴는데 그 중
첫째 불신자들과 친한 자들이다.
위선자들에게는 가혹한 징벌이 준비되고 있다고 당사자들에게 전해줘라. 믿음이 깊은 사람을 젖혀놓고 믿음이 없는 사람과 친구로 사귀는 사람들은 권세라도 얻으려고 하는가? 권세는 모두 알라에게 속하고 있다. -꾸란 4:138 김용선 역

둘째 종교적 의무를 소홀히 하고 재산을 아끼고 무함마드와 이슬람을 위해서 선뜻 희사하지 않는 자들을 위선자들이라고 불렀다.

남자위선자가 그렇고 여자위선자가 그러하거늘 금기한 것은 행하고 의무화한 것은 실천치 아니하며 그들의 손들을 움켜쥐고 알라를 망각하니 그분도 그들을 생각지 아니하시더라. 실로 위선자들은 해악을 끼치는 자들이라. ─구란 9:67 최영길 역

또한 불신자들을 죽이러 가는 이슬람 확장을 위한 전쟁에 참여하기를 꺼리는 자들을 무함마드는 위선자라고 불렀다.

그리고 신자인체 하는 자도 알고 계신다. 오는 것이 좋다. "알라의 길을 위해서 싸워라. 격퇴시켜라."라고 말하였을 때 "만일 우리들이 싸우는 법을 알고 있다면 너희들을 따라갈 것이지만"이라고 그들은 말했다. 그날 그들은 확실히 신앙보다 불신에 가까웠다. 그들은 마음에도 없는 것을 입으로만 말하고 있었다. 그러나 알라께서는 그들이 감추고 있는 일을 잘 알고 계신다. ─구란 3:167 김용선 역

싸움은 그대들에게 과하여진 의무이다. 비록 싫어할지라도. 아마 그대들은 자기에게 좋은 것도 싫은 것도 있을 것이다. 또 자기에게 나쁜 것을 좋아하는 것도 있을 것이다. 알라께서는 잘 아시고 그대들은 아무 것도 모른다. ─구란 2:216 김용선 역

이러한 위선자들의 운명에 대해서 무함마드는 단호하게 이렇게 말했다. 그들은 불지옥에 갈 것이라는 것이다.

참으로 위선자는 지옥의 불길에 던져져 누구 하나 도와 줄 사람을 찾지 못할 것이다. ─구란 4:145 김용선 역

이들은 스스로를 무슬림이라고 하지만 지하드를 좋아하지 않는다. 전쟁에 나가라면 남아 있기를 원하는 자들이다.[25] 그러므로 지금도 자칭 무슬림이라고 하면서 지하드 운동을 하는 진짜 무슬림들(알 카에다, 탈레반 등)을 비난하는 자들은 꾸란에 의하면 알라의 저주를 받을 위선자들인 것이다.

세 번째 무함마드가 증오하던 또 한 가지 부류의 사람들이 있었는데 이는 배신자들이었다.

배신자들이란 일단 이슬람을 받아들였다가 떠난 사람들로서 가혹한 형벌을 면치 못한다. 지금도 이슬람권에서는 이슬람을 떠나 다른 종교를 믿는 자들은 무함마드의 계시인 꾸란에 의해서 죽음을 당하게 될 것을 두려워하며 도피생활을 하고 있는 사람들을 많이 볼 수 있다.

그들을 위해 용서를 구해도 좋고 구하지 않아도 좋다. 가령 그대가 그들을 위해 70회 용서를 구한다 해도 알라께선 결코 용서하시지 않을 것이다. 그것은 그들이 알라와 그 메신저에 대해 배신의 태도를 취했기 때문이다. 알라께선 사악의 무리를 인도하지 않으신다.

―꾸란 9:80 김용선 역

그와 같은 자들은 자기들이 믿지 않는 것같이 너희들도 믿지 않는 것을 바라고 있다. 그렇게 되면 너희들도 동등한 것이 되기 때문이다.

---

25. 꾸란 9:44, 알라의 종말의 날을 믿는 사람들은 생명과 재산을 내던지고 싸우는 일에 빠지려고 그대에게 남아 있기를 원하는 법이 없다. 알라께서는 경건한 사람들을 잘 아신다(김용선 역).

그러면 그러한 자들이 알라의 길 쪽으로 옮겨 올 때까지는 그들을 친구로 삼아서는 안 된다. 만일 그들이 배반하면 너희들이 그들을 발견하는 대로 그 장소에서 잡아 죽여라. 그들을 친구로 하든가 조력자로 해서는 안 된다. -꾸란 4:89 김용선 역

또한 무함마드는 불신자들과 이교도들, 다신교도들을 증오했다. 이들의 운명은 이 세상에서는 죽음이요 저 세상에서는 불붙는 지옥이다.

그런데 4개월의 신성월(神聖月)이 지났으면, 다신교도를 발견하는 즉시 죽여라. 잡아라. 억류하라. 모든 길에 복병을 두고 기다려라. 그러나 만일 그들이 회개하여 예배를 지키고 희사(喜捨)를 한다면 방면해 주라. 알라께서는 관용하시고 자비로우신 분이시다.

-꾸란 9:5 김용선 역

그러나 불신자들에게는 쇠사슬과 멍에와 타오르는 불지옥을 준비하였고. -꾸란 76:4 최영길 역

무함마드가 가장 싫어하고 증오하던 또 한 부류의 사람들이 있었는데 그들은 유대인들과 기독교인들이었다. 그들은 무함마드가 계시를 받았다고 할 때마다 신·구약 성경과 비교하여 그것은 거짓이라고 말하는 자들이라고 꾸란의 여러 곳에서 말하고 있다. 그러므로 이들보다 더 악한 자들은 세상에 없다고 하는 것이 무함마드와 꾸란의 교리인 것이다.

대체로 알라에게 터무니없는 거짓된 날조로, 진리가 나타나도 이를 거짓말이라 이르는 자처럼 악한 자가 더 있을까. 지옥 속에는 믿지 않는 자들을 위한 거주지가 마련되어 있지 않았다는 말인가?

—꾸란 29:68 김용선 역

결과적으로 이슬람을 해롭게 하는 이런 위선자, 배신자, 이교도, 불신자, 기독교인과 유대교인들이 소동을 일으키지 못하도록 무력으로 지하드(Jihad)하여 진압하고 온 세상의 종교가 오로지 알라(Allah)에게 속하도록 하라는 것이다.

　　소동이 없어질 때까지 그리고 종교가 모두 알라께로 귀일할 때까지 그들과 싸움을 계속하라. 만일 그들이 그만둔다면 알라께서 그들의 행동을 다 보고 계시다. —꾸란 8:39 김용선 역

이 구절에 대한 최영길 박사의 주석을 보면 이븐 압바스(Ibn Abbas)의 해석을 인용하여 "지구상에 한 사람의 불신자도 존재하지 아니할 때 까지 지하드를 해야 한다"고 설명하고 있다.[26] 여기서 우리는 메카에서 아랍인들에게 '성경이 진리임을 확증하라'고 보냄을 받았던 무함마드가 이제 아라비아 반도를 넘어서 '세계를 정복하고자 하는' 자로 목표를 재설정한 것을 확인할 수 있는 것이다.

---

26. 최영길 『성꾸란 의미의 한국어 번역』, 8:39 주석 참조, 309p.

타끼야(Taqiyah: 위장)전략

세상을 정복하려면 이슬람보다 강한 군사력을 가진 사람들을 만날 수도 있는데 이럴 때는 무모하게 대항하지 말고 타끼야(Taqiya: 위장) 전략을 사용하면서 시간도 벌고 재정비하여 기회를 보라는 것이 꾸란의 교리이다.

> 너희의 맹세 속에 비의도적인 것에 대해서는 책망하시지 아니하시나 너의 심중에 있는 의도적 맹세는 책망하시니라. 알라는 관용과 은혜로 충만하심이라. -꾸란 2:225 최영길 역

> 너희들이 땅 위에서 여행을 할 때 또는 믿지 않는 자들로부터 학대받을 우려가 있을 때는 예배를 간략해도 죄가 되지 않는다. 참으로 믿지 않는 자들은 너희들의 적이다. -꾸란 4:101 김용선 역

이 타끼야(Taqiya: 위장) 전략은 지금도 지구상의 도처에서 실행되고 있다. 특히 비 이슬람 지역에서는 이슬람의 치부를 감추기 위한 모든 위장이 정당화 된다. 예를 들면 꾸란을 번역할 때도 불신자들의 "목을 치라"(꾸란 47:4)는 구절을 "목을 때리라"(최영길역)고 번역을 하는가 하면 매스컴이나 방송을 통해서도 정직하게 말하면 이슬람이 혐오스럽게 여겨질 가능성이 있을 때는 거짓말을 하는 것이다. 예를 들면 MBC 시선집중 프로에서 전주 이슬람 사원을 취재했는데 취재기자가 일부다처에 대해서 묻자 한국어가 가능한 외국인 이맘(이슬람 성직자)이라는 사람이 "원래 하나님께서 선지자들에게 많은 아내를

허락하셨지만 이슬람에서 일부다처를 말하는 것은 여자를 위해서이며 특히 이슬람에서는 한 번 결혼하면 이혼을 죽을 때까지 허락하지 않는다고 강조했는데[27] 사실은 이슬람만큼 이혼을 쉽게 할 수 있는 종교는 없다. 꾸란에 이혼은 두 번 까지 허락한다고 기록되어 있을 뿐 아니라(꾸란 2:229) 아내 바꾸기도 허락하고 있고(꾸란4:20) 이혼을 하려면 이렇게 하라고 이혼하는 방법을 설명해 주는 이혼 장(꾸란 65장)도 있는데 이맘이 꾸란을 몰라서 그렇게 말하지는 않았을 것이다. 한국 사람들은 이혼에 대한 거부감이 있기 때문에 정직하게 말하면 이슬람이 혐오스럽게 보일 것 같으니까 일부러 거짓말을 하는 것이다.

이슬람은 무슬림들의 숫자가 적은 나라에서는 항상 평화로운 집단을 가장하지만 이슬람의 세력이 커지고 강해질수록 이들은 과격한 집단으로 변모하여 간다. 영국의 여론조사 기구인 유거브(You Gov Survey)에서 조사한 바에 의하면 영국 내의 무슬림들이 2001년에는 자신이 급진주의(radical) 무슬림이라고 답변한 사람이 15퍼센트였는데 2006년 통계에는 40퍼센트로 증가하였다고 한다.[28] 이는 무함마드의 행동지침으로서 그의 전례를 그대로 본받아 답습하는 행동이다. 무함마드가 메카에서 힘이 없을 때 평화를 표방하다가 메디나에서 와서 세력을 얻은 후에는 과격해 진 바로 그 모범을 따르는 것이다.[29] 이슬람은 이러한 전략으로 세계를 정복하고자 하는 것이다. 그러므로 평화스런 무슬림들의 숫자가 많아지는 것은 우려할 필요가 없다고 주장하는 사람들의 생각은 옳지 못하다고 생각한다. 왜냐하면 그들이 언제까지나 평화를 사랑하는 무슬림들일 수가 없기 때문이다. 그렇게 주장할 수 있는 근거는 그들의 경전이 그렇게 가르치고 있고 또한 그들이 본받고 따라가야 할 모범이라고 하는 이슬람의 창시자 무함마드가 그렇게 행동을 했기 때문이다. 꾸란의 내용을 모르는 초신자 무슬림들은 평화스럽게 머물러 있을 수 있지만 꾸란의 내용과 무함마드의 교리를 깨닫고 나면 그들은 이슬람을 떠나든지 아니면 과격해지든지 둘 중의 하나를 택하게 된다. 이는 바로 유럽의 예를 참고해볼 때 더욱 확실해지는 것이다.

---

27. http://www.youtube.com/watch?v=I8zBi5_O8zc
28. 콜린다이, 『영국의 이슬람화 그 대책은 무엇인가?』 11p.
29. 무함마드의 행동모범을 아랍어로 순나(Sunna)라고 하고 그의 행동모범대로 따라 해야 한다는 교리를 가르치는 무슬림들을 순니(Sunni)파 무슬림들이라고 한다.

SECTION 4

선교에 적용

Why Muhammad's revelations are
changing repeatedly?

21세기 이슬람권 선교의 내용을 보면 많은 사람들이 상황화 전략 혹은 C5전략이나 C6전략이라는 용어를 사용하고 있음을 쉽게 발견할 수 있을 것이다. 이는 복음을 전하는데 있어서 선교지의 문화적 상황에 따라서 다양하고 폭 넓은 전략을 사용하여 그 문화권의 사람들이 거부감 없이 받아들일 수 있도록 하고자 하여 사용되는 방법이다.

이는 복음이 타 문화권에 쉽게 정착되도록 돕는 역할을 하는 것으로 선교지에서 즐겨 사용되고 있다. 예를 들면 교회 건물을 불교권에서는 불교 사원처럼 짓는다든지 목회자의 복장을 굳이 서양에서 예식 때 입는 성의를 입지 않고 그 지방의 전통 복장을 활용한다든지 또는 찬송가를 그 지방의 민요나 토속 음악의 가락에 맞춰 복음적인 가사를 삽입하여 부르는 등 여러 가지 측면에서 효과적으로 적용되고 있는 것을 확인할 수 있다.

그러나 이것은 어디까지나 문화의 옷을 갈아입는 것을 말하는 것이지 복음의 핵심까지 양보하면서 이방 문화의 흉내를 내라는 것은 아니라고 본다. 복음만 확실하게 전할 수 있다면 문화의 옷은 얼마든지 갈아입어도 좋다고 생각한다. 예를 들면 한국 사람들은 예로부터 어른들에게 깍듯이 예의를 지키는 문화가 있었다. 어른들 앞에서는 항상 무릎을 꿇고 앉는 것이 예의바른 행위라고 배워왔다. 그런데 교회에서 우주의 창조주이신 하나님 앞에 의자에 앉아서 예배를 드린다는 것을 용납할 수 없는 일이라는 의견이 지배하고 있었다. 그런데 서양인들에게는 무릎을 꿇고 장시간 앉아있는 습관이 되어 있지 않아서 예배를 드릴 때마다 고통을 당해야 했다는 것이다. 그러자 어떤 이가 환자들이나 노약자들을 위해서 뒤에 한 줄만 의자를 놓자고 건의한 것이 받아들여지자 차츰 의자를 놓는 것이 일반화되어 이제 교회에서 장의자를 사용하지 않으면 이상할 정도가 되었다는 것이다. 앉아서 혹은 서서 예배드리는 것은 문화다. 강대상에 신을 신고 올라가는 것에 대한 반발이 얼마나 많았던가? 이런 것들은 지역문화나 전통에 따라서 얼마든지 바꿀 수 있는 것이다.

그런데 이슬람권에서 소위 상황화 전략이라고 하면서 도저히 납득할 수 없는 타협을 하는 것을 보고 놀라움을 금치 못하게 된다. 그것은 이슬람권에서 들어간 기독교 선교사들이 오랜 기간 동안 사역을 해 봐도 열매를 얻지 못하고 무슬림들에게 접근조차 못하게 되자 소위 상황화 전략이라는 이름으로 비상수단을 사용하기 시작한 것이라고 생각된다.

그들은 이슬람권에 들어가서 자신은 분명히 기독교인이지만 누가 "당신도 무슬림입니까?" 라고 물으면 "예, 저도 무슬림입니다." 라고 대답한다는 것이다. 그리고 "당신도 알라를 믿습니까?" 라고 물으면 "예, 저도 알라를 믿습니다." 라고 대답한다는 것이다. 어떻게 그럴 수가 있느냐고 물으면 알라(Allah)는 하나님과 같은 신이니까 나도 알라를 믿는다고 말할 수 있고 무슬림이라는 말은 "알라(Allah)에게 복종하는 자" 라는 뜻이니까 나도 무슬림이라고 하는데 전혀 죄의식이나 거리낌이 없다는 것이다. 그러면서 무슬림들과 어울려 이슬람 사원에 가서 "알라후 아크바르(Allahu Akbar) 알라(Allah)는 위대하다" 를 고백하면서 하루 다섯 번씩 하는 이슬람식 예배를 그들과 함께 드린다는 것이다. 그렇게 해서 그들이 의심을 품지 않고 선교사를 형제로 받아들이게 되면 서서히 복음을 전한다는 것이다.

나는 개인적으로 이런 행위를 하는 것을 옳지 않다고 본다. 왜냐하면 하나님의 말씀은 부끄러운 것이 아닌데 핍박을 면하기 위해서 양심을 속이고 자신을 무슬림으로 고백한다는 것은 양보할 수도 없고 양보해서는 절대로 안 되는 복음의 핵심부분을 양보해 버린 것이라고 생각하기 때문이다. 우리가 믿는 하나님은 저들이 믿는 알라(Allah)와는 전혀 다른 신이다. 알라는 삼위일체 신도 아니고 성육신하지도 않았으며 십자가를 통한 구원의 진리를 거짓이라고 모독하는 신이다.[1] 자신이 무슬림 행세를 하면서 어떻게 기독교인처럼

---

1. 꾸란 4:157.

사는 진실한 개종자를 만들어 낼 수 있다는 것인가?

　방글라데시에서 14년간 사역을 하다가 호주 멜보른에 가서 목회를 잘 하고 있는 로빈슨 박사(Dr. Stuart Robinson)의 말을 들어보면 "자신이 아는 사람 중에 방글라데시에서 그런 방법으로 무슬림들을 많이 모아서 이슬람의 모스크처럼 생긴 교회까지 건축하고 성공적인 사역자로 자처하면서 다니던 한 사역자가 있었는데 어느 날 그의 정체가 발각되면서 그 마을에서 사기꾼의 대명사처럼 불리는 망신을 당하고 다시는 이 마을에 발을 들여 놓으면 죽이겠다는 위협과 함께 추방당한 일이 있었다."고 한다.[2]

　거짓은 결국 밝혀지고 만다. 거짓을 수단으로 진리를 전하자는 것은 이치에 맞지 않는다. 목적이 아무리 좋아도 방법이 선하지 않으면 비록 그 일이 잠시 성공을 거두었다고 할지라도 하나님께서 기뻐하시지 않으며 하나님의 영광에도 유익이 되지 않는다고 생각한다.

성경적 선교 전략

　이슬람권에서는 우리가 그들과 비슷하다는 것을 강조하는 것보다는 오히려 그들과는 다르다는 것을 보여 줄 필요가 있다고 생각한다. 이슬람권에서 태어나서 그 문화에 젖어 사는 사람들 중에는

---

2. Stuart Robinson, 2008년 11월 5일 09시부터 사랑의 교회에서 열렸던 이슬람 세미나 강의 내용 중 발췌함.

162　무함마드의 계시는 왜 자꾸만 바뀔까?
Why Muhammad's revelations are changing repeatedly?

자신들의 문화에 문제가 있다는 것을 알고 있는 사람들이 많이 있다. 왜냐하면 이슬람이라는 종교는 이슬람의 창시자인 무함마드가 살았던 7세기 문화를 그대로 보존하고 실행하자는 것이기 때문이다.[3] 그들의 경전이 그렇고 그들의 문화가 그렇다. 21세기 최첨단 과학 시대에 살고 있으면서 오히려 7세기의 문화를 고수하고자 하는 것이니 얼마나 답답하겠는가? 이슬람의 하디스나 순나가 무엇을 말하는가? 무함마드가 그렇게 말했다거나 무함마드가 그렇게 행동했다는 것을 순나(Sunna)라고 하는데 그것들을 그대로 배우고 지키자는 것이 순니(Sunni)파다. 지구상의 대부분의 무슬림들이 순니파에 속한 사람들이다. 그가 옷을 입었던 방법, 그가 음식을 먹었던 방법, 그가 화장실을 이용하던 방법, 그가 목욕하던 방법, 그가 기도하던 방법 등 신앙생활 뿐 아니라 일상생활의 모든 것을 그대로 따라하자는 것이다.

과거에는 무조건 따라했었던 젊은이들이 이제는 출판물이나 방송 및 인터넷을 통해서 다른 세계에 사는 사람들의 모습을 쉽게 접할 수 있게 되었다. 그래서 그들은 전통 이슬람 문화의 문제점들을 느끼면서도 정작 그런 느낌을 나눌 수 있는 사람을 발견하기 어려운 여건에서 갈등하며 살아가고 있는 것이다. 누군가 그들의 내면의 고민을 들어주고 바른 길로 안내해 줄 사람이 필요하다. 그들은 이미 복음을 들을 준비가 된 사람들이다. 사도 바울이 전도하기 위해서 고린도에

---

3. 최영길, 『무함마드와 이슬람』, 146~188p. 여기서 저자는 무함마드 당시부터 15세기 동안 지켜지고 있는 무함마드의 말과 행동을 기록한 꾸란과 하디스와 순나를 그대로 따라하고 있는 이슬람 문화에 대해서 매우 자랑스럽게 미화하고 있다.

갔을 때 주님께서는 그에게 놀라운 말씀을 하시는 것을 볼 수 있다.

"밤에 주께서 환상 가운데 바울에게 말씀하시되 두려워하지 말며 잠잠하지 말고 말하라 내가 너와 함께 있으매 아무 사람도 너를 대적하여 해롭게 할 자가 없을 것이니 이는 이 성중에 내 백성이 많음이라 하시더라" - 사도행전 18:9-10

그들을 누가 전도했는가? 그 당시 아직 아무도 고린도에 있는 사람들에게 복음을 전했던 사람은 없었다. 그럼에도 불구하고 주님께서는 이 성중에 내 백성이 많다고 하셨다. 그 말씀은 무슨 뜻일까? 복음은 사람이 전하는 것 같지만 사실은 주님께서 그 마음을 열어 놓지 않으면 사람이 아무리 천사의 방언을 하더라도 듣는 이가 믿음을 가질 수가 없다. 바울이 두려움 없이 담대하게 말씀을 증거하면 주님께서 듣는 이들의 마음을 열어서 듣게 하고 믿게 하고 구원하기로 작정하셨다는 것이다. 그렇게 준비된 백성들을 주님께서는 이미 내 백성이라고 부르시면서 그 당시 우상숭배와 음란과 죄악이 지배했던 고린도에 그런 준비된 주님의 백성이 많이 있다고 말씀하신 것이다.

그러므로 그 곳이 이슬람권이든 공산권이나 불교권이나 힌두교권이든지 거기에는 이미 주님께서 구원하시기로 작정하신 주님의 백성이 많다고 하는 믿음을 가지게 되면 담대함이 생기게 된다. 그 담대함에 진정한 사랑과 희생적 섬김과 복음의 능력이 함께 하면 풍성한 결실이 맺어지게 될 것이다.

필자가 19년간 사역했던 이란은 이슬람을 배신한 자들을 핍박하기로 유명한 나라이다.[4] 1994년에는 가까이 지내던 현지인 기독교

목사들이 6개월 만에 3명이나 비참하게 칼에 맞아서 혹은 총에 맞아서 순교한 사건들이 일어났었다. 그런데 그 소식이 전국에 퍼졌고 이슬람을 배신하면 언제 그 같은 일을 당할지 모르는 상황인데도 개종하고 예수를 믿겠다는 청년을 만났다. 그래서 개종하면 사회적으로 얼마나 많은 불이익을 당하고 얼마나 위험한 일이 발생하게 되는지를 아느냐고 물었다. 그랬더니 잘 알고 있다고 대답하는 것이었다. 그래서 그럼에도 불구하고 예수를 믿겠다는 이유를 물었다. 이에 대한 그의 대답은 "미아르제(miarze)"라는 한 마디였다. 번역을 한다면 "그럴만한 가치가 있다"는 것이다. 죄 사함 받고 하나님의 자녀가 되어 천국에서 주님과 함께 영원히 살 수 있는 방법이 이 길 밖에 없다면 잠시 머물다 갈 이 세상에서의 부귀영화를 포기하고 핍박을 받는 정도의 대가는 당연히 지불해야 하는 것 아니냐는 것이다.

이런 사람들이 목마르게 진리를 기다리고 있는데 가서 "나도 너 같이 알라(Allah)를 믿는 무슬림이니 친하게 지내자"고 하면 어떤 결과가 나오겠는가를 생각해 보자. 복음만이 진리라는 것이 확실하다면 정직하게 자신이 기독교인임을 밝히고 자신을 핍박하는 사람들을 섬기고 사랑하면서 그들의 신뢰를 얻어가면서, 그들 중에서 목숨을 걸고 개종할 각오가 되어 있는 준비된 무슬림들을 찾아내서 진리로 양육하여 구원에 동참 시키는 것이 올바른 선교라고 생각한다. 일단

---

4. 이란은 세계 7대 인권 탄압국가로 지정된 나라이다. 이란의 인권탄압에 대한 반기문 UN 사무총장의 경고가 2008년 11월 10일 자 인터넷 미국의 소리(Voice of America) 신문에 게재되어 있다. http://www.voanews.com.edgesuite.net/korean/2008. 11. 10. voa19.cfm.

하나님의 진리인 성경 말씀으로 양육된 사람들은 어떤 핍박이 와도 심지어 순교의 위협 속에도 담대하고 평안한 마음으로 상황을 받아들이며 순간의 평안을 위해서 복음의 위대성과 절대성을 포기하며 세상과 타협하지는 않을 것이다.

그렇지만 우리는 핍박이 심하다고 해서 그들과 타협해서도 안 되지만 절대로 무슬림들을 미워해서도 안 될 것이며, 그들과 싸워서도 안 될 것이다.

"우리의 싸움은 혈과 육에 대한 것이 아니요 정사와 권세와 이 어두움의 세상 주관자들과 하늘에 있는 악한 영들에게 대함이라."

-에베소서 6:12

우리가 무슬림들과 싸워서는 안 되는 이유는 우리의 대적은 그들을 속이고 있는 영들이며 그들은 적그리스도의 영에 속고 있는 불쌍한 우리의 형제들이며 이슬람의 영에 의해 가장 큰 피해를 입은 상처받은 영혼들이기 때문이다. 그들은 하나님의 양들이지만 다른 울타리 속에 들어가서 참 주인에게로 돌아갈 수 있는 길을 강제로 차단당한 안타까운 상황에 처한 피해자들이며 우리의 도움이 절실히 필요한 사람들이기에 우리마저 포기한다면 영원히 구원받을 수 있는 기회가 없을지도 모른다.

그들은 적그리스도의 영에 속아서 우리를 까닭 없이 미워할지라도 우리는 그들을 미워할 이유가 없다. 아니 이유가 충분히 있어도 미워해서는 안 되며 오히려 축복하라[5]는 것이 주님의 가르침이며 우리의 사명이기 때문이다. 왜 주님께서는 어린 양을 이리 가운데

보내실까?⁶ 그것은 우리에게 엄청난 상급을 준비해 놓으시고 우리가 과연 그 상을 받기에 합당한 사람들인지 아닌지를 확인하고자 우리의 담대함을 시험하기 위해서 그리고 우리의 순종을 시험하기 위해서 이기도 하지만 가서 잡아먹히고 죽을 수도 있음을 알면서도 가라고 명하시는 말씀 속에는 우리의 목자 되시는 주님께서 철저하게 보호해 주시겠다는 약속이 포함되어 있는 것이라는 사실을 잊어서는 안 될 것이다. 따라서 우리의 지혜를 짜내어 스스로 보호하려고 무리한 방법을 사용하지 말라는 것이다. 그러면 주님께서 부족하지만 우리를 사용하셔서 많은 열매를 거두시고 스스로 영광을 받으실 것이며 우리는 그 일에 선택받았음을 감격해하면서 그 영광에 동참하게 될 것이다.

---

5. 로마서 12:14, 너희를 핍박하는 자를 축복하라. 축복하고 저주하지 말라.
6. 누가복음 10:3.

SECTION 5

결론

Why Muhammad's revelations are
changing repeatedly?

결론

　이슬람은 이제 세계를 정복하려고 '양동작전'을 벌이고 있다. 양동작전이란 한 쪽에서는 평화를 외치면서 또 한 쪽에서는 폭력과 테러를 통해서 이슬람에 대한 공포심을 불러일으키는 것이다. 유럽 등 서방세계에서는 이미 이슬람이 자신들의 목소리를 낼 수 있는 규모로 성장을 했고, 자체 테러조직들이 구성되어 이슬람의 세계정복 전략을 방해하는 해로운 인물들은 과감하게 테러를 가할 수 있을 만큼 세력을 갖추었다. 알 카에다는 "팔레스타인에서 수행되고 있는 순교적인 자살폭탄 테러에 여성들이 참여하는 것은 거룩한 장소에서 유대인들이 자행하는 신성모독적인 많은 행동과 점령된 땅으로서 그곳의 상황을 볼 때 가장 칭찬받아야 할 예배의 표현 중 하나이다."라고 했다.[1]

　이란의 최고 지도자 호메이니(Khomeini)는 영국에서 이슬람을 모독

한 책『악마의 시(Satanic Verses)』를 저술한 살만 루시디(Salman Rushidy)[2]를 살해하는 무슬림에게는 300만 불의 상금을 준다고 하여 그를 보호하려는 경찰과 그를 죽이겠다는 무슬림들 때문에 많은 사상자를 내며 심지어는 그 책에 관심을 가지고 번역한 사람들을 일본과 이태리에서 암살하는 등 세계적인 물의를 일으켰으며,[3] 네델란드에서는 히르시 알리(Hirsi Ali)라는 국회의원 출신의 여자가 저술한 이슬람 여성들의 핍박상을 그린『굴종(Submission)』이라는 책을 영화로 만든 세계적인 화가인 반 빈센트 고흐의 동생인 테오 반 고흐의 증손자인 테오 반 고흐(Van Gogh)라는 네덜란드 국민 영화감독이 자전거를 타고 가는데 한 무슬림이 총을 쏘았다. 피투성이가 되어 땅에 구르면서 자기를 쏜 사람에게 손을 저으며 "말로 하자"고 했으나 그는 총을 4발을 더 쏘아 죽이고 목에 칼을 꽂고 또 그 영화의 시나리오 작가인 '히르시 알리'에게 죽음을 경고하는 5장의 경고장을 칼로 가슴에 박아 놓는 끔찍한 사건이 발생했다.[4] 유럽에서는 이제 더 이상 이슬람의 정체를 마음 놓고 밝힐 수 있는 기회가 사라져 버렸다고 해도 과언이 아닐 것이다.

그러나 대한민국은 아직 이슬람 인구가 1퍼센트가 안 되는 나라다.[5] 그래서 그들은 평화를 가장하며 세력이 커질 때까지는 과격한

---

1. 콜린 다이,『영국의 이슬람화 그 대책은 무엇인가』, 도움번역 위원회 역(대전: 도움, 2008), 13p.
2. Ibid. 28p.
3. 살만 루시디,『악마의 시』, 김진준 역(서울: 문학세계사, 2007), 속표지 내용 참조.
4. 동아일보(2006.7.1) 국제면 "불행을 부르는 여자, 네덜란드 전 의원 히르시 알리"
5. 한국 이슬람 중앙회의 공식 통계는 2007년도 현재 13만 5천 명 정도로 대한민국 국민의 0.28 퍼센트 정도 된다.

행동을 자제하고 있는 상황[6]이며 아직 자생테러 단체도 생기지 않은 상태다.

지금 이슬람의 정체를 밝히지 않으면 몇 년 후에는 이슬람의 정체를 밝힐 수 있는 기회를 영원히 놓치고 만다.

따라서 이 책은 무함마드가 계시를 받았다고 하는 꾸란과 이슬람의 율법의 기초가 되는 하디스 등을 살펴가면서 그의 계시가 상황에 따라 변하는 모습을 통해서 이슬람의 영의 정체를 밝히고자 했다. 그 영은 성령과는 상관이 없는 다른 영이라는 것을 그들의 경전과 교리를 근거로 제시했다.

물론 무함마드의 계시가 상황에 따라 달라진 경우들은 이 책에서 다루지 않은 부분들도 많이 있다. 예를 들면 간음하지 말라[7]고 해 놓고 만일 간음을 범하는 자들에게는 처음에는 알라(Allah)가 데려갈 때까지 가두어 두라[8]고 했다가 나중에는 백대의 태형에 처하라고 했다[9]가 후에는 4명의 증인이 없으면 정죄하지 말라고 했다[10]가 천국에서는 많은 처녀들과 침상에서 즐길 수 있다[11]고 발전되었다든가

또는 술 마시는 자들에 대한 계시도 처음에는 술 취했을 때는 깰

---

6. 한국에 선교사 신분으로 와 있는 서울대학교 내의 무슬림들은 "자신들은 한국인들을 전도하기 위해서 온 사람들이 아니라"고 한다. 다만 이슬람을 오해하는 사람들이 있으면 그들의 궁금증을 풀어주고 싶다고 하여 한국인들의 경계심을 완화시키고자 한다(에바다 해외선교회 홈페이지 임웅철이 올린 글 인터넷: http://cafe.daum.net/e.p.t/WgYB/4).

7. 꾸란 17:32.

8. 꾸란 4:15.

9. 꾸란 24:2.

10. 꾸란 24:4.

11. 꾸란 55:70.

때까지는 예배를 드리지 말라고 했다(꾸란 4:43)가, 나중에는 술은 사탄의 도구이기에 완전히 금하라(꾸란 5:90)고 했다가 후에는 천국에서는 마음껏 술을 즐길 수 있다(꾸란 76:15)고 발전되었다.

무함마드의 계시는 일관성이 없다는 것은 군이 누가 주장하지 않아도 여러 곳에서 확연하게 드러난다. 그의 계시는 계속 상황에 따라 변경되었다. 이미 내린 계시와 완전히 모순되는 계시들이 많이 있기에 알라(Allah)의 계시는 절대로 취소할 수 없다(꾸란 6:115)던 그가 이미 내린 계시를 취소하라(꾸란 2:106)는 계시를 받았다는 것이다. 평화를 주장하는 무슬림들이 기회 있을 때마다 주장하는 유명한 구절 "종교는 강제로 하지 말지니라."라고 한 '꾸란 2:256'은 "불신자와 이교도는 발견하는 대로 죽이라."는 '꾸란 9:5' (칼의 구절)에 의해서 취소된 것을 무슬림 학자들은 다 알고 있다.[12] 그러나 그들은 이슬람을 잘 모르고 아랍어도 모르는 사람들에게 이슬람을 평화의 종교라고 소개하기 위해서 이미 취소된 구절을 가장 애용하고 있는 것이다.

이런 일들은 무엇을 말하는가? 그의 계시는 성령의 계시가 아니며 그들의 정체를 알고 있는 이슬람의 지도자들도 정직하지 않다는 것을 증명하는 것이다. 심지어는 이슬람의 하디스에 의하면 그가 알라의 세 딸들의 중보기도를 알라께서 받으실 것이라는 "마귀의 계시"를 받았다가 다시 "알라의 명령에 의해서 그것을 취소하라는 계시"를 받았다고 한다.[13] 과연 그가 마귀의 계시를 받은 것이 "알라의 세 딸들"에 관계된 것뿐이었을까?

예수 그리스도께서 하나님의 아들 되심과 그의 신성을 부인하며 (꾸란 6:101), 삼위일체를 부인하며(꾸란 4:171, 5:73), 예수 그리스도의 십자가에 달리신 사건을 부인하며(꾸란 4:157), 예수 그리스도의 부활을 부인하며(꾸란 4:158) 유대교인들과 기독교인들을 저주하는 계시(꾸란 5:51, 9:29, 98:6)를 받았을 때도 그는 성령이 아닌 인류의 구원을 가로막고 있는 적그리스도의 영을 받았음을 아무도 부인할 수는 없을 것이다.

---

12. 인터넷 사이트 http://www.thequran.com 에 들어가서 영문 번역본 꾸란들을 검색하여 꾸란 2:256 "종교는 강제로 하지 말지니라"라고 하는 구절을 찾아 보면 바로 밑에 "이 구절은 꾸란 9:5에 의해서 취소된 구절임"이라는 설명이 첨부되어 있는 것을 확인할 수 있다.

13. 알 타바리(Al Tabari) 의 하디스 제 6권 107p.

2002년 이후 해외에서 발생한
한국인 납치 및 피격사건 일지

2002년 이후 해외에서 발생한 한국인 납치 및 피격사건 일지.

(★은 이슬람과격단체에 의한 테러임)

▶ 2002.11.13 발리섬 한국인 테러기사 한국인 2명 사망.

▶ 2003.11.30 오무전기 직원들, 이라크 티크리트 고속도로서 차량
이동 중 피격. 김만수 곽경해씨 사망, 이상원 임재석씨 부상.

★ 2004. 4. 5 지구촌나눔운동의 한재광 사업부장과 무역업체 직원
인 박모씨, 이라크 나시리야에서 시아파 지도자 무크타다 알-사
드르 추종민병대원들에 의해 억류됐다가 14시간여 만에 석방.

★ 2004. 4. 8 변 모씨 등 한국인 목사 7명, 이라크 바그다드 서쪽
250㎞ 지점에서 차량 이동 중 이라크 무장세력에 의해 억류된
뒤 7시간만에 석방.

★2004. 5.31 가나무역 직원 김선일씨, 물건배달을 위해 바그다드에서 팔루자로 트럭을 이용해 이동하다 무장단체 '알 타우히드 왈 지하드'(유일신과 성전)에 피랍.

★2004. 6.22 김선일씨 참수된 채 팔루자 인근 도로에서 시신 발견.

★2004. 8. 7 이라크 취재 중이던 외국언론사 소속 한국인 기자 조모씨, 무장단체에 억류된 뒤 15시간30분만에 석방.

▶2005. 2.18 나이지리아 교민, 몸값 노린 무장세력에 피랍 뒤 석방.

▶2005. 7.28 아이티 교민 서모씨, 수도 포르토프랭스에서 몸값 노린 무장괴한에 의해 피랍. 사흘만에 석방.

★2006. 3.14 KBS 용모 특파원, 팔레스타인 가자지구에서 무장단체 PFLF (팔레스타인 해방전선) 소속으로 추정되는 무장괴한들에 의해 피랍. 하루 뒤 석방.

▶2006. 4. 4 동원수산 수속 원양어선 제628호 동원호 소말리아 인근 해역에서 조업중 현지 무장단체에 피랍. 최성식 선장 등 한국인 8명, 인도네시아인 9명, 베트남인 5명, 중국인 3명 등 총 선원 25명 피랍. 117일만인 7월 30일 석방.

▶2006. 6. 7 대우건설 근로자 3명, 한국가스공사 직원 2명 등 한국인 5명 나 이지리아 유전지대 포트 하코트 내 대우건설 현장에서 현지 무장 단체에 의해 피랍. 다음 날 석방.

▶2007. 1.10 나이지리아 남부 바엘사주 오구지역서 대우건설 소속 한국인 근로자 9명과 현지인 1명 등 10명이 무장단체에 피랍. 사흘만인 13일 석방.

▶2007. 5.3 나이지리아 유전지대 포트 하코트 내 화력발전소

건설 현장에서 대우건설 소속 직원 3명이 현지 무장단체에 의해 납치됐다 6일만에 석방.

▶ 2007. 5.15 소말리아 주변 해역에서 한국인 4명 탑승한 원양어선 2척 무장단체에 피랍. 173일만인 11월 4일 석방.

★ 2007. 7.19 아프가니스탄 탈레반 무장세력에 의해 분당 샘물교회 자원봉사자 23명 피랍.

★ 2007. 7.25 탈레반, 한국인 인질 배형규 목사 살해.

★ 2007. 7.31 탈레반, 남은 인질 22명 중 심성민씨 추가 살해.

★ 2007. 8.13 탈레반, 김경자, 김지나 씨 석방.

★ 2007. 8.29 탈레반, 한국인 인질 12명 3차례에 걸쳐 석방.

★ 2007. 8.30 탈레반, 남은 인질 7명 석방. 인질사태 종료.

▶ 2007.10.26 과테말라 거주 교민 무장괴한에 납치됐다 하루만인 29일 석방.

▶ 2007.10.28 아프리카 소말리아 근해에서 한국인 선원 2명 탑승한 일본 선박골든노리호 해적단체에 피랍, 1명은 당일 탈출, 전우성 씨는 45일만인 12월 12일 석방.

▶ 2007.12.24 중국 상하이(上海)에서 유학중인 한국 대학생 1명이 한국인이 낀 납치범들에게 납치됐다가 이틀만인 26일 중국 공안이 범인들을 검거하면서 무사히 구조.

▶ 2008. 3.29 필리핀 민다나오섬에서 한국인 사업가 1명 피랍, 55일만인 5월 23일 석방.

▶ 2008. 4.28 아프리카 소말리아 해역을 지나던 한국 선적 화물선 알렉산더칼 호가 해적단체로부터 피습, 피랍은 모면.

▶ 2008. 5.31 필리핀 마닐라 북부에서 한국 여성 교민 1명 납치
되었다가 나흘만인 6월 4일 석방.

▶ 2008.11.15 한국인 5명이 탄 일본 국적 화물선 해적에 피랍,
3개월여 만인 2009년 2월13일 석방

★ 2009. 3.15 한국인 관광객 18명, 예멘 고대 유적지 시밤지역
에서 폭발물 공격으로 이중 4명 사망 3명 부상

★ 2009. 4. 해군 청해부대 소말리아 파병

★ 2009. 6.12 한국인 엄영선 씨를 포함한 국제의료 자원봉사단
원 9명, 예멘에서 피랍

★ 2009. 6.16 예멘에서 피랍되었던 엄영선 씨를 포함한 외국인
의료봉사단 9명 전원 사망 확인

★ 2009. 12.9 탈레반, 한국 재 파병시 '나쁜결과'를 맞을 준비
해야할 것이라고 경고함

★ 2010. 2.25 아프간 재 파병 국회 통과

국내 도서

- 공일주. 『이싸냐 예수냐』. 서울: 죠이선교회 출판부, 1997.
- 김성철. 『종교학 대사전』. 서울: 한국사전연구사, 1998.
- 김용선. 『이슬람의 역사와 그 문화』. 서울: 명문당, 2002.
- 김용선. 『무함마드』. 서울: 명문당, 2003.
- 김정위. 『이슬람 입문』. 서울: 한국외국어대학교 출판부, 2001.
- 김정위. 『이슬람 사전』. 서울: 학문사, 2002.
- 김종빈. 『갈등의 핵 유태인』. 경기: 효형출판사, 2007.
- 유해석. 『이슬람이 다가오고 있다』. 서울: 쿰란출판사, 2005.
- 이명권. 『무함마드와 예수 그리고 이슬람』. 서울: 코나쿠스, 2008.
- 이희수. 『초등학생이 꼭 알아야 할 이슬람의 모든 것』.

　　서울: 김영사, 2009

- 정수일.『이슬람 문명』. 서울: 창작과 비평사, 2002.

- 진원숙.『충돌의 역사』. 서울: 신서원, 2002.

- 최영길 외 6인(21세기 중동 이슬람문명권연구사업단).
　『중동종교운동의 이해2』. 파주: 한울, 2005.

- 최영길.『꾸란의 이해』. 서울: 성천문화재단, 1995.

- 최영길.『이슬람 문화』. 서울: 도서출판 알림, 2004.

- 최영길.『이슬람문화사』. 서울: 송산출판사,1990.

- 최창모.『이스라엘사』. 서울: 대한 교과서주식회사, 2007.

번역 도서

- H.A.R Gibb.『이슬람』. 이희수 최준식 공역 .
　서울: 도서출판 주류성, 1997.

- Huseyin Kirdemir.『한국인들이 이슬람에 대해 궁금해 하는
　33가지』. 이형주 역. 서울: 아담출판사, 2005.

- P. J. 스튜어트.『펼쳐보는 이슬람』. 김백리 역. 서울: 풀빛, 2004.

- 가토히로시,『이슬람 그들은 누구인가』. 남구형 조영렬 역.
　서울: 고도, 2001.

- 돈 리처드슨.『코란의 비밀』. 이희민 역. 서울: 쿰란출판사, 2008

- 레자 아슬란.『알라 외에 다른 신은 없도다』. 정규역 역.
　서울: 이론과 실천, 2006.

- 마크 A. G. 『이슬람과 유대인 그 끝나지 않은 전쟁』. 4HIM 지음.
  서울: 도서출판 글마당, 2009.
- 미르치아 엘리아데. 『샤마니즘 고대 접신술』. 이윤기 역.
  서울: 까치글방, 1992.
- 사피 아르라흐만 알무바라크푸리. 『인간 무함마드』. 최영길 역.
  서울: 도서출판 알림, 2006.
- 살레 H. 알아이드. 『이슬람국가에서의 비무슬림의 권리』. 최영길 역.
  서울: 도서출판 알림, 2006.
- 압둘 마시흐. 『무슬림과의 대화』. 이동주 역.
  서울: 기독교문서선교회, 2004.
- 엘리엇 애런슨 & 캐럴 태브리스. 『거짓말의 진화』. 박웅희 역.
  서울: 추수 밭, 2007.
- 요하킴 그닐카. 『성경과 코란 무엇이 같으며 무엇이 다른가』.
  오희천 역. 서울: 중심, 2005.
- 윌리엄 와그너. 『이슬람의 세계변화 전략』. 노승현 역.
  서울: Apostolos Press, 2006.
- 이즈쓰 도시히코. 『이슬람: 종교, 법, 그리고 정신의 내면』.
  조영렬 역. 서울: 무우수, 2007.
- 콜린 다이. 『영국의 이슬람화 그 대책은 무엇인가』.
  도움번역 위원회 역. 대전: 도움, 2008.
- 폴 존슨. 『유대인의 역사 3 홀로코스트와 시오니즘』.
  김한성 역. 서울: 살림, 2005.
- 프랜시스 로빈슨. 『케임브리지 이슬람사』.

손주영 역. 서울: 시공사, 2006.

- 하르트무트 보브친, 『무함마드는 이렇게 말했다』. 염정용 역.
  서울: 들녘, 2005.

- 하르트무트 보브친. 『무함마드는 이렇게 말했다』. 염정용 역.
  서울: 들녘, 2005.

- W. 푀르스터, 『신 · 구약 중간사』. 문희석 역.
  서울: 컨콜디아사, 1979.

외국서적

- Dashti. A Study of the Prophetic Career of Mohammad. translated from Persian by F.R.C. Bagley. U.S.A CA: Mazda Publishers, 1994.

- E. M. Blaiklock. The Zondervan Pictorial Bible Atlas. Michigan U.S.A.: Zondervan Publishing House, 1981.

- Ibn Warraq. Why I am not a Muslim. U. S. A. New York : Prometheus Books, 2003.

- L. Esposito, John. UNHOLY WAR: Terror in the Name of Islam. U.K.: Oxford University Press, 2002.

- L. Esposito, John. The Oxford History of Islam. New York: Oxford University press, 1999.

- Mark Gabriel. The unfinished battle Islam & Jews. Fl. U.S.A : FrontLine , 2003.

- Patrick A, O'Boyle, D.D. New Catholic Encyclopedia. U.S.A :

Washington, 1967.

- Robert A. Morey. Islamic Invasion. U. S. A. California: Chick
  Publications, 2000.

- William Montgomery Watt. Muslim-Christian encounters.
  London: Routledge, 1991.

- Zwemer, Samuel. The Influence of Animism on Islam. U. K.
  :London, 1920.

성경

- 대한성경공회. 『신·구약 성경』. 개역 한글판, 1956.

꾸란

- 김용선. 『한역 꾸란(이슬람 경전)』. 서울, 어학사.
- 이슬람 국제 출판국, 『코란』. 서울: 이슬람 국제 출판국, 1988.
- 최영길, 『성꾸란 의미의 한국어 번역』.
  서울: 파하드 국왕 꾸란 출판청, 1996.
- 영어 꾸란: Arberry 역.
- 영어 꾸란: Hilali 역.
- 영어 꾸란: Khalifa 역.
- 영어 꾸란: Palmer 역.
- 영어 꾸란: Pickthel 역.
- 영어 꾸란: Rodwell 역.

- 영어 꾸란: Sale 역.
- 영어 꾸란: Shakir 역.
- 영어 꾸란: Sher Ali 역.
- 영어 꾸란: Yousuf Ali 역.
- 이란어 꾸란: 이란 Ministry of Islamic Guidance & Culture 역.
- Sahih al Bukhari. Volume 1, Book 1.
- Hadith al Tabari. volume 6.
- Sahih al-Bukhari, Volume 6, Book 60.
- Tirmidhi and Ibn Maiah. ishkat al-Masabih. Vol. 1.
- Al-Imam Zain-ud-Din Ahmad bin Abdul-Lateef Az-Zubaidi, Summarized Sahih Al-Bukhari, translated by Dr Muhammad Muhsin Khan. Riyadh Saudi Arabia : Maktaba Dar-us-Salam, 1996.

신문, 잡지

- 동아일보. 2006.7.1 국제면 "불행을 부르는 여자, 네델란드 전 의원 히르시 알리"

인터넷

- http://www.faithfreedom.org/Articles/skm30804.htm.
- http://www.islammission.org/islam/ramadan/2001_ramadan/011212.htm.
- Sayyid Qutb, 『Milestones』 Revised Edition, Chapter 4 "Jihad in the

cause of Allah". internet site research: http://www.answering-islam.org/Hahn/jihad.htm#fn7

• Sheikh Muhammed Salih Al-Munajjid. '이슬람 Q & A'. (http://www.islam-qa.com/en/ref/1528)

• 늘사랑교회홈페이지. (http://www.everlove.or.kr/community/?kind=7&cate=77&mod=2&page=1&idx=625&searchKind=&searchText=&subCate=)

• '이슬람선교' 웹사이트 (http://www.islammission.org/islam/introduct/islam.htm)

• 인터넷 동영상: 마크 G. 박사의 증언, http://www.youtube.com/watch?v=Tds8-EOEsk.

• 인터넷 동영상: http://kr.youtube.com/watch?v=0AxKT_taS0s.

• 인터넷 동영상: http://kr.youtube.com/watch?v=bL9XoM1rbG8.

• 인터넷위키백과 '꾸란' 참조: http://ko.wikipedia.org/wiki/%EC%BD%94%EB%9E%80.

• 인터넷조선일보, http://news.chosun.com/site/data/html_dir/2007/07/24/2007072401064.html.

• 파파울프, '이슬람의 적신월' 웹사이트. 참조 (http://idealist.egloos.com/3683555)

무함마드의 계시는 왜 자꾸 바뀔까?

저 자 이만석
감 수 4HIM
만든이 이만석

2010년 4월 8일 1판 1쇄 발행

만 든 곳 4HIM
등   록 제 25100-2010-000002호

서울시 강북구 도봉로 176(미아동 125-25)
전 화 02) 989-5688
팩 스 02) 989-5688
E-mail : msltkc@yahoo.co.kr

값 **10,000원**

ISBN 978-89-964279-0-2 03280

Other Books by Vivian Vande Velde

heir
apparent

heir apparent

Vivian Vande Velde

sandpiper

Houghton Mifflin Harcourt
Boston New York

www.hmhco.com

The text of this book is set in Berling LT Std.

The Library of Congress has cataloged the hardcover edition as follows:
Vande Velde, Vivian.
Heir apparent/by Vivian Vande Velde.
p. cm.
Summary: While playing a total immersion virtual reality game of kings and
intrigue, fourteen-year-old Giannine learns that demonstrators have damaged the
equipment to which she is connected, and she must win the game quickly or be
damaged herself.
[1. Virtual reality—Fiction. 2. Science fiction.] I. Title.
PZ7.V2773He 2002
[Fic]—dc21
2002002441

Manufactured in the United States of America
DOC 20 19 18

4500549659

This book is dedicated with affection for
but no patience with
those who would protect our children through
humorless moralizing and paranoia about fantasy

contents

heir
apparent

GIFT CERTIFICATE

RASMUSSEM ENTERPRISES

$50.00

FIFTY DOLLARS AND 00 CENTS

721068076

A gift to ___Giannine Bellisario___

NOT REDEEMABLE FOR CASH

Nigel Rasmussem

THIS CERTIFICATE MUST BE PRESENTED IN ORDER TO BE REDEEMED.

Valid at any Rasmussem Gaming Center™ Virtual Reality Arcade, Total Immersion Game Rooms, or concession counters. Some restrictions may apply. If total value of certificate is not used at any one time, another certificate or Rasmussem Gaming Center™ tokens may be substituted as reimbursement, at manager's discretion.

RASMUSSEM ENTERPRISES IS NOT RESPONSIBLE FOR REIMBURSEMENT IF THIS CERTIFICATE IS LOST OR STOLEN.

Acceptance of this certificate by Rasmussem Enterprises in no way constitutes nor implies liability for any loss of property that occurs on premises, nor for personal injury incurred. A small minority of those participating in Total Immersion situations may experience such usually short-term effects as but not necessarily limited to light-headedness, decreased appetite, increased heart rate, blurred vision, memory loss, inability to concentrate, and/or loss of motor control.

See disclaimer on back for further details.

CHAPTER ONE

Happy Birthday to Me

It was my fourteenth birthday, and I was arguing with a bus. How pathetic is that?

Even before the bus had started in on me, my mood wasn't exactly the best it's ever been. Birthdays do that to me. This year I didn't even have a good excuse: I had actually received my birthday gift from my father on time, which might have been a sign he was making an effort to be a more considerate and involved dad. Of course, if he was really considerate and involved, he wouldn't have had his secretary call to ask me what kind of gift certificate I wanted for my birthday.

Whatever. Birthday = don't-mess-with-me mood.

So there I was, on my way to cash in my gift certificate, riding on a bus powered by artificial intelligence—emphasis on the *artificial*.

I saw the picketers just as the bus paged me: "Passenger Giannine Bellisario, you asked to disembark at the

Rasmussem Gaming Center, but there is a civil disturbance at your stop. Do you wish to continue to another destination, or would you prefer to be returned to the location at which you boarded?" The voice was kind and polite and only slightly metallic.

I was not polite. I sighed. Loudly. "Are they on strike?" I asked into the speaker embedded in the armrest.

There was a brief pause while the bus's computer brain accessed Central Information. "Rasmussem employees are not on strike," the bus reassured me, at just about the same time that I could make out the picketers' signs. "The demonstration is by members of CPOC."

I sighed even louder. They pronounce it, *C pock*. It stands for Citizens to Protect Our Children. As a fourteen-year-old, I qualify—by society's definition—as a child. I am willing to accept protection from stray meteors, ecoterrorists, and my seven-year-old cousin, Todd. But I don't feel in need of protecting by CPOC, which strongly believes that only G-rated movies should be made and that libraries should stock only nice, uplifting books that promote solid family values—*nice* being defined as nothing supernatural, nothing violent, nothing scary. That about kills my entire reading list. I think there are a couple alphabet books they approve of. Still, as far as I knew, this was the first time they'd ever come after Rasmussem.

I have excellent timing like that.

As the bus passed by the patch of sidewalk the picketers had claimed, I could read their signs: MAGIC = SATANISM and VIOLENCE BEGETS VIOLENCE and INAPPROPRIATE FOR OUR CHILDREN.

"Why can't you drop me off?" I asked. "Legally, they aren't allowed to obstruct anyone from going in." I'd learned that in Participation in Government class.

"Rochester Transit Authority is prohibited from letting a minor disembark into a situation that might be hazardous," the bus told me.

A little bit of artificial intelligence can be an annoying thing. "What are they going to do: smack me on the head with a pamphlet?" I asked.

The bus didn't answer and kept on moving. I was not going to win an argument, I could tell.

"Well, then," I said, "let me off at the next stop."

"Not if you intend to return to the Rasmussem Gaming Center stop," the bus responded.

I checked our progress on the real-time electronic route map displayed on the back of the seat in front of me and told the bus, "Of course not. I want to be dropped off at the art museum."

"That is on this vehicle's route and is only one block away," the bus told me. "Estimated time of arrival, thirty seconds."

So much for artificial intelligence. A human bus driver could have guessed that I had not developed a sudden craving for culture. Then again, a human bus driver probably wouldn't have cared, any more than the other passengers did.

The bus stopped in front of the museum. "Have a nice day, Giannine Bellisario," the bus told me.

I smiled and gave a Queen Victoria wave, and muttered under my breath, "Your mother was a toaster oven."

———

AS I APPROACHED the gaming center, I could see the picketers were quiet and orderly; so using my *human* intelligence, I deduced they weren't dangerous. Once I got in front of the building, I sprinted for the doorway. It was beneath a large red-and-gold sign flanked by rearing dragons: RASMUSSEM GAMING CENTER.

At least one of the picketers realized my intent and started quoting some Bible verse at me, complete with *yea*s and *thou*s and *wicked one*s.

I started walking faster, and he started quoting faster, which would have been fine except he was also moving to cut me off. I reached the door and a Rasmussem employee opened it for me, which was better service than they'd ever provided before. He was probably set there to make sure the picketers didn't physically interfere with the customers. Once the door was shut behind me, that blocked out road noise and protester noise alike.

The lobby of a Rasmussem Gaming Center looks pretty much like the lobby of a movie theater. Lots of slick posters advertising the latest games, a concession stand, booths where you can feed in tokens and play some of the older virtual reality arcade-type games. For a Saturday on a nice May afternoon, the place looked dead, though the popcorn machine was going, wafting the enticing smell of fresh popcorn all the way down to the doors where I'd come in.

But I was self-disciplined and resisted. I went up to the reception desk in the waiting area. The total immersion gaming rooms were beyond, where they hook you up to the computer—as an individual or with a group— to experience a role-playing fantasy.

There were a pair of older boys, late high school or maybe even college age, sprawled in the comfy chairs in the waiting area, looking as though they'd been there awhile. They glanced up hopefully when they spotted me, then returned to leafing through their catalogs and poking at each other and trying to look cool for the receptionist, who was tapping her computer keys with the speed, concentration, and fervor of someone who had to be playing Tetris instead of working.

She must have made a game-ending mistake for she scowled and looked up. "Welcome to Rasmussem Gaming Center," she said. She wore a gown that was a medieval style but that shimmered and slowly shifted color, going from pink to lavender to deep purple to blue. I knew that if I watched long enough, it would cycle through the rainbow. There was one of those new genetically engineered dragons on her desk, hamster-sized and unpleasant: It had been trying to tip over the receptionist's nameplate, and when I placed my gift certificate on the desk, the little beast lunged at me. "He's just playing," the receptionist assured me as I snatched my hand back. "It's his way of greeting you."

Sure. I have an uncle who'll tell you the same thing about his rottweiler.

The receptionist looked at the gift certificate. "This will get you half an hour of total immersion game time or forty-five tokens for the arcade games up front. You can play your own module, or you can join other players." She pointed toward the older boys. Her desk dragon dove and nipped at the trailing edge of her sleev~~d tiny chain that tethered him to her pen ~~

him up short, and he hovered, his leathery wings fluttering. The receptionist ignored him. "They're trying to form up a foursome to play Dragons Doom. Interested?"

I don't like to play role-playing games with people I don't know, and besides, I figured an eighth-grade girl with a seventh-grader's figure probably wasn't exactly what they'd been hoping for, either.

"No, I'll play with computer-generated characters," I said.

The receptionist nodded. I could see her set herself on automatic pilot. "Because the computer directly stimulates your brain, you will feel as though you're actually experiencing the adventure." She must have said this about a million times a day, because she spoke quickly and without inflection, so that if I hadn't known what she was talking about, I wouldn't have known what she was talking about. "Half an hour of game time will take you through the three days of your chosen computer adventure. You will smell the smells, taste the tastes, feel the texture of the clothes you're wearing and the things you touch. You will experience cold if your computer persona is in a situation where he or she would feel cold, just as you will feel hunger and you might feel pain. If your persona is killed off, you will not, of course, feel that pain. You are guaranteed at least thirty minutes of playtime. If you get killed before your thirty minutes have been used up, you will be given another life and the adventure will automatically restart. Once you have started a life, you will be able to continue until you successfully finish or until you are killed, even if your thirty minutes ut partway through. Any questions?"

8

I shook my head.

"Want to check out the promos?" She pointed to the alcoves, and her dragon once again lunged and missed.

At the promo station, the computer recognized my handprint and showed the names of the games I'd played the other times I'd been here, as well as the game I'd played when I'd visited my cousins in Baltimore and we'd gone to the Rasmussem Center there. The screen showed the dates I'd played and the scores I'd received. I pressed the button indicating I wanted to view the trailers for games that could be played in half an hour or under.

Alien Conflict I didn't even bother with, nor Dinosaur Safari. I watched the promo for Lost in Time and decided it looked too complicated. It was probably the kind of game where you had to come back four or five times before you got anywhere. Weatherly Manor was a haunted-house game that looked like a possibility, though the computer knew my birth date, which meant I would get the toned-down version for those under sixteen. A Witch's Stew sounded too young even though this list was supposed to be age specific. Sword of Talla looked interesting, and I was thinking I'd probably go with that, when I pressed the button for Heir Apparent.

The voice-over described Heir Apparent as a game of strategy and shifting alliances. "The king has died," the voice said. "Are you next in line for the throne, or next in line to die?" There was a flurry of quick scenes: a castle on a hill, an army assembling, a dragon, someone being pursued through the woods, a wizard tossing
der into the air, and an eagle forming fr

and lunging—talons outstretched—so that he looked about to come straight out of the screen, and I instinctively jerked back. "Who can you trust?" the voice asked. The screen went dark with an ominous thud like a dungeon door slamming. A child's voice whispered, "Bad choice," and cackling laughter echoed while the name Heir Apparent flashed on the screen, then slowly faded.

I found myself more inclined toward Heir Apparent than Sword of Talla, and knew myself well enough to know why. In the montage of scenes, there had been some really good-looking guys. Probably *not* the smartest way to choose a game. On the other hand, it made no sense to pick a game specifically because it had nobody interesting-looking.

I went back to the receptionist. "Heir Apparent for girls as well as boys?"

The receptionist had been filing her nails while waiting, and now that she paused, the desk dragon leaped and clung on to the emery board, gnawing at the edge. She shook him off. "Yes," she told me, "a female character can inherit the throne and become king if she makes the right decisions."

"Is there only one set of right decisions?" I asked. That could make for a frustrating game, the kind you have to play over and over.

"Heir Apparent," she said, "is like bean soup."

"Excuse me?" I said.

"Playing Heir Apparent," she explained, "is like making bean soup, whereas Dragons Doom is more like making a peanut butter and jelly sandwich."

10

I had *no* idea what she was talking about.

"With Dragons Doom, all you've got to do is remember you're making a peanut butter and jelly sandwich, and you'll end up with a peanut butter and jelly sandwich. Barring, of course, dropping the bread, peanut-butter-side down, onto the floor."

"Of course," I agreed, just to humor her.

She continued, "But with Heir Apparent, you can approach in any one of several ways, and still end up with bean soup. You can use pinto beans or black beans or navy beans. You could maybe add macaroni, or not, and you'd still end up with bean soup. But there're all sorts of dangers—if you *do* decide to use macaroni but you add it too late, it's undercooked, maybe even crunchy. Add it too early, and it becomes mushy. You can have too much salt, not enough pepper. Tarragon might help, or it might make the whole thing bitter." She leaned forward confidentially. "And that's not even getting into the question of boil or simmer."

Just my luck to get an explanation from someone who didn't know when to give up a bad metaphor. "Not just one set of right decisions?" I interpreted. "Okay, I'll go for it."

Just then her desk dragon pooped on the desk.

I should have taken it as an omen.

CHAPTER TWO

Off to a Fantastic Start (Not!)

Rasmussem Enterprises must have a vice president in charge of bad smells.

It makes you wonder—or at least it makes *me* wonder: What kind of person takes a job where, when you go home every night and your family asks, "How did the day go, dear?" you answer, "Oh, very nice, thank you. Some kid I don't know paid a couple weeks' allowance money to get hooked up to the computer to enjoy a nice fantasy game, and I got to plunk her into a pile of sheep dung"?

I woke up thinking I'd been set down in a barn, which is sort of a Rasmussem specialty, I guess. But I could hear birds chirping, and I could feel grass prickling me through my clothes, and when I opened my eyes, there was blue sky and a warm sun above me. I could hear sheep bleating not too far off.

I sat up and was amazed to find nothing under me ex-cept the grass.

Which was when I realized that the stink was coming from me.

My shapeless, scratchy, rough-spun, and many-patched dress of unbleached wool was a far cry from the rainbow-hued gown of the Rasmussem receptionist. The people who work for Rasmussem have a pretty weird sense of humor.

Why do I put myself through this? I wondered. When my dad, who rarely calls except for the week before my birthday and the week before Christmas, had asked—through his secretary—what kind of gift certificate he should send for my birthday present, I could have named a clothes store or an electronics store or a bookstore. But no, I asked for Rasmussem, and I'd crossed a CPOC picket line to get here.

On the other hand, as soon as I stopped sending mental hate messages to Rasmussem, the computer conditioning kicked in. My mind filled with details of memories I'd never had. The effect is like holding two pieces of tracing paper up to the light, one on top of the other: At first all you can see is a jumble, but as you concentrate on one drawing—or on one life, as the case may be—then suddenly you can make it out by ignoring the pieces that don't fit.

So I ignored those parts that were Giannine Bellisario, eighth grader at St. John the Evangelist School. I ignored Rasmussem Enterprises and its overpriced computer that lets you see, hear, feel, taste, and—yes, thank you very much—*smell* a fantasy adventure in quarter-hour segments that seem to last for days.

13

I let myself become Janine de St. Jehan, sheepherder. Along with the identity came all sorts of snippets of information that I'd have known if I'd been born and raised in the village of St. Jehan.

Most of that information had to do with sheep.

If one of those woolly critters came over here, I could milk it, shear it, cure it of ringworm by an infusion of ringwort, castrate it, or help it in case of a breech birth. Not all at once to the same animal, of course.

"Janine!" a voice called. "Janine, come back to the house."

A dog came bounding up to me, black and white, with floppy ears. Did animals in this world talk? No, my implanted memory told me—well, mostly not. And definitely not in this case. This was merely Dusty, who helped me with the sheepherding. Dusty was old and her energy came in bursts, but you wouldn't guess that from the way she put her front paws on my shoulders and licked my face to greet me after my midmorning nap.

"Hiya, Dusty," I said at the same time I tried to fend her off.

The voice called again: "Janine!" And this time I recognized it as my mother's voice.

That distant, half-buried part of me that was my true self surfaced long enough to bark, *Ha! Fat chance.*

I tried to bury me even deeper. *Play the game,* I told myself. *Did you pay big bucks just to find fault with everything?* My real mother lives in New York because that's where her employer wants her to be, so I only see her one weekend a month during the school year, when she comes and stays with my grandmother and me. That, and for two weeks during the summer, which—apparently—is all she can take of me in her New York apartment, which is, as she says, "cozy for one." I told myself not to be bitter about my mother's attitude toward me. It is, after all, better than my father's: My father demanded a paternity test before the divorce settlement, when I was five. And—excuse me very much—but while five might be too young to catch all the nuances, I didn't need nuances to understand that my father wasn't willing to love me, much less pay child support, unless my mother could prove I was his.

But none of this, I told myself, was true in *this* lifetime, so none of it was important. In *this* lifetime I lived with my mother, named Solita, and my father, Dexter, who was a peat cutter, and my three younger sisters and two younger brothers. And we all loved each other unconditionally.

I stood, despite Dusty's attempts to knock me over. Instinctively my eyes found the right hut out of a cluster of eight—the entirety of the village of St. Jehan in all its glory. All the huts were made of straw and held together with sheep you-can-probably-guess-what. There was my mother, nearly as broad as she was tall, waving to me from the front yard, a swirl of chickens and small children stirring up the dirt around her skirts. "Stay, Dusty," I ordered the dog. "Guard the sheep."

Dusty lay down on the spot I'd vacated, resting her head on her paws. I assumed that if a wolf or thieves came, she would know what to do.

I waved my woolen cap at my mother and started down the hill.

The part of the scene below that didn't fit was the man standing beside my mother. He had an ostrich-feather-plumed hat and was holding the reins of a fine horse that had obviously never pulled a plow. Between the two of them, man and horse, there was enough gold trim to keep the village of St. Jehan fed for a year. I could see he'd been talking with my mother, though he took great care to keep out of the way of chickens and children alike.

"Hello, Mother," I said when I finally reached them. "Hello, sir." It couldn't hurt to be polite, whoever he was.

The man wrinkled his nose. "Is this the lass?" He pulled out a lacy handkerchief and breathed through that. Did I smell *that* bad?

"Yes, sir," my mother said. "Stand straight, Janine, and don't fidget." When my mother in the real world deigns to visit, she has the same sort of advice for me, as does my grandmother. It must be a mother thing.

I stood straight and didn't fidget.

My mother shooed off the children and as many of the chickens as she could. "Janine," she said, "I have something to say to you, which I probably should have told you before. I wish I could delay it until your father gets home from the bog."

The well-dressed man waved his handkerchief at her. "Get on with it, woman."

Just because she was a computer-generated figment of my imagination was no reason for him to be rude.

"Hey," I told him. "That's my mother you're talking to."

If my real mother hung around more, I'd defend her, too.

But, "Wrong," the man said. "That's the whole point."

Quick on my feet as always, I said, "Huh?"

"This woman is not your mother. And the man you take to be your father is also no relation to you."

It made sense, considering the Heir Apparent scenario had indicated I was one of several in line for the throne. But if ever there was someone who obviously delighted in delivering bad news, this was the man. And meanwhile, "this woman," as he'd called her, looked ready to cry. She told him, "Sir Deming, you said *I* could break it to her."

"You took too long."

I shoved him away from her, even though I was a full head shorter. I was mad enough to tell him, "Look, as far as I can tell, you're just some well-dressed messenger boy. You say one more word to my mother, and I'll set the dogs on you."

Actually, we only had Dusty, and the chances were she was asleep by now. But "I'll set the dogs on you" sounds more impressive than "I'll call my dog, and if she hears me, and if she obeys, she'll make her way down here and maybe even bite you with whatever teeth she has left." And it certainly sounds more impressive than "I'll set the chickens on you."

Deming looked down his nose at me and sneered.

I told him, "I'm assuming you were paid to deliver a message?"

With his lip still curled, Deming said, "These people who have raised you are in truth your foster parents. You

17

were delivered to them for your own safekeeping. Your true parents..." He rolled his eyes. "Well, your mother was a servant woman."

I could tell he enjoyed telling me that. "And my father?" I asked, suspecting, because of the nature of the game.

With a sigh, Deming admitted, "King Cynric, God rest his soul."

"'God rest his soul'?" my mother repeated. "The king has died?"

Deming removed his ostrich-feather-plumed hat and bowed his head for a moment of silence. I suspected his sincerity when the first thing he said after that was, "And he chose a very inconvenient time to do it."

My mother fanned herself with her hand.

"I have brothers?" I asked. As an inhabitant of this land, I had heard talk of princes; but as a lowly inhabitant, I wasn't familiar with their names.

"Yes," Deming said.

"For someone who was so eager to talk before," I told him, "you certainly seem tongue-tied now. What are their names, and what are they like?"

"There are three princes," Deming said. "All older than you. Which gives them priority over you for the crown. As does your..."—he gave a patronizing smile—"irregular birth."

He let the smile drop. "Wulfgar is the firstborn," Deming told me. "He was educated away from home and has...certain..." He paused to consider. "Perhaps the word I'm thinking of is *exotic*. He has certain *exotic* ideas."

Something about the way he said it made me suspect that *exotic* wasn't the word he was thinking of at all. "Ideas about what?" I asked.

"Everything," Deming said. Which was no help at all. "The second son is Abas, a young man of incredible physical prowess in the classical sense."

" 'Classical sense'? What does *classical sense* mean?"

Deming ignored me. "And lastly Kenric, who displays—as far as *I'm* concerned—altogether too much interest in the magical arts."

I fought off a mental image of someone in a black cape and top hat, pulling coins out of people's ears and sawing lovely assistants in half, for I seriously doubted that was what Deming meant. "What—" I started.

"Perhaps it would be best if you waited to form your own impressions." Deming gave a toothy smile.

My mother asked, "You're bringing her back to court?"

Deming nodded.

"But I thought she was in danger there?"

Deming pursed his lips to indicate it wasn't his idea. "The king commanded it."

I said, "I thought the king was dead."

Deming sighed to let me know what an idiot he found me. "*Before* he died. It was his deathbed wish. Of course, he was quite feverish by then." Deming clearly thought the king hadn't been in his right mind. "When you were born, you were a royal embarrassment. Your servant mother had died during the long and difficult labor, and there were those among King Cynric's advisers

19

who pointed out that there was nothing unusual about a young mother and her firstborn *both* dying under such a circumstance. But the king was a kindhearted man." Deming sniffed—or snorted—into his handkerchief.

I'll bet. It was hard not to picture my *real* father as the king. "So, when he knew he was dying, he had a twinge of conscience?" I finished for Deming. "He decided to see if I was alive after all?"

"Oh, he knew you were alive," Deming assured me. "He sent for you to have you named his heir."

"Oh my!" my mother gasped.

I had assumed that the succession had been left unclear—that I'd have to fight it out with the other three. The other three, who were all older than me and who, presumably, had *two* royal parents. "Why me?" I asked.

Deming stuffed the handkerchief back into his sleeve. "Heaven knows," he said. He wiggled his fingers at me. "Go on," he said, "get on the horse. Time to pull yourself away from the sheep."

I didn't tell him that so far I liked the sheep more than I liked him. I kissed my mother and my brothers and my sisters good-bye.

"You're leaving now?" my mother cried in dismay. "Without saying good-bye to your father? I sent word to him that Sir Deming was here, and he should be coming home from the bog soon."

I was eager to get the game moving. Rasmussem builds in a little extra time, for soaking up the local atmosphere and because they assume people playing a game for the first time will make a fatal mistake or two and have to rely on additional lives—how many depends on how soon they mess up badly enough to get killed. I don't know how many players actually make it through a game in the first sitting, but my grandmother couldn't afford to send me here on a regular basis. That—and remembering the last time I'd said good-bye to a father—had me frantic not to wait around.

"I'll send for you when things get settled," I promised. Even if the game ended before I could, saying it was worth the look on Deming's face.

CHAPTER THREE

Fun and Games with the Family

When Deming and I arrived at the castle, there were pages to blow a trumpet fanfare, and guards who saluted and called me "Highness" without the superior mockery of Deming's tone. In the courtyard, two squires rushed forward to help me dismount. Having never, in the real world, ridden anything livelier than a carousel horse, I'd been pleasantly surprised that my character had memories of riding a horse. Of course, that had been bareback on the plow horse the community of St. Jehan shared, but if I didn't try to analyze and I just let my character's instincts take over, it wasn't too hard to stay on.

A good thing, because I suspected that if I'd fallen, Deming would just have left me, king's wishes or not.

But now servants lifted me off his horse as though I were a delicate lady, and both I and my character enjoyed that.

Deming disappeared into the crowd—probably to

take a bath, if I was to take all his sniffing and whining seriously.

A gray-haired man in a crushed-velvet suit was waiting by the entrance to the castle proper. "Welcome, Princess Janine," he said, bowing. "I am Counselor Rawdon, one of King Cynric's advisers. Allow me to escort you to the Great Hall, where the royal family awaits."

Though his smile looked sincere, I kept in mind what Deming had said about the king's advisers' suggestions at my birth.

I was half expecting that the people at Rasmussem would give me a castle that was a wreck—run-down and rat infested—but it was the one I had seen in the promo. It was like a magnificent old cathedral, except without the incense: polished stone walls and floors, high vaulted ceilings, stained-glass windows.

Rawdon led me down a wide gallery; one wall was made of mirrors, the other was a series of marble arches opening onto a formal garden with fountains and crushed-stone walks. I tried not to gawk like a tourist.

Finally we came to a massive set of carved doors. Two guards in ceremonial dress saluted, then opened the doors, while a third man blew yet another fanfare.

"Her Royal Highness," Rawdon proclaimed, "Princess Janine."

My first impression was that I had just been announced to an empty room, but then I saw that everybody—and everybody was only four people—was clustered around two thrones way down at the other end.

Rawdon whispered, "Good luck," my first hint that he was about to abandon me.

I whipped around to see him bowing his way backward out between the doors. Once he cleared the opening, those two guards swung the doors shut with a massive *thud*.

Leaving me with my back exposed to . . . ? My three half brothers would have been the obvious guess. And the woman I'd glimpsed? One of their wives, perhaps. Or she could be the queen, my dead father's wife, and mother to his sons. I hadn't thought to ask Deming if she was still alive or what her name was, putting me at a definite social disadvantage.

Obviously, I wasn't going to find out anything by standing with my back to them, the closed doors five inches from my nose. Someone tittered, and I had the impression it wasn't the woman.

"Hello," I said, turning to face them. There was a huge leaded-glass window behind them, so that they were little more than dark silhouettes. My footsteps echoed hollowly as I crossed that vast distance all alone, aware of the four sets of eyes watching me, evaluating. Should I have waited to be invited to approach? *No*, I thought. *I'm a princess.*

Or at least half princess.

Princesses do not wait to be summoned.

Do they?

Close up I determined the woman was definitely the queen. For one thing, she was sitting on one of the thrones, and she had a crown. She was also forty or fifty years old, a bit old for any of these guys—even for an arranged marriage. The princes ranged from one who was only a couple years older than me to the other two, who were probably in their early to mid twenties. They were the good-looking guys I'd noticed in the coming attractions.

"Hello," I said again, remembering to stand straight, and trying not to fidget, which was tough, considering I didn't know if I was supposed to bow, seeing as how we were all royalty. "It's a great honor to—"

The queen turned to the prince who stood at her right. That one was Abas, I thought. I suddenly understood what Deming had meant when he'd said Abas was strong in the classical sense. He looked like he'd stepped out of one of those old Hercules movies: huge muscles bulging out of an outfit consisting mostly of leather straps with metal studs. His skin was tan and slick—I wouldn't have looked that healthy with a whole tube of skin bronzer.

"This *girl*," the queen said to Abas, "smells like a goat."

The prince wrinkled his nose. "Yes," he said in a strained voice that sounded as though he was trying not to inhale.

"Ahm," I said, "a sheep, actually."

The queen gave me a look like oh-I-didn't-know-turds-could-talk.

"I've been working tending sheep." *Don't get started*, I warned myself. She didn't want explanations or clarifications—she just wanted to put me in my place. But the

25

silence sat there and sat there, so I babbled on, "I probably smell more like sheep than goats."

One of the other princes snickered. *Wulfgar?* I speculated, *the foreign-educated one?* since he wore a goatee—not a wispy end-of-the-chin–Colonel Sanders look, but a sexy one—while all the other men I'd seen so far were clean shaven. He was looking at me with undisguised contempt.

The third prince—the youngest, who would be Kenric—fidgeted, using his hand to cover a smile. He was sitting sideways on the arm of the empty throne, which might indicate he was trying to insinuate himself into the kingship. When he saw me looking at him, he flashed his smile openly, which could have meant that he was friendly or that he was amused or that he realized I was too dumb to be serious trouble.

"I think," the queen said, "we should kill her now and be done with her."

"All right," Abas said agreeably. One of those straps crisscrossing his chest must have been a harness to hold his sword on his back, for he reached over his shoulder and whipped out a blade almost as long as I was tall.

"Wait a minute." I scrambled backward. Lucky for me, I had outgrown my stinky and patched gown, so that the edge of the dress came only halfway down past my knees. Although this clearly showed my bare and dirty feet, at least I didn't trip as I took a couple hasty steps backward. "Wait a minute," I repeated, as a grinning Abas stepped toward me. I had a skinning knife on my belt, all of about four inches long. Abas's sword was

26

broader than that. All things considered, it was probably best not even to go for it.

"Just don't move," Abas told me in his calm, slow voice. "It'll be faster, and you won't bleed as much."

Was he concerned about hurting me, or about messing the inlaid marble floor?

"But," I said, dodging him, "but…"

"You can't kill her," his brother Kenric pointed out. "She's already been seen by too many people. If you wanted to kill her, you should have done so before."

Well, gee, thanks. I think.

Abas glanced at his mother for confirmation.

"I suppose," she conceded, clearly disappointed.

And only then did he lower his sword.

Wulfgar spoke for the first time. "How about if we start all over again?" He smiled at me in a way that was definitely not friendly nor amused nor even, I suspected, you're-too-dumb-to-count. "You come in, you're introduced, we ascertain exactly what it is that you smell of. Let's start there."

"No," I said, beginning to be ticked off at all this, "how about if we go back to the introduction phase, and *you* introduce yourselves to *me*? Sort of an as-subjects-to-your-new-king kind of thing."

The prince's smile momentarily froze, but then he said, "Certainly. I am Prince Wulfgar, the firstborn. By common tradition, the heir apparent. This bulwark of humanity"—he indicated Mr. Olympia—"is Abas, the second born. And this is Kenric, the youngest." Abas let that sit for a couple seconds. "Excluding yourself, of course." His hand swept in the direction of the queen, who looked miffed to be introduced *after* the others. "Our mother—that is, the mother of the king's *legitimate* children—Queen Andreanna."

The queen sat forward in her throne. "Now," she said, "Janine." Her tone indicated what she thought of that name.

Before I could learn what she was about to say, the room went black, as though someone had turned the lights off.

Except, of course, that medieval castles don't have light switches.

And except that we were in a room with about twenty floor-to-ceiling windows—not even counting the big leaded-glass one behind the thrones, through which, a moment ago, the midmorning sun had been streaming.

"What—" I started, but was drowned out by a crash of thunder that seemed to go off about half an inch from my ear. Simultaneously, jagged lightning streaked past the window behind the royal group.

Usually, Rasmussem is more subtle with its special effects. I could feel my scalp get all tingly from the electricity, which I thought was a great detail, but the storm didn't *look* right. They should have darkened the sky more gradually, and as I glanced around the room, I saw that there were identical bolts of lightning in each of the windows, which was pretty shoddy, like cheaply made anime, where they use the same background in multiple scenes, hoping you won't notice what's going on behind the main characters. Still, I couldn't help but jump. The thunder continued to boom and crackle as though the lightning bolts were striking at the parapets of the castle itself.

"Princess Janine." The queen sounded impatient, and I realized she had repeated my name several times already.

"I'm sorry!" I raised my voice over the thunder. "I didn't hear." I tapped my ear just in case *she* couldn't hear *me.*

In the flickering light of the near-continuous lightning, I saw her look at her sons. They were all watching me warily. Maybe they were worried about how they'd been treating me. Maybe they'd realized they shouldn't have been so open in their hostility. The queen said something I couldn't hear.

"What?" I said. "I can't hear you over the thunder."

Again the royals exchanged a look among themselves. The queen raised her eyebrows; Kenric, sitting on the arm of the throne, stopped swinging his leg and leaned forward; Wulfgar took a step away from me as though nervous; and Abas, still holding his sword, raised it defensively.

And no—I decided as the queen said, *"What* are you talking about?"—no, that wasn't a this-is-someone-we-shouldn't-have-threatened look. That was a maybe-this-is-someone-who's-totally-out-of-her-mind look.

At which point the lightning moved inside the castle.

And not a one of them twitched.

I took a step backward as a jag of lightning lit up the area between the back wall and the royal family.

"Move!" I screamed at them. Obviously, the storm was not natural. But that didn't mean it couldn't fry us all. "It's getting closer! The next one will hit you!"

Weren't the little hairs on *their* arms all standing up and marching around from the charged air? Sure, they wouldn't know the word *ozone,* but couldn't they smell it?

Wulfgar tapped his head in a loose-screw gesture, and the queen rested her face in her hand as though I was a bigger burden than she'd ever anticipated. Abas was obviously waiting for his mother to tell him what to do. Kenric stood and took a hesitant step toward me, the only one to trust my warning even that far.

And then the light came back. No lightning, no vestigial rumbles of dying thunder. The sky was blue and bright outside the window.

"Oh," I said. "Never mind. It went away."

Magic, obviously. But whose, and why? Deming had said Kenric dabbled in magic, but why would he call up a storm only I could sense? If it was to make a fool of me, then why was he the one person to heed my warning and step away from the window?

And judging from his face, *he* was thinking that *I* was the one who had set out to make *him* look foolish in front of his family.

"There was a storm," I said. "In here, in this room. With thunder and lightning, and my skin all goose bumpy from the electricity."

"I never knew you were so gullible, Kenric," Wulfgar smirked. "I'll remember that."

That was sure to endear me to Kenric.

"Enough of this nonsense," the queen said. "Janine, I don't know what you think you're doing, but stop it or I may yet change my mind about having you killed. For the time being, my husband—in the derangement of his dying—named you his successor. Let's see how long you can keep the job. And your head. Come, Abas." She swept out of the hall with a rustle of stiff skirts, which nearly toppled me as she brushed past.

Hercules Jr. followed, putting his sword back into its harness with a glance at my neck as though evaluating for future reference how hard he'd have to swing for a decapitation. Kenric glowered as he passed, and Wulfgar grinned before he followed—which didn't look quite as friendly as his brother's glower.

Ouch. Not a very good first impression on my family.

And what was that awful smell?

Oh yeah. That was me.

CHAPTER FOUR

A Heavenly Visitor

The point of Heir Apparent is to make good decisions, choose capable and trustworthy friends and advisers, and survive long enough to be crowned as king two days from now, game time.

Judging from what I'd seen of my family, none of them would fit very snugly into the trustworthy-friends-and-advisers category.

Maybe my first decision should be to have the guards throw all four of them into the dungeon. But, seeing as the only other people I'd met here at the castle—not counting stable boys, doorkeepers, and trumpeters—were Deming and Rawdon, it didn't seem a good plan to throw four-sixths of the people I knew into prison.

I had to find an ally—and *fast*. As I ran after my family like a puppy that doesn't want to get left behind, I considered.

The queen had every reason to hate me, as her husband's illegitimate child. Also, she had the welfare of her three offspring to advance if she could not gain the throne for herself.

Abas seemed to be the queen's favorite—after herself, of course—but he obviously wasn't going to make any move that his mother hadn't previously approved.

That left Wulfgar and Kenric, both clearly troublemakers.

I based my decision on something totally frivolous: Kenric was dressed all in black. That might have been a heavy-handed hint on Rasmussem's part that he was the villain, or it might have meant that—with his dark hair and light eyes—he knew he looked good in black. On the other hand, it might mean that he was in mourning. If so, he was the only one. I didn't know anything about King Cynric, whether he'd been a just king or a loving husband or a kind father. But so far nobody had said a word about the poor guy being dead except in how it related to the succession to the throne.

"Kenric!" I called. I don't know what I'd have done if he'd ignored me, but he waited for me to catch up as the others moved on without us.

Still, he didn't look happy. He had no reason to trust me any more than I trusted him.

We were standing by one of the gates leading outside, with sunlight and the chirping of birds and a soft breeze that carried the scent of lavender, as though nature wanted to rub in the idea that I'd imagined or made up the storm.

"Are there wizards that live nearby?" I asked.

From his expression, it was a dumb question. From his expression, everybody knew. Kenric crossed his arms over his chest. "Xenos and Uldemar."

"Well," I said, "apparently one of them magically created a storm that I and only I could see."

"Uh-huh," he said. "Why?"

"I don't know," I admitted. "Maybe to make me look like a crazy person."

"Uh-huh," Kenric said again. "That you did." But he looked more amused than angry now, which I suppose was a step in the right direction.

Before I could ask if *he* could think of any reason one of the wizards might have called up the storm, there was a commotion in the courtyard. Two guards in chain mail were dragging along a boy who couldn't have been any older than nine or ten. The boy was crying and trying to squirm away, and the guards were not being gentle about holding firm. "Prince Kenric," one of the men called out, "and, uh, Princess Justine..."

"Janine," I corrected.

The man shrugged, like *What's the big deal? Didn't I get it mostly right?* He was looking at Kenric as the person in charge, not me, and no doubt considered himself extremely gracious for even acknowledging me. "We caught this boy poaching. He killed a deer. The usual punishment?"

Kenric opened his mouth to answer, then turned to me. "I don't know. Janine?" His voice and manner dripped with innocence. "What do you think, the usual?"

One thing I was certain of: He wasn't asking for advice; he was testing. "What's the usual?" I asked, ignoring the answer the Rasmussem program was prodding forward from my subconscious.

"First-time offense for poaching small game might be branding or to have his hand cut off," Kenric told me. "For deer, it's the death penalty."

"No," the boy whimpered. "I didn't do nothing. I found 'im dead already. I was dressing 'im down so's the meat wouldn't go to waste, but I didn't kill 'im."

Kenric was watching me appraisingly.

I said, "The boy says he didn't do it."

"Of course he does," Kenric said.

I looked at the boy, all ragged clothes and tear-streaked, with his bones showing under his dirty skin. "Did you see him kill the deer?" I asked the guards.

"No," said the one who was doing all the talking, "but look at his hands." They were bloody to the elbows.

"He already admitted to dressing down the carcass," I said. "Did you see him kill the deer?"

For an awful moment, I thought one of them was going to say yes. But then both guards shook their heads.

"Then let the boy go." My first command as the would-be king.

The guards looked to Kenric, unwilling to take my word for it. Kenric spread his hands out, indicating it was my decision. The guards let go of the boy and saluted smartly. Perhaps too smartly. Like when you jump out of your seat and shout, "Good morning, sir!" to the teacher you hate the most.

I didn't know what to do next, so for a moment I did

nothing. Kenric turned and walked away, back into the castle. I suspected I was probably supposed to say or do something to make him stay, but the game's time limit for my trying to figure what that should be must have run out. The guards, too, left to do whatever guards here did when they weren't terrorizing nine-year-old boys. Probably another missed opportunity.

"Are you all right?" I asked the kid.

He was watching me through the fringe of hair that hung down in his eyes, looking like a headlight-startled rabbit. He was so dirty, I couldn't tell if the guards had beaten him.

"Are you all right?" I repeated, tipping his face up by the chin.

He kicked me, hard, on the shin, and ran off.

"Ungrateful wretch," I muttered as he ran over the open drawbridge, vaulted over a short fence, and took off through the meadow beyond.

I turned to go back into the castle, when suddenly there was a brilliant shaft of light from the sky. Clouds billowed up out of nowhere, then rolled back; harp music sounded, an angelic choir sang a note of infinitely sad sweetness, and a white-robed figure descended on a golden beam.

"Giannine Bellisario," the white-robed figure said in a voice like the voice of God from the videos they show in religion class.

Outside of the fact that I was too stunned to speak, he was calling me by the wrong name. Here, I was Janine de St. Jehan.

And this sure didn't sound like any Rasmussem program I'd ever heard of.

"Giannine Bellisario," the white-robed figure repeated.

The closer he got, the more I could see he wasn't God after all, which was a relief no matter how you look at it. For one thing, his white robe turned out to be a lab coat, and for another, he was wearing glasses. I felt fairly certain God wouldn't go around wearing glasses.

The figure came to rest with his Reebok'd feet about six inches from the ground, so that—even though he couldn't be much taller than me—I had to tip my head back to look him in the face. "Giannine," he said, "this is Nigel Rasmussem. Don't panic."

I'd been surprised and confused but doing fine until he said that.

"There has been a slight emergency. Nothing to worry about."

I began to hyperventilate.

"People from the Society to Prevent Cruelty to Children...What?" Somebody I couldn't see or hear must have corrected Mr. Rasmussem. He waved the interruption away. Which was good. He was already speaking infuriatingly slowly, like someone who doesn't trust the mental capacity of his audience.

"What do you mean, 'emergency'—" I started, but he talked over my question.

"People from the Society to Protect Our Children," he said, still getting it wrong, "have broken into the building. They have damaged our equipment. Don't worry. There is no physical danger to your body. The intruders have been removed by the police."

"What do you mean, 'no *physical*'—"

But again he kept on talking.

He can't hear me, I realized. He probably couldn't see me. I shut up and listened, since I wouldn't be able to ask him to repeat.

"We are working to regain control," Mr. Rasmussem was saying, which wasn't comforting at all, especially from someone who had ink stains on his lab coat where he'd forgotten to use his pocket protector. "There are fail-safe measures to keep external stimuli, like power failures or surges, from affecting your mental state. But while these safeguards are in effect, you will find it difficult to exit the Heir Apparent program."

I was stuck here?

"The only route," Mr. Rasmussem said, "is to successfully complete the game. Unsuccessful solutions will loop you back to the start of the program."

I can do that, I thought. What he was telling me was that I was getting free extra tries. I began to breathe normally again.

"Unfortunately," Mr. Rasmussem said, and my breath caught again, "this is the last time we will be able to communicate with you. And, unfortunately, I cannot tell you the solution to the game since there is no one, single, right path. There are an infinite number of permutations, depending on which characters you take into your confidence, how you react to the problems with which you will be presented, and what policies you set for your government."

Mr. Rasmussem might have been counting on this going over my head, but I could figure it out: If there were an infinite number of possible right ways that could get me out of here, there had to be an infinite number of wrong ways that would set me back on that hill in St. Jehan.

"Don't panic," Mr. Rasmussem said again. Their readouts on my heart rate and blood pressure must have been going wild. "All you have to do is play the game as well as you can as quickly as you can."

And while that was still sinking in, while I was mentally repeating *quickly?* Mr. Rasmussem said, "Wait!"

Wait? That seemed all I could do. But he wasn't talking to me.

He was beginning to float upward again. The heavenly choir started humming. The clouds took on a pink hue. Mr. Rasmussem was again talking to someone else, arguing. "No, this is foolish. She needs to know the urgency." He turned back to me, speaking in a rush now, so that I suddenly suspected his earlier comments had been scripted. "What I said before isn't entirely accurate. I don't want to frighten you—you should be fine. But there is no time to waste. The prolonged direct stimulation to your brain is dangerous. The longest game we have is supposed to be over in an hour, and our equipment would normally be safe for up to five times that exposure. But with the damage these people have inflicted, your safety zone is much, much less. We don't know how long you have, but the longer you're in the game, the more you risk fatal overload."

Overload? What was he saying? And *fatal overload?*

39

Now it was my turn to cry, "Wait!" to him. But even if he could have heard me, it was obvious that there was nothing he could do about remaining.

"Advice," Mr. Rasmussem called down at me as the clouds foamed about him. "Kenric and Sister Mary Ursula don't work well together."

Who in the world was Sister Mary Ursula?

Mr. Rasmussem's voice was fading despite the fact that he was obviously shouting. "And next time, don't forget the ring."

"What ring?" I shouted back up to him. All I could see, far above, were the bottoms of his sneakers.

"And whatever you do, don't..."

But, naturally, I couldn't make that out.

SUBJ: URGENT--Emergency Situation
DATE: 5/25   03:37:02 P.M. US eastern
         daylight time
FROM: Nigel Rasmussem
         <nrasmussem@rasmussem.com>
TO: dept. heads distribution list

BACKGROUND: The Rochester, New York,
facility has been compromised by
unauthorized persons who have forced
entry and damaged equipment *while it
was in use*.

See attached file for damage assessment
and equipment specifics.

The intruders have been removed and
arrested by local authorities. Security
believes them to be politically
motivated local individuals working
spontaneously in an isolated incident
rather than organized terrorists, BUT
TIGHTEN SECURITY IN ALL GAMING CENTERS
NONETHELESS.

See attached file for background on
CPOC political lobby group.

At the time of the raid on the
facility, 2 gamers were in the VR
arcade and were not harmed, one group
of 4 TI gamers had just gone under and
were successfully retrieved by the
premises technologist, but a lone player
was already fully in total immersion

and the technologist believes serious bodily harm would result from disconnecting this gamer before successful completion of the game.

Access code #703-592-B-3 to monitor subject's vital signs.

Note: Gamer is a 14-year-old minor believed to have limited gaming experience.

Using the residual power in the grids, contact was made with the gamer to apprise her of the situation, though on the advice of Lisa in psychology, the risk was downplayed so as not to cause nonfunctional anxiety. Once that power drained, contact was obstructed and cannot be reestablished.

CURRENT SITUATION: We do not know exactly how much time we have and we need all possible input from all available technologists with all possible speed. We require estimates, advice for repairing the equipment in minimal time, contingency plans to disconnect the gamer in case of systems failure before game completion.

Legal is working to make sure we are covered, but I DO NOT want R.E. to be the first VR company with a fatality.

CHAPTER FIVE

Simple Math

What kind of cheesy outfit was Rasmussem that crazies could walk in and endanger innocent kids? A picture flitted through my brain of the Rasmussem Gaming Center receptionist—the last defense between immobilized semiconscious kids and crazed CPOC members taking out their frustrations on Rasmussem's equipment. She'd probably been too wrapped up in her nails or in a game of Free Cell to notice the intruders. And what about those idiots at CPOC? Wasn't their whole purpose to protect kids? Did I not count because they considered me some sort of evil deviant for having come in here?

You're wasting time, I told myself.

I tried to work it out in my head: Rasmussem's engineers said I *should* have had five hours for the supposed safety zone. Since Heir Apparent took only half an hour to play, that should have given me ten tries. . . . Except those CPOC demonstrators had caused enough damage that however much time I had, it was less than that. And time before...what? What did "overload" mean?

Stop it, I told myself. *Panicking is not going to help. Think calmly; plan things out.*

Would my brain literally fry, getting so hot that I would feel fevered, or like I was stranded in a desert, or like I was being cooked alive?

Don't be melodramatic, I told myself.

It would probably be more like an electrical shock. Or an epileptic convulsion.

Would I—immersed in the game—feel it? Would I know it was happening?

I tried to drag myself away from that line of thinking. Lots of drastically wrong things could be happening inside a person's body without that person even knowing. It wouldn't necessarily hurt.

On the other hand, I knew that the Rasmussem technology sometimes made it so that a sick person who didn't even know she was sick would—while playing the game—feel sick. The gaming-as-diagnostic-tool scenario.

Not that I felt sick yet.

Did I?

I felt all clammy and my stomach was in a knot and my throat was tight and my chest hurt, but that was probably from the tension. Probably. I touched my forehead and didn't think I had a fever. Or at least not yet.

At the most, I would have had ten tries, feeling like thirty days, which would have been a long time to feel sick. But Mr. Rasmussem said I had less time than that— "much, much less," I remembered him stressing. What was much, much less time than thirty days—half of that? A quarter?

Did I, in fact, have only one try?

No. He'd said, "Next time..." So, at least one more try. I hoped.

There is a possibility, I told myself firmly, *that you will make it. You need to play smart and maximize your chances.*

Nigel Rasmussem had talked about infinite possibilities of ways to play Heir Apparent correctly.

I might stumble on one. In...whatever time I had left. If I played carefully.

I was so preoccupied, I wasn't aware of anyone approaching until someone grabbed me from behind—which I guess was a pretty good indication I wasn't playing carefully enough. Someone spun me around, and I saw that I was facing a group of about twenty of the castle guards.

Something about them was spooky. I mean, in theory, weren't they there to guard me, the officially named heir apparent of this realm? Surely it wasn't proper guard etiquette to come up behind the person who's scheduled to be crowned as your king, to lay hands on her and spin her around. And several of them had swords or knives drawn.

I glanced around. Maybe something had happened, I thought. Maybe they were here to rescue me from some danger?

Right.

"She's too weak to be a proper king," said the guard who'd spun me around, the guard I'd ordered to release the boy accused of poaching. "She'll be the death of all of us."

And with that he stuck a knife into me.

It didn't hurt. I felt fizzy, like an ice cube in a glass of ginger ale, all covered with carbonated bubbles. My knees gave out from under me, and my eyes grew heavy. When I opened them again, I was on the hill above the cluster of huts that was the village of St. Jehan, and my mother was calling, "Janine! Janine, come back to the house."

So much for playing smart.

CHAPTER SIX

"Do Not Pass Go;
Do Not Collect $200"

O*K*, I thought, *that brings me down to . . . what?* Whatever I'd had before minus half a day.

Never mind, I told myself. *Just play smarter this time.* Nigel Rasmussem had given me two hints: *And next time,* he'd said, *don't forget the ring.* OK, I'd be on the lookout for a ring. And, *Kenric and Sister Mary Ursula don't work well together.* I'd be on the lookout for Sister Mary Ursula. I would concentrate on being a good heir apparent so that I would win the game, and I wouldn't distract myself by keeping a running calculation on how much time I might or might not have left.

Just as last time—until I did something different, *everything* would be just as last time—Dusty, my dog, leaped on me and began licking my face. "Down, Dusty!" I ordered. "Stay. Guard the sheep."

Dusty lay down and either guarded the sheep or went to sleep.

I ran down the hill. "Hello, Mother," I said. I glanced at her hands. No rings. Of course not, she was a simple peasant woman, and peasants don't wear jewelry.

I asked, "Who's this?" Even though I knew Sir Deming's name and business, my character wouldn't.

Sir Deming was just as rude as last time. Waving his handkerchief as though to dissipate the smell I brought with me, he asked, "Is this the lass?"

Who cared what he said? I saw he was wearing a ring. *Aha!*

"My, what a nice ring," I said, talking over my mother, who was telling me to stand straight and not fidget.

Deming looked as though he suspected I was a ring thief as well as a sheepherder, and he crossed his arms over his chest, tucking his fingers under his arms.

In games, certain events are keyed to certain actions. It was probably too early for me to actually get the ring.

I listened, antsy with impatience, while I was told, once again, that I had been living with foster parents; I learned, once again, about the death of King Cynric, my father.

When Deming said that the dying king had sent for me, I eyed his hand and asked, "Did he send some token?"

"He sent me," Deming said in his snooty, snotty manner.

OK, maybe it was still too early.

I didn't bother asking about my half brothers or the queen—we could discuss them on the ride to the castle, without taking any extra time.

Once again my foster mother wept when I left, saying

that my foster father would be heartbroken to miss saying good-bye to me. (*Yeah, yeah.* In my experience—in two worlds now—fathers were just big sentimental softies.) If I had felt rushed the first time, now I knew myself to be in a race. No time to waste on characters who were there just for the scene-setting.

This time as we rode away on Deming's horse, I asked Deming all sorts of questions about my new family, to show I was interested. Deming, of course, was *not* interested.

"Who's Sister Mary Ursula?" I asked.

Again Deming gave me a suspicious look. "Interfering old busybody," he said. "Has she been in clandestine contact with your family?"

Oops. I realized I shouldn't give away that I knew things I shouldn't know yet.

"No," I said.

"Then where have you heard her name?"

"I can't remember," I said.

Deming snorted.

I still didn't like him, and he still didn't like me.

As we approached the castle, I once again tried for the ring. "I can't help but notice the interesting design on your ring," I told him. "What do you call that?"

"I call it," he said, "the letter *D*."

D was his initial—not mine; not King Cynric's. Maybe this was the wrong ring after all.

When we got to the castle, I traded in Sir Deming for Counselor Rawdon, who was not wearing a ring. OK, so it had to be one of the royal family. That made more sense, anyway.

Queen Andreanna and her three sons, Wulfgar, Abas, and Kenric, were just as charming as last time, lounging about the thrones in the Great Hall, looking down their noses at me.

"Hello," I said. Last time I had approached timidly and hesitantly, wanting to make friends. I was determined not to make that mistake twice. Going for brisk, confident, and assertive this time, I said, "May I offer my condolences—"

"This *girl*," the queen said to Abas, "smells like a goat."

Back to that again. I wouldn't let myself get caught up in that argument.

"Excuse me," I said in a tone that would have gotten me a lecture from my grandmother, "I believe the king died and named me his heir. That makes you my subjects. Obviously, you're so overcome by grief at the death of your old king that you're forgetting yourself. I will forgive you this once, but from now on you are to show me proper respect."

"*'Proper respect'?*" the queen snapped. "Abas, show her the respect she's due."

Luckily for me, sarcasm was a bit beyond Abas's mental grasp. He began to bow. This gave me time to take a quick step back.

"Kill her," Queen Andreanna clarified for her son.

I remembered Kenric's reasoning from last time. "Too many people have seen me already," I said.

Abas had unsheathed his sword and wasn't even slowing down.

I ducked behind a pillar.

"Everyone would know who killed me," I called back to the queen. No use trying to reason with Abas. If the queen didn't call him off, my attempts at logic certainly wouldn't.

For such a big guy, Abas was incredibly quick and agile. He jabbed with the sword, left and right of the protective column, and sooner or later I was going to move too slowly, or he was going to correctly anticipate my next dodge.

I said, "You'll be in trouble for killing the appointed heir." That sounded feeble, even to me.

Abas's sword caught on the trailing edge of my dress that swirled a second slower than I did. With his free hand, he caught hold of my hair and dragged me from behind the column.

"She's probably right," Wulfgar drawled.

"Probably," the queen agreed equably.

Her voice was the last thing I heard.

CHAPTER SEVEN

Shuffle and Deal Again

Janine!" my foster mother's voice called. "Janine, come back to the house."

I couldn't believe it. I'd wasted another half day. What was the matter with me? Surely, the programmers at Rasmussem didn't intend for their game to be so complicated that a reasonably intelligent fourteen-year-old couldn't get beyond the first hours of a three-day game.

Was my brain overloading already? Was the damage the CPOC saboteurs had inflicted making me stupid?

All in all, I preferred to believe that I just wasn't playing this game as well as Rasmussem's average teenage gamer.

"OK, OK," I told Dusty as she once more licked my face. "Sit. Stay. Guard."

At the foot of the hill, I again rushed my mother and Sir Deming through the introductions. Did Rasmussem *have* to start me at the very beginning every single time?

Deming told me the king had named me his heir. I acted surprised. My foster mother wept that I had to leave. I told her to give my love to my foster father. I spared a thought for my real-life father, who'd given me the Rasmussem gift certificate. *Gee, Dad,* I thought, *you shouldn't have.*

When I was introduced to Counselor Rawdon, I interrupted him when he said he'd take me to meet my family.

"And what are they like?" I asked, though I knew well enough. "Are they to be trusted?"

"'Trusted,' Princess Janine?" Rawdon repeated.

"Do they present a danger to me?"

"Well..." Rawdon said, and I was sure he was going to give an evasive answer. But he said, "Probably."

OK, I liked that honesty. "Should I take steps?" I asked.

"Assuredly," he told me.

For a counselor, he wasn't very forthcoming with counsel.

"Would, for example—just in theory here—would it be a good idea to have my family confined?"

"It *might*," Rawdon agreed. "On the other hand, you *are* new here. An unknown element. The soldiers who would have jumped to your late father's orders might not be so quick to respond to you." He smiled and added, "In theory."

"I understand," I said. No royal beheadings on the first morning.

I sighed, suspecting that I wasn't imaginative enough

to figure out half of what needed to be figured out. I was already in a rut: hill, Deming, Rawdon, family, death by various unpleasant means. I said, "Perhaps I should dress more suitably before I meet my royal kin. So I don't offend them."

"Certainly," Rawdon told me.

After I was scrubbed and coiffed—that was the word Lady Cynthia, my newly appointed lady-in-waiting used, *coiffed*—and perfumed, I was given a beautiful gown of burgundy-colored velvet.

I almost did feel like a princess as Lady Cynthia brought me to the Great Hall.

The guards blew their fanfare, opened the doors for me to walk in, closed the doors after me.

And nobody was there.

Oops.

Apparently my royal kin didn't like to be kept waiting—even more than they didn't like me smelling of sheep. Who could have guessed?

I went out the way I had gone that first time with Kenric. No sign of the royal family in the courtyard, although one of the guards was raking the dirt. I started to go over, then realized what he was doing: covering up blood. With a sinking feeling, I remembered the peasant boy accused of poaching. Apparently by taking the time to bathe, I'd missed the opportunity to keep the guards from chopping his head off.

It was just a game, but I didn't like the turn it had taken.

"Guard!" I called the man over to me so that I wouldn't have to go any nearer.

"Princess Justine," he said.

I didn't correct him. "Where's the queen?" I asked.

"I believe she and Prince Wulfgar are in the topiary maze."

Maze. I sighed. "I don't suppose you know the way through?"

He looked surprised that I would ask such a thing. "It would be more fun if you figured it out on your own."

"Show me," I ordered.

The hedges were boxwood, which is a smell that always makes me think of cat pee. The bushes were full, so that I couldn't see through them at all, and they were about seven feet high, which is about two feet taller than me. I was just thinking that I should have been paying closer attention to the turns, when we found ourselves in the center, an open area with a pair of stone benches, and sitting there—drinking tea—was Queen Andreanna. But the guard was mistaken: With her was her youngest son, Kenric, not Wulfgar.

"Ah," Andreanna said, "the sheep princess. I thought I smelled something bad."

"I *did* take a bath," I said.

"A bath," the queen said, "no matter how long, is not sufficient to wash off the stink of a bad birth." She waved her hand at the guard, so that her ring caught a glint of the sun. "You," she ordered him, "go."

"I'm sorry I kept you waiting," I said. "I tried to make myself presentable before appearing before you. I know this is a difficult time for you—"

"Oh, hush, you tiresome thing!" the queen commanded. "Kenric, can't you do something about her?"

55

"What exactly?" he asked.

"Well, I was thinking you could kill her."

Apparently there was no pleasing the woman.

"She *has* been seen here," Kenric pointed out.

"Maybe she'll have an accident," Andreanna said wistfully.

"Maybe," Kenric agreed.

"Listen," I said, "obviously you're upset by the king's decision to name me—"

"Go away," the queen ordered me. "You may speak to us at supper." She gave a dismissive wave, fluttering her fingers.

Maybe, I thought, *I was playing too cautiously.* This time I caught her hand. "My, what a lovely ring."

Kenric grabbed my wrist even as the queen demanded, "Unhand me immediately."

"Sorry," I said. I let go; Kenric did not, and his grip was beginning to hurt. "I was just wondering if that ring was meant for me."

"It's my wedding ring, you stupid twit of a sheep girl."

"Sorry," I repeated. How could it not be the right ring? Mr. Rasmussem needed a good shaking. "Sorry."

"Just leave."

Kenric finally let go of my wrist.

"Could one of you—" I started.

The queen gave a snort of impatience.

All right, all right. I'd make my own way out of the maze.

Except I *really* should have paid more attention to the turns when I'd been with the guard.

I was sure three right turns, then a left, would bring me to a Y-shaped intersection I remembered, but it didn't. Maybe three left turns, then a right? I tried backing up but realized I'd bypassed one turn, yet when I went back, I lost track of which way I'd been facing: I thought I should be at a T intersection, but found myself in the middle of an X—and by then I had no idea where I was.

OK, I thought. *There is a strategy to mazes.* In most mazes, if you consistently choose one direction, you eventually find your way—maybe not the quickest way, but *a* way. So, I told myself, I would choose left.

The sun was hot on my velvet gown, and the smell of boxwood was making me cranky and itchy.

Come on, I told myself. Surely I should be out of the maze by now, or back in the center.

And then I heard a sound behind me, a single footfall. Andreanna? Kenric?...Except I had the momentary impression of an animal. I'm not sure why. Maybe it was the growl.

I didn't have a chance to turn around. Something struck me hard on the back, knocking me face first to the ground. I cried out at the pain in my palms and knees— and at the back of my neck. I felt fizzy bubbles all over my skin. "No!" I screamed. Then I heard my foster mother call, "Janine! Janine, come back to the house."

I pounded my fists on the ground. "I hate this! Hate this! Hate this!" I screamed.

Dusty licked my face to show me that she loved me.

CHAPTER EIGHT

Hey, Loser, Start Over Again (Again)

I was going to die. I was *never* going to get past the first step of the game, and I was going to die. And this was going to be the rest of my life—this hill, and the trip with Sir Deming, and fatally ticking somebody off moments after arriving at the castle, and experiencing a death that, while not painful, was fizzy and disorienting—I would relive that whole boring, frustrating routine for whatever was left of my life.

I'll be READY to die by then, I told myself.

But I knew that wasn't true. I didn't want to die now, and I wouldn't want to die in the few hours I had left, either. Boring was one thing. Feeling like a dissolving Alka Seltzer was another thing. But the prospect of really dying was something else entirely.

Well, then, I told myself, *DO something*. I got out from under Dusty, who was still trying to lick my face to let me know how glad she was to see me. If I had any time to spare, I might have tried just staying here, refusing to go to the castle, where I would be surrounded by surly retainers, murderous family, and treacherous guards. *No, I could tell Deming, I'm not interested. Go away. Let somebody else be king. I'll just stay here with the dog and the sheep.*

But I doubted the Rasmussem program would allow this. It would probably have the sheep get rabies and attack me. Or have Dusty lick me to death.

I forgot to tell Dusty to tend the sheep, but apparently she didn't need me to tell her her job. She was obviously a smart dog. She could probably make better choices in this game than I had. I started down the hill, and she stayed behind.

All right, I thought, *I was supposed to already have gotten the ring by the time Mr. Rasmussem came to me, after the family conference.* It had to be the lack of the ring that was causing me to bomb out so quickly. When I thought about it, Rasmussem was doing me a favor: It would be worse to let me keep on playing for three days, get to the end of the game, then fail because of something I had overlooked in the first minutes of the first day. This was like—in the old games—not being able to make it to the next level.

OK, I thought. It probably wasn't a member of the royal family who had the ring, since my three half brothers didn't appear to have any rings and the queen had only a wedding band. I doubted I was supposed to bully a widow out of her wedding band. Besides, the person who had been the friendliest and most helpful—Rawdon—didn't know anything about a ring. Still, who else had I met before Mr. Rasmussem's appearance?

I mentally retraced my steps.

And could have smacked myself on the forehead when I got to the boy accused of poaching. Of course, a normal peasant boy wouldn't have a valuable ring. But a boy who was willing to break the law by poaching might also be a thief, and there was no telling what kind of goodies a thief may have accumulated.

Exasperated that it had taken me so long to reason this out, I ran the rest of the way down the hill. I sailed through the preliminaries with my mother and Sir Deming: The king is dead? Gee, that's too bad. I've been named his heir? Well, how nice. Hang around long enough to say good-bye to Dad? I don't think so.

Deming and I once again rode to the castle in sullen silence. When I spoke to my family, it was humbly and quietly, with no attempt to defend myself against their rudeness. The queen once again ordered Abas to kill me, and Kenric once again came to my defense, in his own sentimental way, by advising against killing me now that I had made a public appearance at the castle.

This was the exact point at which—during the first game—the strange storm only I could see had moved inside the Great Hall. I now knew that the storm was the physical manifestation of the CPOC demonstrators damaging the Rasmussem Gaming Center, setting the equipment to which my brain was linked to "deep fry."

I got to hear what the thunder had previously prevented my hearing.

"Now," Queen Andreanna said, wearing the same pained-and-disgusted-but-still-trying-to-carry-on expression that might flicker across your face if you realized you'd just publicly sat on a plate of Jell-O, "Princess Janine. Obviously, you are neither trained for nor suited to life in the political arena. Between the barbarian hordes waiting at our northern border for the first sign of weakness, and the peasant uprisings in the east, now is not the time for an inexperienced sheepherder to play at being king. For your own safety, as well as that of the country, it would be best if you left the rulership of this kingdom to those who understand its intricacies. My suggestion is that we send you to one of the manor houses in the country. You can bring your foster family with you, if you wish. There will be servants under your command, guards to protect you, luxury to surround you."

I said, "And I won't need to worry my pretty little head about all that nasty politics and complicated decision making and stuff."

The queen smiled tightly, as though looking at me gave her a headache.

"That's a very kind offer," I told her. "But King Cynric named me his heir apparent, and I don't intend to shirk my duty."

"There are those who would eat you up," the queen warned.

Pass the barbecue sauce—I knew that already. "Thank you for your concern," I said.

She swept to her feet. "It's your funeral."

Unfortunately, I knew she meant that literally.

Her three sons made to follow her out of the room. Since Nigel Rasmussem had seemed to warn me away from Kenric, I switched to a different prince. "Wulfgar, may I walk with you?"

Wulfgar bowed. Remembering that Deming had said

Wulfgar had been raised abroad, I tried to believe his courtesy was foreign manners, but I suspected he was just being ironic.

The queen didn't react well to my talking to her oldest son. "Wulfgar," she snapped, just as she might have to any lowly subject, "I need to speak with you in the topiary maze."

Wulfgar grinned, obviously relishing being the prize in a power play between the queen and the heir apparent. "In a few moments, Mother," he said.

Even I could see that was the wrong answer. She linked arms with Abas and Kenric, as though afraid I would try to steal them away, too, and walked out of the Great Hall in a huff.

"So, Wulfgar..." I said as we trailed them. Slowly. So they couldn't listen in. (Make alliances, the Heir Apparent directive said. I realized I had no idea how to go about doing that. Talk sweetly. Make nice. That was what my mother did, in her New York job.)

Wulfgar didn't help. He waited for me to say something.

"I think we need to call together the old king's advisers," I said, proud of myself for remembering to say "we," for including him, which his mother seemed not inclined to do. "We should have a counsel, decide what direction the kingdom needs to take."

"All right," Wulfgar said.

"I was thinking your advice might be helpful."

He seemed to like that thought. "All right," he said again. Just as I was fearing he was no help at all, he said,

"That would be Sir Deming, Counselor Rawdon, and Sister Mary Ursula."

Finally! "Oh," I said, "Sister Mary Ursula—what's she like?"

"She's a fusty old meddler," Wulfgar said, which surprised me—since Mr. Rasmussem had said *Kenric* didn't work well with her. "Why do you ask about her in particular?"

Was I ever going to learn not to give away too much? "No special reason," I assured him. "It's just, I've already met Deming and Rawdon."

That answer seemed to satisfy him. He said, "You should also meet with those in the kingdom who know magic."

"That sounds like a fine idea." In my eagerness to please him, to flatter him, to make sure he liked me, I suspected I was sounding like an overly enthusiastic kindergarten teacher. "Who would they be?"

"Orielle," Wulfgar said, which was a new name to me. "And Xenos and Uldemar," whose names Kenric had mentioned.

"Anything I should know about any of them?"

Wulfgar paused to consider. "Orielle is better-looking than Xenos and Uldemar."

"OK," I said. If I were a fifteen-year-old boy, that might impress me.

By then we had entered the courtyard. And we were once again just in time to see the armored guards dragging along the boy accused of poaching—the boy I was convinced had the ring I needed.

"Prince Wulfgar and Princess Justine," one of the guards called out to us.

"Princess *Janine*," Wulfgar corrected, and he rocketed up in my estimation.

"Sorry, sir," the guard said, apologizing to the person who was important rather than to the one he had actually slighted.

"What's all this?" I asked, though I already knew. I had been thinking I wasn't going to be too sympathetic to the boy—remembering how he had kicked me. I needed to rescue him because I needed what I'd deduced he had—but he looked so young and scared, I couldn't help myself.

Still looking at Wulfgar, the guard said, "We caught this boy poaching. He killed a deer. The usual punishment?"

"Yes," Wulfgar said.

"No," I said.

Wulfgar gave me an annoyed look.

The boy whimpered, "No. I didn't do nothing. I found 'im dead already. I was dressing 'im down so's the meat wouldn't go to waste, but I didn't kill 'im."

Wulfgar gave *him* an annoyed look, too.

I said to the guards, "Let the boy go."

The guard who was doing all the talking protested, "Punishment for poaching is death."

"You didn't actually see him poaching, did you?" I asked.

Looking sulky about it, the guards shook their heads.

Wulfgar leaned in to me and hissed, "You asked for my advice. So heed me now: This is not wise."

Impatiently I gestured for him to back away from me.

"There have been uprisings among the peasants. Now is not the time to be *soft* with them." He practically spat the word *soft,* as though to get the taste of it out of his mouth.

"On the contrary," I said. "Perhaps the whole problem is that you have been too harsh with them." I realized as soon as I said it that I shouldn't have said "you." I meant "the old regime," but it came out sounding as though I was criticizing Wulfgar himself.

Wulfgar spun on his heel and left. The guards saluted and left.

Well, that hadn't gone particularly well. And I'd have to figure out some way to protect myself from the guards who would be spreading the word that I was weak and unfit to rule. In the meantime, I grabbed hold of the kid by the shoulder of his grimy tunic so he couldn't run away and spoil everything. "It looks," I told him, "as though you owe me a favor."

"Yeah?" he asked, sounding not at all grateful to me for antagonizing both Wulfgar and the guards on his behalf. "You looking for a payment? You need to be bribed into mercy? I coulda guessed your fine talk was all a act. You're worse'n the rest of 'em."

"It wasn't," I protested. "I'm not." *Worse than let's-just-kill-her Queen Andreanna?* "I only meant..." Well, to be honest I only meant: *If you've got a ring, hand it over.* But obviously I couldn't say so. "Sorry," I finished lamely.

"If you wanna get paid," the kid said, "you gotta talk to my father—I got nothing."

"I don't want to get paid," I insisted. "Is your father near here?"

"Somebody's sure to have told him I got brought in. He's probably in the woods nearby."

I noticed that the two guards I'd humiliated by taking the boy's side were talking to another pair of guards, and all four of them were glancing over in my direction with looks that reminded me that they'd already killed me once today.

"Look," I said, getting a whole new picture of what making alliances could mean. "I'm new here. The royal family hates me, the guards distrust me, and from what I can see, things here have obviously been run badly for a long time. I think it's time for a change. I want to talk to your father, to some of the regular people in this king-dom." Peasant unrest, did the queen say? Maybe I could start my own revolution.

The kid looked at me for at least five seconds before he remembered to close his mouth. Then he grinned. "All right," he said. "Follow me."

He led me over the drawbridge and through a meadow and into the forest. Once we were among the trees, he put his hand to his mouth and gave a whistle that sounded like a birdcall. I didn't know woodland birds enough to know if someone answered.

I heard a rustling and a thud, and I felt a dull pressure in my back. It shouldn't have been enough to knock me over, but I fell to my knees and then fell forward again, onto my face. Looking over my shoulder, I could see an arrow sticking out of my back, and that was when I realized that I felt all fizzy. I wanted to tell the boy that he could keep the damn ring. But by then he was jumping over a fallen log and running to embrace a big man who had to be his father; and a couple other woodsy-looking guys were coming out from between the trees, some of them carrying bows, and I was just so tired I had to rest my head on my arms and let the fizziness take over.

CHAPTER NINE

Stop Me If You Think You've Heard This One Before

When I woke up to hear my mother calling me, I cracked. OK, the ring wasn't with the royal family or with the poachers, it *had* to be the one Deming had. I went tearing down the hill, Dusty barking her encouragement to me.

As my foster mother said, "Hello, Janine. Stand straight now, dear—" I launched myself at Sir Deming. We hit the ground hard, scattering chickens and younger siblings alike. I had his arm pinned and tried to unwedge the ring from his fat little finger. But with the element of surprise having run its course, he squirmed out from beneath skinny little me.

My mother was fluttering worse than the chickens, crying, "Janine! Janine, what are you thinking?"

I bit Deming's hand, and I would gladly have gnawed off his finger if he hadn't pulled out a knife and stuck it between my ribs.

"Oh, Janine!" Mother cried. "How am I ever going to explain this to your father?"

As the fizziness bubbled over me, the last thing I saw was her wringing her hands helplessly.

"There is no ring," I observed, trying for defiant, but recognizing that my voice was only a faint mumble. This was all just an evil plot thought up by Nigel Rasmussem to torment me in my last hours.

"Of course I have no ring," my mother told me as my vision blacked out. "It's your father who took the ring."

CHAPTER TEN

Family History

I'd been sabotaging myself. I blamed Rasmussem, of course: In this day of fractured families, what made them think the average gamer would be willing to hang around just for a parental good-bye?

The next time I went down the hill, I spoke politely to my foster mother and to Sir Deming. Then, when my mother said, "Aren't you going to stay long enough to say good-bye to your father?" I drove thoughts of paternity suits and cheap birthday-and-Christmas gift certificates from my mind.

"Why, of course, how could I leave without saying good-bye to my father?" I said.

"Oh, for goodness' sakes!" Deming snapped. "We haven't the time!"

"Sure we do," I told him.

He continued to grumble and complain, but from what I'd seen in playing this game so far, there was absolutely nothing I could do or say to make the man act pleasantly.

My father didn't take long to arrive. He came running over the hill that my computer subconscious identified as the direction of the bog. "Janine!" he cried, sweeping me up into a great bear hug that took me totally by surprise. He was such a big guy, I found my face pressed into his chest. Considering that he had come straight from cutting peat in the bog, this was not the best position in the world in which to be. I held my breath, trusting that he would let go before I suffocated.

I could hear my little foster siblings chanting for his attention, "Father! Father!"

"Hush now," my mother said. "Run along. Your father, your sister, and I must speak with this man."

Then—still pressed against my father's chest, I could both hear and feel the rumble of his voice—my father asked, "She's been told, then?"

"Yes." Deming sighed impatiently.

My father held me out at arm's length to look me over, and I was amazed to see that his eyes glistened with tears. "I was hoping we'd have more time," he said.

He was going to miss me? My father was saying he was going to miss me?

Though he was just a stupid computer simulation, I felt my throat tighten. "I'll come back," I promised. "Or, better yet, I'll send for you."

He forced a smile. "We'll come," he assured me. Then he glanced in Sir Deming's direction before he said to me, "Janine..."

He hesitated, and Deming said, "Get on with it, man. Shake her hand, wish her luck, repeat after me: 'It's been nice knowing you; good-bye.'"

I sincerely hoped that at some time during the progress of the game, I would be called upon to kill Deming. Surely *one* of the infinite variations Mr. Rasmussem had talked about could accommodate that. "Could we have some privacy here?" I asked.

Yet again Deming sighed, but he strode several long steps away.

"Janine," my father said, "when you first came to us, you were less than a week old—just a tiny little bundle, wrapped in a blanket."

My mother nodded mutely, dabbing her eyes.

I glanced at my father's rough and dirty hands and saw no ring, but why would a peat cutter have a ring?

He continued, "The midwife who brought you said that you were the daughter of the king and of a servant woman who had died in childbirth."

From off to the side, Deming complained, "She's been told all this."

"Go *farther* away," I ordered him.

He took a few more steps, and I wiggled my fingers at him to keep going, until he was practically at our neighbors' pigpen.

In a lowered voice, Father continued. "When your birth mother died, and she didn't have any relatives to send you to, your uncle Mayer, who was the king's gardener, suggested to the king that we might take you in. The king knew that at court your life would be in danger because the queen was obviously not pleased by the idea of your competing with her own children."

"And the king favored you," my mother said, "because he'd loved your mother so, and because the queen brought up her sons to love only her, not him."

That explained some things.

Father glanced at Deming, who was facing the other direction and was a good thirty yards away. Still, Father lowered his voice to a whisper. "So the midwife brought you here, but she also brought something else."

"Yes?" I prompted.

He nodded. "A ring."

"Really?" I said. "Imagine that."

"It's a magic ring," Mother told me.

Now, that was interesting. I'd been assuming it was just a keepsake to prove I was the king's choice. "What kind of magic does it do?" I asked.

Father said, "The midwife didn't say. She just said it was something your mother had asked with her dying breath to be given to you if you were ever summoned to court."

When that seemed to be the end of his story, I said, "Which I just have been."

"Which you just have been," he agreed.

"So . . . where's the ring?"

"The midwife has it. I decided it would be safer with her, just in case the queen knew of its existence and tried to get it from us. I didn't even tell Solita here."

OK. That made sense. Sort of. "Where's the midwife?"

73

"She has become a hermit," Father said, "in service at the Shrine of Saint Bruce the Warrior Poet."

I'd heard of it, but no memory stronger than name recognition surfaced.

"So I need to go to the shrine," I said.

"If you want the ring," Father agreed.

After what felt like a dozen false starts because I *didn't* have it?

"Be safe," he told me.

"Be good," my mother told me.

I kissed them both. I kissed my brothers and sisters. This time I really felt as though I were leaving my true family behind. I was tempted to go back up the hill and kiss Dusty, but I was sure Deming would ride off without me if I tried.

"Are you *finally* quite through?" Deming asked.

Father stepped to within a nose length of him and said, "She's your new king, little man. Treat her respectfully."

For some reason—maybe because Father was about a foot taller and about two feet wider—Deming bobbed his head and stammered, "Yes, of course. I meant: Does it please you to go now, Highness?"

My father winked at me as Deming lifted me onto the horse before he mounted in front of me, the first time he hadn't left me to scramble on by myself.

"Good-bye, good-bye," my family and I called out. I kept looking back and blowing kisses until I could no longer see them.

Maybe the people at Rasmussem need to develop a new game called something like Happy Family, where there's no gathering treasure or fighting hostile warriors or solving puzzles, just nice people who speak kindly to you and don't make you feel like one of those Christmas trees you see by the curb on December 26. I bet other people, besides me, would be interested.

Maybe.

OK, probably not.

When we got to the crossroads beyond the boundary of St. Jehan, I told Deming, "We need to go to the Shrine of Saint Bruce the Warrior Poet."

"Why?" he demanded, his newfound respect strained.

"Because I'm your new king and I command it," I told him.

Deming sighed but turned down a different road from the one we had taken in all the previous games. "I don't even like poetry," he complained.

It was the first thing he'd said that I could relate to.

THE ROAD led into the woods, where Deming chose a path that more or less followed a stream. He insisted that, though not a lover of poetry, he knew the way. I wondered if we were going to meet the bow-happy relatives of the poacher boy, which got me to wondering what would happen to him, since I wasn't going straight to the castle. But if I was supposed to play a part in that, his capture by the guards must be triggered by my arrival at the castle.

It wasn't a long ride before we reached what looked like an about-to-fall-down lean-to of twigs and hide that sagged against a hill.

"There she is," Deming said, stopping the horse half a city-block length away. "Feordina the Knitter. I'm not going any closer."

Feordina the Knitter? I squinted my eyes in the direction he was looking, at what I had supposed was a heap of forest debris piled by the wind into a corner formed by the lean-to and the hill. I became aware that the pile of debris had looked up and was watching us.

"Wait for me," I told Deming, dismounting.

"Yeah, yeah," he said. He, too, got off the horse and led it to the stream to drink.

I approached the lean-to. "Good day to you," I said.

The reason the person—Feordina—looked like a compost heap was that her clothes seemed to be made entirely of vegetation. She had a basket by her feet that was filled with dandelions, and that was what she was knitting with. I mean, she had knitting needles made of smooth sticks, but she was using dandelion stems as yarn. Dandelion stems not being very long, every few stitches she'd reach down into the basket for a new dandelion, lop off the top with her thumb, then add this new stem to the garment she was knitting. And I knew it was a garment she was making because she seemed to be wearing last season's model, over a fashionable chemise of what I was guessing to be moss and lichen, with accent points of leaves and a hint of heather. She had a two-foot-wide mushroom cap on her head.

"Hold on," she told me, "I'm counting knits and purls."

I waited while she got to the end of the row.

"So"—she didn't set her project down, but she looked up at me through her bushy eyebrows, which themselves almost looked knitted—"who are you and why are you here?"

"I'm Janine," I told her.

She looked at me blankly.

"Janine de St. Jehan." Still no reaction. "You were midwife at my birth. In the king's castle. Where my mother died. You brought me to my foster parents, Solita and Dexter the peat cutter." She *was* the right woman, wasn't she?

"You don't look like the Janine I remember," she said.

"Well"—I was beginning to get worried—"it *has* been fourteen years."

"Hmmm," she said noncommittally.

"My parents—my foster parents—said that they left a ring with you that my mother wanted me to have."

"We'll see," Feordina said. She carefully set her knitting down in the basket and stood, creaking and snapping. I couldn't tell if that was her bones, or something she was wearing. She was even shorter than me, probably only four feet tall. "Well, come in, then."

She motioned me to follow her into the lean-to, which hardly looked big enough for two. But it turned out to be only an entryway, protecting a huge crack in the side of the hill. There were burning torches set into nooks and crannies in the cave surface, so I had no trouble seeing.

The cave must have been formed by an offshoot of the stream we'd been following, for it was quite damp, which made me sneeze. The cave was roundish and about as big as, say, your average one-stall-and-a-sink public bathroom, which it also kind of smelled like. At the far wall was a life-size statue of a man who most likely was Saint Bruce the Warrior Poet. What was kind of neat was that, even though his face was carved wood, his armor was real: a plate-metal helmet (the visor was up, which was how I saw his face), gauntlets, shin protectors, and a surcoat of mail—thousands and thousands of interlocking circles of metal.

"Wow," I said. "Impressive."

When Feordina didn't say anything, I asked, "Uhm, what does this have to do with me and the ring?"

She waggled her finger at the statue, and my heart sank. "I hid the ring in the coat of mail." She smiled apologetically, showing little brown teeth, and I winced, not for the teeth but because I saw what was coming. "I wish I could remember where."

I ran my fingers over the metal, but nothing came loose. "Any hints?" I asked. "Arms? Shoulders? Back?"

She just shook her head. "But the rightful owner—and according to you, that's you—can call it forth."

"How?"

"Why, by reciting poetry, of course."

Of course.

I asked, "You mean like"—I paused to remember—"'Listen, my children and you shall hear / Of the midnight ride of Paul Revere'?"

"Cute," she said, "though a bit short."

"No, that wasn't the whole thing." I started panicking because I didn't *know* the whole thing. I'd just said all I remembered. Did I know any poem in its entirety?

No matter, for she said, "But it has to be a poem of your own making."

"Oh," I said. How hard could that be?

"Of course," Feordina said, "if Saint Bruce doesn't like your poem, he chops your head off."

CHAPTER ELEVEN

A Poem
Can Be a Home
to Those Who Roam
(Or, Like, Whatever)

If Saint Bruce didn't like my poetry, he got to chop my head off? That was even stiffer than my teacher Mrs. Kascima, who isn't satisfied with the quality of her quizzes unless half the class fails.

"I don't know," I said, though a moment before, I'd been convinced this ring was my only chance to succeed in the game—or at least to succeed in *starting* the game.

Feordina folded her arms across her chest and sighed. "That's all right; don't worry about me," she said in a tone that was just the slightest bit insincere. "Take your time; think it over." As though I couldn't hear, she muttered, presumably to Saint Bruce, "Like she's got a choice in the matter." She smiled brightly at me, then a moment later heaved another sigh.

"What, exactly, does this ring do?" I asked.

"I'm not going to answer that question at this point," she said, "not until I know it's really you."

Well, it wasn't like getting killed would be a new experience for me. "All right," I said. "Any rules I should know about?"

"Nope," Feordina said. "Just so long as it's your own poem." She considered before adding, "And Saint Bruce was very well-read, and was known for his incredible memory."

Which sounded like she was saying I looked like a cheater. I was offended but suspected it wasn't worthwhile defending myself to her.

"And he chops people's heads off," I asked for clarification, "if he suspects the poem is somebody else's . . . ?" I drifted off, hoping that was the extent of it.

"Or if the poem stinks," Feordina finished for me. "You wouldn't believe the number of people who come in here with stinky poems. What a mess. Speaking of which, I should probably get the mop and bucket out now. Well, never mind, we'll see." She gave me that bright smile again. "Did I forget to mention there's a time limit?"

"You most certainly did." Could things get any worse? Silly question: Things can *always* get worse. "You mean there's a limit to how long the poem can be?"

"I mean there's a limit to how long you can wait between entering the shrine and starting—*and ending*—the poem. Bruce doesn't like a lot of dithering, you know."

Before I had time to throttle her, she added: "I'd say your time's probably . . . oh, about half gone."

Which didn't give me enough time to throttle her *and* think up a poem. "Any particular subject or type of poem he prefers?"

I figured she'd say he wanted a *rondel* or a *sonnet* or some other kind of poem I could name but not remember how to structure; I also feared that he might be especially fond of deep, meaningful, symbolic poetry. But she just shook her head. And glanced warily at that sword the statue held aloft, as though revising her estimate of how much time I had left.

Did I detect a smear of red along its length, or was that just the light from the torches?

All right. What, exactly did I have to lose? I announced: "An Ode to Saint Bruce." He had to like a poem praising him—didn't he?

No reaction.

OK.

Except, of course, that my mind was blank.

OK...

It made no sense to just stand there without trying while my time ran out. I started:

"A warrior poet named Bruce..."

My mind ran through a series of words rhyming with "Bruce," none of which seemed particularly apt.

"...wrote odes to his horse and his goose."

I fully expected the sword to come down then, but it didn't. I cleared my throat. OK, that took care of the "poet" part, what about the "warrior"?

"He won honor and prizes..."

Prizes? What was I thinking of, *prizes*?

"...'gainst foes of various sizes..."

'Gainst was poetical, even if the line itself was forced. And now what about the "saint" part?

Knowing it sounded like the pathetic begging it was, I finished:

"...and protected young poets from abuse."

Feordina winced and ducked.

I closed my eyes and braced myself for the blow from the sword.

No pain. No fizziness. No maternal call of, "Janine! Janine, come back to the house."

Maybe I was still alive. I peeked to check.

The statue just stood there, like a good statue should. *Stood/good/should:* Now the rhyming was coming to me.

Feordina lowered her arms from protecting her head and gave a snort of disbelief. "He must be in a good mood," she proclaimed. "Lucky you: He's accepted your poem."

I couldn't fault Feordina for being surprised. I was amazed myself. "Now what?" I asked.

"Now you ask for what you want," Feordina said, "and if it's within Saint Bruce's power, he'll grant it."

I closed the mouth I had opened to ask for the ring. "If it's within his power," I repeated.

She nodded. "'If it's within his power.'"

"What does that mean?" I asked.

"It means: If he can do it." Feordina rolled her eyes despite her polite smile.

Oh, well, thank you very much for clarifying that particularly challenging question. Though I had come to get the ring, suddenly I wondered if the ring was my best option. "What sorts of wishes does he grant?" I asked. "And what sort doesn't he grant?"

"Well," she said, "I've never known him to turn down a request for facility at rhyming or meter, which I do have to point out are areas in which you seem to be particularly weak."

83

"Ahh," I said, suspecting that she wouldn't recognize sarcasm, "very useful to peasant girls who need to take on the royal court."

"Hmmm," she said as though maybe she *did* know sarcasm when she heard it. "Of course, Saint Bruce does tend to get cranky with greedy people who are granted one wish then ask for more."

"Cranky," I said. "As in..." I glanced at the upraised sword.

"Hmmm," Feordina agreed.

"So what do you suggest?" I asked.

She sighed audibly. "You came here looking for something in particular. Is your attention span so short that you've forgotten?"

"I came looking for my mother's ring," I said.

Feordina leaned close as though she was about to whisper something to me, but instead she shouted: *"Well, then, ask for it!"*

"I wish for my mother's ring," I said.

There was a slight *ping* as something metallic fell—I couldn't see from where on the statue—and hit the floor of the cave. I caught the glint of metal as the ring rolled to bounce off my right big toe.

"Oy!" Feordina smacked her palm against her forehead. "Was that so difficult?"

I picked up the ring. It was a pewter band with a design I recognized from the medieval paraphernalia catalogs as a Celtic knot. "Thank you," I said to Saint Bruce. All right, he was a statue, but what could politeness hurt? I asked Feordina, "Now do you believe I'm Janine de St. Jehan?"

Feordina sighed. Feordina was great at sighing. "I suppose."

"Then can you tell me about this ring?"

"If you give it to someone," Feordina said, "that person will do your bidding."

"You mean...like..."—I shrugged—"...what?"

"I mean, like, your father put the ring on your mother's finger, and—even though she knew better—she was compelled to love him."

"Eww!" I said. "You mean she didn't want to, and had to because of the ring?" The king, who had never been high in my estimation, took an express elevator into the subbasement. "She shouldn't have accepted the ring," I proclaimed.

Feordina looked close to smacking her palm against *my* forehead, but she refrained. "You don't listen too well," she said. "You really should learn to listen. *Compelled.* Did you not hear me say *compelled,* or don't you know what the word means?"

"You said," I reminded her, "that once my father put the ring on my mother's finger, she was compelled to love him—and, yes, I know that *compelled* means she had to, whether she wanted to or not. You never said she was *compelled* to accept the ring."

She put her hands on her hips and stood on her toes to stick her face up into mine. "Well, I should think that was obvious."

I raised my voice to match hers. "Well, then, OK." But getting her mad wasn't going to help. Making an effort to sound pleasant, I said, "OK, thank you."

"Don't you take *that tone* with me," Feordina snapped,

which made me wonder if her character might not be based on my grandmother, who can discern *a tone* at fifty paces.

"Sorry," I said meekly. "But, no, really, thank you. That is valuable information. You're saying that when I give the ring to someone, that person *has* to accept it, and then he or she *has* to do whatever I command."

Feordina nodded. "You can give the ring only once, and that person will do all your bidding, or die trying, for as long as he or she lives, never able to remove the ring, no matter what you bid, even if it's to jump off a castle battlement. Which—not that you asked, but I'll give my opinion, anyway—would be a wasteful thing for you to ask for, because even if your person dies within moments of getting the ring, you can't take it back. Well, you can, but it won't work for you again."

Seeing what looked like a flaw in her reasoning, I asked, "What if I bid the person to take the ring off?"

"What are you, a fledgling lawyer?" Feordina asked. "Can't be done."

"Just wondering."

She shook her head. "I really hate lawyers," she said. She turned to complain to the statue of Saint Bruce. "Who would have ever guessed that my little Janine would grow up to be a lawyer?" She waved me away. "Go on, go on," she said. "I have a sweater to finish knitting before the nights start getting chilly. Don't you have a kingdom to inherit or something?"

SUBJ: URGENT RESPONSE NEEDED--Repair
        Team
DATE: 5/25   03:50:13 P.M. US eastern
        daylight time
FROM: Nigel Rasmussem
        <nrasmussem@rasmussem.com>
TO: dept. heads distribution list

The patch suggested by the Palo Alto
group didn't work.

The gamer has only now broken through
level 1 for the first time. We are
concerned over her lack of progress,
which makes it seem unlikely that she
will finish the game in the short time
she has left.

Note that we're already seeing
degeneration of the bios, even earlier
than forecast. We do have medical
personnel present.

Options needed immediately for
stabilization. Please respond ASAP.

CHAPTER TWELVE

One

So, tying the ring to the laces of my bodice, I said good-bye to Feordina the Knitter and the statue of Saint Bruce the Warrior Poet, and I woke up Sir Deming, who'd fallen asleep on the stream bank, though he claimed he was just thinking with his eyes closed.

"Are you quite ready yet?" he asked as he helped me mount the horse. "Maybe we can go visit the seashore next, or perhaps you'd like to tour the great cathedrals of the midland provinces? I mean, it isn't as though there's any sort of rush or anything, with the old king dead and the new king not yet crowned."

What had he done—awakened on the wrong side of the stream?

"The new king," I said, "doesn't appreciate sarcasm."

I could give him the ring and order him to like me— or at least to be civil to me and protect me from others' rudeness—but I suspected that would be a frivolous waste.

Once we had been riding for a long silent while, he asked, "What did you ask for, back at the shrine?"

I'd had plenty of time to consider what I might answer should he ask that question—something clever, I'd calculated, and believable, and at the same time implying that I was not someone to be taken lightly or messed with: a deception he might pass on to the royal family so that they would have a healthy fear of me. But the best I'd come up with was, "That's for me to know."

Deming shrugged and didn't say anything else the whole ride to the castle.

SIR DEMING ONCE again handed me over to Counselor Rawdon, and I once again decided to forgo the bath and change of clothes. After all, if this kingdom included people dressed like Feordina, whose fashion sense began and stopped at forest edibles, the royal family would just have to accept my sheepherder's garb.

Ah, my royal kin. What can I say? After a short interval of aristocratic abuse, punctuated by my polite little apologies (I'm sorry I smell, I'm sorry I was born, I'm sorry the king liked me better than he liked you), the audience was once again over.

"Wulfgar," I said to my eldest half brother, "may I please have a word with you?"

Queen Andreanna went off in a huff, sweeping Abas and Kenric away with her.

"I'm guessing," I told Wulfgar, "that I'm going to be needing a lot of help."

"Yeah," he agreed.

"I'm thinking it can't have been easy for you as the firstborn son, with a domineering mother and two brothers who, I suspect, have always been ready to betray you to advance their own causes."

Wulfgar didn't have to say anything—I could tell I was right by his expression.

"There's nothing I can do about our father passing you over to name me heir." It'd be a lot easier to just give him the ring and *force* him to help me than it would be to *convince* him, but I had to try it this way first, in case I needed the ring during the rest of the game. I said, "Fathers..." I tried to get rid of the mental image of me with my ear pressed to the wall, hearing my own father demand, "How can I even be sure she's mine?" "Fathers," I said, "can be a disappointment."

"'Disappointment,'" Wulfgar snorted.

"You don't have to be abandoned to be abandoned," I told him, and at that he looked thoughtful, and then nodded. I repeated, "There's nothing I can do about our father's decision. But I suspect you would have had competition for the throne even if I had never been born, even if King Cynric had officially named you his heir."

"Oh, I can imagine," Wulfgar agreed.

"If we work together," I said, "that's the power divided between two rather than among four."

Wulfgar looked at me appraisingly, then nodded. "All right," he said.

By then we had walked out into the courtyard, and I saw that same old pair of guards dragging the poacher boy toward us. Though he and his kin had murdered me once already, I couldn't stand by and let the guards execute him for being hungry. That was no way to start my kingship. Still, I remembered that Wulfgar hadn't reacted well to leniency. "What we need to do," I said hurriedly, "is call together a council: the old king's advisers, plus those in the kingdom who know magic. I'll leave *who* to you. And *when*. You make the arrangements. I'll handle this."

Wulfgar noted the approaching guards. He obviously dismissed the oncoming situation as within my abilities and turned to go back indoors.

One of the guards called out, "Prince Wulfgar!"

Wulfgar gave a vague wave and continued walking away.

I stepped into the path of the guard. "May *I* help you?" I asked. "I'm Princess Janine." I smiled sweetly.

The guard bobbed his head in what may have been a bow. "Princess Janine, this boy has been caught poaching deer. We were about to deliver the usual punishment."

"Indeed?" I said, trying to sound regal.

"I didn't do nothing," the boy sniveled. "I found 'im dead already. I was dressing 'im down so's the meat wouldn't go bad, but—"

"You didn't kill him, right?" I turned to the guards. "Were there witnesses to the actual killing?"

The two men shuffled their feet. "No," they admitted, and I was sure I saw disappointment on their faces.

"Then let the boy go," I said. "Prince Wulfgar and I discussed this." Well, only if you counted my saying, "I'll handle this," as discussion, but I remembered how the guards had killed me once before because they perceived me as weak. I couldn't very well give the magic ring to the entire barracks to make them love and respect me.

The guards saluted smartly and released the boy.

"I will not be so lenient again," I said, which was for everybody's benefit.

As though afraid I might change my mind, the boy dashed away—across the courtyard, over the drawbridge, and into the woods.

The guards walked away, shaking their heads and muttering—which didn't look promising.

Surely, I thought, *I'm not supposed to let them kill the boy—that couldn't be the right track to take?*

I was so busy watching the guards, I wasn't aware of anyone approaching until someone laid a hand on my arm. For once I lucked out, for it was a gentle touch, and when I looked up, I saw an old woman. She was about four-and-a-half-feet tall by four-and-a-half-feet wide, and she was dressed in a simple brown gown decorated with feathers and bits of seashell and smooth, polished stones of various colors. *I wonder if she's related to Feordina?* I asked myself. Or was this just the kingdom of the fashion impaired?

The old woman said, "Blessed is the way of the One."

"The one what?" I asked.

"All is One," she answered cryptically.

So I retaliated with a smart-mouthed, "And one is all."

But the old woman didn't take my comment as sarcastic. "That is very profound," she told me, and—while I checked her expression to see if *she* was being sarcastic—she added, "I guessed you might be One."

I was going to ask, "One what?" but I suspected we'd start going in circles again. So instead I asked, "Are you Sister Mary Ursula?" because I wondered if maybe we were talking about religion.

Her face lit up. "Yes," she said, obviously unduly impressed by my perceptiveness, when it was really just a case of having gotten a hint from Nigel Rasmussem. "You are truly One with the world, aren't you? I surmised that, by how you treated that boy. You recognized his Oneness. Many would not have."

"Ah, well," I said vaguely. I took it she was complimenting me, but beyond that I was kind of lost.

"You are the answer to my prayers," she told me. Which is the kind of thing I'd always fantasized someone would say to me—I'd just never pictured that someone as a seventy-year-old nun.

"Uhm..." I said.

"Let us give thanks for our Oneness," Sister Mary Ursula said. She clasped my hands, closed her eyes, and hummed nasally. "I feel the world in my bones," she said. "The wind is in my veins; the spirit of the otter is in my liver."

"Are you..." I started. "I mean, you're not..." She opened her eyes and looked at me quizzically. "I'm guessing you aren't a Roman Catholic nun," I said. I go to Catholic school, so I would know.

Like an actress momentarily stepping out of character, she put one hand on her hip and said in a chirpy little voice totally unlike her normal hazy tone, "Definitely not, because—of course—our intent is not to offend anyone," which was probably a Rasmussem programmer's idea of humor. Sister Mary Ursula resumed her slightly foggy manner. "I am," she said, "of the Sisterhood of One."

"That's a regular order here?" I asked.

"No," she said. "I'm the only one. We are *all* the only one."

Of course. How silly of me.

She said, "I'm afraid King Cynric and his family have not always been quite so One as they might have been."

"Well..." I said. I wasn't sure what to answer, but that made no difference, for Sister Mary Ursula had only paused to take a breath.

"But you are obviously someone who takes Oneness seriously. You're a true treasure, like rain on a plain of drought, or like a peach without a pit." Sister Mary Ursula patted my hand. "You and I are going to get along wonderfully well, I can tell. Together we shall unite this kingdom into Oneness with the universe."

Since she obviously wasn't going to give me a chance to get a word in edgewise, I just smiled at her.

But apparently she was through. "Come, come," she said, starting for the castle, moving at a slow waddle. "If the sun is singing in your marrow, tell it to whisper to the acorns instead. We have work before us."

Not knowing what else to do, I followed her.

In the castle we ran into Wulfgar, who was walking with Counselor Rawdon.

"Yes," Rawdon was saying, "if we send a rider to contact Uldemar, he can use his scrying glass to tell the others, and that will certainly save time with trying to track them all down."

"Oooo," Sister Mary Ursula interrupted, "scrying." She shook her head disapprovingly. As far as I could tell, she was totally oblivious to the annoyed looks she was getting from both men. "Not a good thing. Not a good thing at all. Disrupts the cosmic harmonies. Throws off the balance of One—it's like a fat woman trying to stand on one foot. No, not a good idea at all." She placed her fingertips to her temples and hummed, then shuddered as though she'd had a sudden chill. "Good thing we met you in time to stop you."

"You are not," Wulfgar said, "stopping us." To me he explained, "If you want Orielle and Xenos to attend your meeting, having Uldemar use his scrying glass is the most efficient way to reach them."

This made sense to me, but "Oooo," Sister Mary Ursula said as though Wulfgar had said the one thing she dreaded more than hearing that scrying was about to take place. "Wizard, witch, necromancer. They are *so* strayed from One, you might just as well count them as Other. No, no, no, no—not a good way to start your good work, Princess Janine, definitely not."

No magic? Was that what she was saying: There should be no magic? "Surely that can't be right," I said, remembering the promos I'd seen, which included a wizard and a dragon. Were they only in the dead ends? No magic? What kind of fantasy role-playing game had no magic?

But Sister Mary Ursula was shaking her head. "Of course I'm right," she said. "Right and truth are One with pinochle and rye bread."

Rawdon shook his head.

Wulfgar said, "Princess Janine, haven't you listened to enough of this woman's rantings?"

As though Wulfgar wasn't standing only about two feet farther away from her than I was, Sister Mary Ursula whispered loudly, "He's not to be trusted. He was raised by Others, you know." To Wulfgar and Rawdon she said, "Princess Janine and I dance to the same rhythms of the cosmos. She has chosen me to be her counselor, and we are now as two bodies sharing one mind."

That was a scary thought.

And, anyway, *had* I chosen her? All I'd done was pardon the poacher boy, an action she happened to approve. Did that make her my official choice of counselor?

"Princess Janine," Rawdon said, "are you really planning to dismiss me?"

"I never said anything about dismissing..." I started.

But Wulfgar, who'd been looking from me to Sister Mary Ursula, crossed his arms over his chest and demanded of me, "*What* is she talking about?"

Sister Mary Ursula answered for me, and I realized I was getting pretty tired of that. She said, "The princess showed Oneness with a poor peasant boy."

Wulfgar homed in on what she must be talking about. "The poacher?" he asked. "You let the poacher off? Is that what she's saying? Didn't you hear my mother warn you about the peasant unrest?"

"Yes," I said before Sister Mary Ursula could tell me what I thought about this. "I thought the unrest could be due to the severity of the laws over minor matters."

"'Minor matters'?" Wulfgar snarled at me. "The laws of the land are a minor matter?"

How could every conversation get so far beyond me? I said, "Well, this particular one is."

We glowered at each other, until Sister Mary Ursula finally said, "See? One mind."

"You're welcome to each other," Wulfgar said, and he stormed off down the hall.

Rawdon threw his hands up in the air in frustration. "Princess—" he started.

Sister Mary Ursula put her fingers to her temples and said, "No, no, no Rawdon."

And Rawdon, too, left in a huff.

"Can't I have two counselors?" I called after him.

He didn't answer. And Sister Mary Ursula told me, "One. One sun. One underlying song to the universe. One best way to prepare eggplant. One counselor. We must sit down and discuss all that needs to be changed. I am a much better person than Rawdon."

"Counselor Rawdon." I raised my voice and I was pretty sure he could hear me. "I haven't said no, about those magic-users coming. I just"—I sighed and finished lamely—"need to talk to my counselor about it first."

And of course he didn't answer that, either.

CHAPTER THIRTEEN

Disarming the Troops

N ow," Sister Mary Ursula said, "the first thing you must do is cleanse yourself."

How kind of her to notice. "Yeah," I said, checking out the skirt of my dress, "I *am* pretty disgusting."

She sighed. Loudly. "Physical appearance is not what is important."

Yeah, right. Tell that to any girl who hasn't bothered to put on a presentable shirt or fix her hair because she's only running into the grocery store to get a quart of milk for her grandmother, and who does she see tending the 7-ITEMS-OR-LESS cash register but the guy of her dreams, except she can't even say hi—much less try to develop a meaningful relationship—since she looks like the poster child for the terminally geeky.

But Sister Mary Ursula came from a different world from me. I suspected Sister Mary Ursula came from a different world from the other people in *this* world, too, but

I didn't say so. She told me, "You need to cleanse your soul—make it One with the world."

"How do I do that?" I asked.

"Solitude. Fasting. Meditation. Skinny-dipping in the moonlight."

"I think I'll wait until my second week as king for that," I said, willing to risk that I was skipping something I was supposed to do.

Sister Mary Ursula didn't argue. "All ways lead to the One," she said, "though some ways get you there faster."

"Speaking of getting places," I said, "what I want are people to deliver messages for me. Who would I talk to about that?"

"You could talk to me," Sister Mary Ursula said. "But in all honesty, I don't know much about it. Probably the one you need to speak to is Penrod, captain of the guard."

"Fine," I said. "Thank you. I'll see you later."

"Don't you want to discuss the meaning of life?" Sister Mary Ursula took a few steps after me.

But she stopped following when I said, "In a little bit." She was obviously a dead end. I had chosen the wrong counselor, that was all there was to it. There was no way the game was supposed to be played with me spending my first afternoon here cleansing my soul and listening to Sister Mary Ursula philosophize about life. Or, at least, I didn't think so.

I was sure the ceiling would come crashing down on me at any moment now. Or maybe there would be an earthquake or a tidal wave, something to kill me off and set me down at the beginning again. But in the meanwhile, there was no reason I couldn't try to find out information that would be useful for my next try.

I went back out into the courtyard. No guards this time; if they weren't terrorizing the local citizenry, they were probably huddled somewhere conspiring to kill me. I stopped a servant woman who was carrying a basket of laundry. "Any idea where I would find Captain Penrod?" I asked her.

"He might be in the guardhouse." She pointed to one of the doorways.

Luckily, the door was wide open, because I didn't know if—as a princess-about-to-be-appointed-king—I was supposed to knock. I mean, obviously I outranked them, but I didn't want to walk in on a group of guys who might be in the process of getting dressed or undressed, or who might be sitting around scratching or belching and farting or doing whatever it is guys do when there aren't any civilized folk around. But with the door already open, I rapped my knuckles against the doorframe, called, "Hello!" and walked in.

There were about a half-dozen guards, who were neither walking around naked nor conspiring against me—at least not obviously so. Apparently this wasn't where they slept but just where they hung around. A pair of them were seated at a table, playing a game my subconscious identified as knucklebones. Most of the others were clustered around them, and I gathered, from the snatch of conversation I caught before they saw me and stopped, that they were betting on the outcome of the game. One man was napping on a cot in the corner, and another was making some sort of adjustment to his sword belt. All of the men, except the napper, jumped to attention when they saw me. Not guiltily, I thought, just wary.

"Captain Penrod?" I said.

"Yeah?" The man who answered was the one who had been fiddling with his belt. He was also the guard I'd talked to several times this morning—the one who had arrested the poacher. The one who had killed me two or three games back.

I decided not to hold that against him. "I need to invite the magic-users of the realm to a meeting," I said.

"Done," the man said.

Did he mean, "I will do your bidding so quickly, you might as well consider it done already"? Because he certainly wasn't moving, quickly or otherwise.

"'Done'?" I repeated.

"Prince Wulfgar already gave that order."

"Oh," I said, because—excuse me, but—the way Prince Wulfgar and I had left things, Sister Mary Ursula was my adviser, and she had advised me to steer clear of magic, and he had no reason to believe I wouldn't take her recommendation. Sure, that was what I had decided. But *after* he left. I had certainly not told him to go ahead and give the order.

Some of this—not the details but the surprise and annoyance—must have shown on my face. Captain Penrod gave an unpleasant smile and said, "You and Prince Wulfgar need to consult more to get your stories straight."

I took that as indication the captain had found out I'd misled him regarding the poacher. I didn't like the way the other men had moved in closer—even the guy who earlier had been lying down. I braced myself, but so far their weapons were still sheathed.

"You're right," I told Penrod, told all of them. "As I'm starting my rule, I'm sure to make many mistakes. But I want you to know: You and your men are very important to me. I realize you perform some of the hardest, most dangerous, most thankless jobs in the realm." I had no idea what their duties were, but doesn't everybody feel that describes their jobs? I figured it couldn't hurt for me to be sympathetic.

They *did* seem to—well, not mellow or relax, but maybe loosen a bit at my words.

"I want all of you to feel free to come to me with any of your concerns. And I want you to go ahead and give me advice if you think anything in the way this kingdom is being run is wrong."

Well, that was a mistake.

They started complaining to me about everything from my being too soft on the peasants to the fact that they weren't paid enough and weren't paid regularly, and the food was pretty generally lousy, and they really didn't like the way the queen had a tendency to hit on the younger men.

"Wow," I said the instant there was a pause, "I'm going to look into all of those things. First..." I was going to apologize for undermining their authority with the poacher boy; but on second thought, they might take that as permission to enact harsher measures on the nearest peasants. Besides, I didn't think a king should start her reign by apologizing. "First," I said, "the money owed you."

That certainly seemed the right choice for getting their attention. They all spoke at once, their words tumbling over one another, but I gathered that they'd been shorted their salaries several times over the past months.

"Who's in charge of paying you?" I asked.

"Counselor Rawdon," they all said, seven voices speaking as one.

Rawdon, of course, had walked off in a huff. Had he simply left my presence or had he left the castle? "I will get to the bottom of this," I promised. "Who can take me to Counselor Rawdon's room, or..." I still didn't have a clear idea what I was supposed to be doing in this game. "Or, well, to all the places I need to go?"

They all looked ready to volunteer, which was a distinct improvement to their earlier mood. But it was Penrod who said, "I will accompany you, Highness."

"Good. Thank you." I nodded to the other men. "At ease," I said, which was about all the military-speak I knew.

Penrod and I walked back out into the courtyard. "Any idea how soon before the magic-users will be here?" I asked.

"Uldemar is the only one with a regular house in a town, and that's about a half-day's ride from here. The messenger Prince Wulfgar sent should be there by late afternoon. Uldemar has wizardly ways to contact the others. Depending on where they are and if they can come immediately, I should think they'd be here sometime between noon tomorrow and..." He trailed off, indicating no upper limit for how long it could take.

Ouch. OK, so I guessed I wasn't supposed to wait on them.

Then my new top priority was to get the guards happy with me so they wouldn't kill me again. "What—" I started. But I heard a sound, that stomach-churning *whoosh* of an arrow that I recognized from my death a couple times back, when the woodsmen had fired their arrows at me.

What did I do now? I thought things had been going...maybe not *well* but sort of OK. Hadn't they? Had the guardsmen been only pretending to accept my proposals?

Except that I hadn't felt an arrow slam into me, and I didn't feel any fizziness.

I looked back to the doorway of the guardroom, but there was no bowman there. Could I have imagined that sound? I turned to Captain Penrod, and he wasn't where I had left him.

He was, in fact, on the ground at my feet, an arrow through his heart.

There was a supply wagon parked in front of a servants' entrance, and a man jumped out from behind it. He was a huge, hairy guy, and it was hard to tell where his hairiness ended and his tunic—which my subconscious identified as elk hide—began. On his head was one of those horned helmets worn by cartoon Vikings and fat ladies in German operas.

Before I could get out much more than a squeak, he

clapped a massive hand over my mouth. I kicked, squirmed, and tried to bite—but didn't get much reaction.

Still, my pathetic scream must have gotten someone's attention, for one of the guards came to the guardroom door.

A second man, who could have been my attacker's twin, edged out from behind the wagon and let loose an arrow that struck the guard in the throat.

I was still trying to jab my attacker where it hurts—which apparently is a lot easier in the movies than in real life—as he dragged me backward toward the wagon. There were two bowmen behind the wagon, who covered our retreat, as well as others, I now saw, on top of the wall that separated the courtyard from the surrounding woods. At just about the same time I became aware that the placement of the wagon had hidden a rope ladder the attackers had used to get into the castle compound, I also became aware that it wasn't my attacker's hand that smelled so bad, but the cloth he held in his hand over my nose and mouth.

Whatever he'd soaked the cloth in made my knees wobble and give out, and he flung me over his shoulder as he grabbed hold of the rope. The ground spun, and I lost consciousness.

CHAPTER FOURTEEN

Are We Having Fun Yet?

I woke up when someone threw a bucket of cold water on me. Even in my groggy state, I was beginning to figure this was the only bath I was likely to get in this particular lifetime.

Speaking of baths, two big hairy guys who looked as though they'd never *heard* the word—and who may or may not have been some of the ones I'd seen in the castle courtyard—were standing over me, one with an empty-though-still-dripping bucket in hand. This guy said something to me—a whole string of words I couldn't understand.

"I don't speak your language," I said.

The second man switched to whatever language English passed for in this world. "Where do it be?" he demanded. Despite his appearance, his accent was pleasant and musical—sort of Jamaican but not.

I was smart enough not to check to see if the ring I'd tied to my bodice laces was still there.

"Where do *what* be?" I asked.

"Do na play the dumb one," commanded the other guy, his accent thicker. "The crown, to be certain."

That was a surprise. I had no idea who these guys were or why they were looking for the crown, but I couldn't see any reason not to be honest. "I haven't been officially named king yet," I explained. "Not for a couple more days. I don't know where they're keeping the crown in the meantime."

The two guys exchanged a look that struck me as a can-this-girl-be-real? look.

"What?" I asked.

They talked over me as though I weren't there. "Mayhap she be playin' the dumb one?" the one with the bucket said. "Or mayhap she really be as stupid as she seems?"

I resented that, even though I was lying in a puddle of new-made mud, obviously these guys' prisoner. And there were a bunch of other guys, looking just like these two. A *whole* bunch. Like hundreds, I guessed, seeing their tents, their campfires. I was in some sort of enemy camp.

Bucketless stroked his bushy beard speculatively. "It might be that no one has been telling her yet," he said, but he didn't sound as though he really believed it.

"Nobody has told me much of anything," I agreed.

"You be the new king," said the bucket guy. "How can they be na tellin' you what you be needin' to know to rule?"

"Well," I admitted, "I do suspect some of them are trying to get around that me-being-the-new-king thing."

The guy who spoke better English gave a short, sharp

107

laugh, and this time I guessed he believed me. "I would bet," he said. Then he asked, "Do anybody be telling you about King Grimbold?"

I shook my head. "Who's he?"

He grinned, his white teeth flashing. "Me."

A king. Another one. Oh boy. "You're not a contender for the throne of..."—implanted memory floated to my mind's surface, and my kingdom gained a name— "Shelby, are you?"

Grimbold snorted. "I be having my own kingdom, thank you—when Shelban kings be not sabotaging us." He could see I wasn't following this. "In the north," he added, which wouldn't have meant anything to me except for what Queen Andreanna had said about us being threatened by a barbarian army in the north.

I didn't ask if he was a barbarian, which sounded a bit rude to me. Maybe it would and maybe it wouldn't to a barbarian, but I decided not to chance it. I asked, "King Cynric took your crown, is that what you're saying? He took away the actual crown?"

"He be *stole* it away," the other man interrupted. "From Grimbold's father, King Tobrecan."

"I don't know anything about that," I said. "I was raised away from court."

Grimbold gave that barklike laugh of his. "Like Wulfgar."

This was not news to me, but for the first time I wondered if Wulfgar and I had more in common than I had suspected. That he had been educated away from home was the first thing Deming had said about him—but had it been to protect him from court intrigue? Had Cynric seen that Queen Andreanna had enough ambitions for herself that she posed a danger to their son when he was too young to defend himself? I saw there were a lot more questions I should have asked at court.

The barbarian with the bucket said, "But now that King Tobrecan is bein' dead and Grimbold is bein' our new king, and now that Cynric is bein' dead, it is bein' time to reclaim the crown that been fashioned by Xenos for Brecc the Slayer, our firstest chieftain."

"Xenos," I said, recognizing the name. "There's a magician today by that same name."

Again the men exchanged a long-suffering look.

They couldn't be talking about the same man, could they? How long ago had this Brecc ruled, and how old would that make Xenos? But, then again, we were talking about a magician.

"She *do* be as stupid as she looks," the guy with the bucket said.

"I be liking her," Grimbold argued. "She does na know nothing, but I na be going to hold that against her."

"So what do that be meanin'?" the other man asked.

"We shall be letting her live," Grimbold said.

That was a relief.

Grimbold said, "We shall be demanding the crown as ransom for her."

The other gave a dismissive snort. "What makes you be thinkin' they be payin' a ransom for her, useless thing that she be?"

I couldn't help but mentally agree. They were going to ask my family to trade something—presumably of value—for me? This opened up a whole new batch of possibilities for public humiliation.

Grimbold stroked his beard pensively as though his companion had presented a new thought. "We can always be killing her later," he said.

Which I guess showed he wasn't all *that* emotionally attached to me.

"Set a guard on her," Grimbold ordered, "and send a envoy to the castle to be demanding the returning of my crown in exchange for the life of their new king."

I couldn't even use my ring on Grimbold. If I said, "Here, take this ring," and he put it on, and then started doing everything I said, then surely this other guy would catch on that something was wrong.

Nor could I use it on my guard: Grimbold had given his orders. There were too many men in this camp who would question why those orders were being ignored if I got this guy to release me.

The barbarian guard got a length of chain and some shackles—not promising an easy escape at all—then he brought me to a tree in the midst of their campground, and he fastened me there, by my left ankle. All in all, they were being more considerate than I had reason to expect from enemy barbarians. The shackle wasn't tight, and the chain was long enough that I could sit, stand, lie down, or walk around the tree—choosing shade or sunlight as I pleased. But I still felt like a leashed dog.

From the position of the sun, I guessed that it was mid-afternoon. The last meal my stomach remembered was a breakfast of hard bread and salted fish back in St. Jehan—a menu the real me had to keep from dwelling on or I would have gagged. I felt hungry, and these guys would have already had their midday meal and wouldn't be thinking about supper for another several hours.

A guard was posted to watch me. He was given the key to the shackles, which I found reason enough to try to strike up a friendship. It was hard to tell if he didn't speak English, or if he simply didn't want to talk.

There were some women in the camp, and one of them brought me a cup of water.

"Thank you," I said. "Any chance of any leftovers from lunch?"

She looked at me quizzically and said something that sounded like, *"Doe naado?"*

"Food?" I said. I pantomimed eating, but she shook her head. I thought she meant she didn't understand rather than that I couldn't have any, but there was no way to know for sure. My guard certainly didn't offer any commentary.

There were even a few kids. Some of them seemed curious, some seemed to be playing a game of dare—approaching, then running away. When I didn't chase after them, a few got bolder and took up a new game of throw-clumps-of-dirt-at-the-prisoner. My guard napped obliviously in the shade of his own tree.

I didn't even know if my royal family was planning to rescue me. Should I be patiently waiting for them to come swooping in, or was I supposed to be working on some plan of my own?

Of course, it would help if I had even the beginnings

of a plan of my own to get me started in the right direction.

Knowing how difficult it is to judge the passing of time when you're bored, I think I waited about an hour and a half, maybe two. The sun *did* lower a bit in the sky.

This can't be right, I told myself. If anyone was going to rescue me, it was probably going to have to be me.

My opportunity came when a new guard took over.

"Do you speak the language of Shelby?" I asked.

"No," the man answered, revealing himself to be not quite rocket-scientist caliber.

I untied the magic ring from the lacing of my bodice. "Take this ring," I commanded.

Sure enough, he understood me well enough that the magic of the ring compelled him to come forward and take it from my outstretched hand. He slipped it onto one of his own fingers, and I figured that had to be another of the ring's magical properties—that it would fit anyone—either that or my mother had had very fat fingers.

"I want you to like me," I told the guard.

"Oh, I do," the man assured me so warmly I feared we were veering into a direction I certainly didn't want to go.

"I want you to like me as your best buddy," I clarified. "I want you to only want good things for me. I want you to want me safe and happy."

"'Safe,'" he repeated, nodding his head energetically. "'Happy.'"

"I want you to release me," I said, "and to get me out of this camp."

He came forward and tried to tear the chain in half with his bare hands.

It looked as though I would have to do the thinking for both of us.

I said, "Take the time to release me without attracting attention."

The guard paused to consider, then took out the key he'd been given when he'd relieved the other guy. He unlocked my shackles.

I stood. "Put your hand on my shoulder. Act as if Grimbold has ordered you to bring me to him, except lead me out of the camp instead. If anyone asks, tell them you're acting under Grimbold's orders. Do you understand?"

"Yes," he told me. "Buddy."

We were fine for about ten paces. Then King Grimbold came around the corner of a tent, and we found ourselves face-to-face.

"What do you be doing?" Grimbold demanded.

And my guard, compelled to do my bidding, answered, "Grimbold's orders."

"I be ordering no such thing!" Grimbold protested. "Bring her back and secure her once more."

My guard tried to stiff-arm Grimbold out of his way.

"Stop," Grimbold ordered.

"Uhm…" I said. What in the world was the way out of this?

My guard waited one second to see what I would bid, then he once again tried to shove past his king.

Grimbold stopped the man the only way he could.

He whipped out his sword and stabbed my escort in the chest.

Well, that was too bad, but I wasn't going to let it slow me down. I made a break for the trees.

Grimbold yelled something in his own language, and barbarians came pouring out of the tents. What felt like about seventeen of them tackled me and jumped on top of me before I'd made it more than a tenth of the way I had to.

They took their time about getting off me, too. Now I know what a football feels like.

My captors dragged my bruised body back to where Grimbold knelt beside the dead guard. Though he spoke in Shelban for my benefit, he addressed his men. "I be having to kill Isen because she be having some sort of power over him. I be thinking this may be the source of her power." He held up the ring to show them.

"No," I assured him.

"Give me her finger," he commanded his men.

With this crowd I was lucky none of them was stupid enough to chop one off and hand it to him. I struggled, because he didn't know that all he had to do was order me to take it, but I knew it was a losing battle. The ring slipped snugly over my finger.

"Now tell me true," he said, "do you have to be doing what I say to you?"

Because he phrased it as a command, I had to answer, and I had to answer truthfully even though I tried to deny it. "Yes," I said. The best I could do was to mumble, my hands over my mouth.

For once everybody caught on quickly. One of my captors pulled my hands behind my back.

Grimbold said, "Tell me true. Do you be knowing the whereabouts of my crown?"

"No," I told him.

Obviously, he would be worried that the ring only worked once. "Stand on one leg," he commanded.

I balanced on one leg.

"Sing a song," he commanded.

Maybe it was because I was standing on one leg ready to tip over, but the first song that came to me was "I'm a Little Teapot."

Those who understood Shelban gleefully translated the stupid little ditty for those who didn't.

With great hilarity, the barbarian horde shouted out suggestions to Grimbold, just in case he couldn't think of enough humiliating things to have me do. Dance, spin, spit—they loved that I couldn't stop any act unless specifically ordered to stop, even if I was simultaneously feeling compelled to complete another action. You try spinning, singing, and spitting at the same time—all balanced on one leg.

Luckily, though Rasmussem has nothing against killing off a paying customer, they won't allow sexual harassment, so that was one thing I didn't need to worry about.

"Pretend you be a chicken," Grimbold said.

My singing changed to clucking, and I couldn't help myself—I began flapping my arms.

Barbarian humor.

I was saved from new indignities when the messenger they'd sent to the castle returned. He spoke in his native language, which I didn't have to understand—I could tell by everyone's sour expressions that Grimbold's offer had been refused.

Now what? Would they kill me?

Maybe, maybe not—Grimbold obviously needed time to consider.

"Go back to the tree," he ordered.

Of course, as soon as I tried walking using only one leg, I immediately tipped over.

"You may be walking on both feetses," Grimbold told me.

I walked back to the tree, still clucking, scratching at the ground with my toes.

Even so, Grimbold didn't trust me and had me once again shackled.

Enough with the chicken routine, I thought at him, but apparently he figured his camp needed the entertainment. I suppose I was lucky he rescinded the commands to sing and spit.

If time had passed slowly for me as a prisoner, it passed even more slowly for me as a chicken. The sun set, the smells of cooking carried to me, and still I couldn't stop clucking and scratching at the earth. Thank goodness I found no worms. I *did* try to lay an egg, though.

After those in the camp had eaten, and after it got dark, they finally became bored with me. They returned to their campfires and tents, leaving me with only one guard. I tucked my head under one arm and tried to sleep.

I was awakened when Grimbold himself came to take

the guard's place. "What will I be doing with you?" he asked. He leaned against the tree all the guards seemed to favor, which was out of my range in case I decided to try to peck him to death. "You truly be a useless thing— useless to me, useless to your own peoples. Maybe I be selling you into slavery to one of the nomad tribes. Or maybe I be selling you to the orcs, which have a tasting for human flesh."

I sure hoped the Rasmussem program would send me back to the start of the game before anyone began roast- ing me on a spit. I tried to tell him that I was sure I could be useful: I was willing to side with him and turn on my royal family. My pleading came out as frantic clucking.

Grimbold started laughing. "I wonder," he said, "when the orcs be cooking you, if you be tasting like human or like chicken."

He was still having a good time with that thought when he gave an odd sound, something like choking but more bubbly. He pitched forward onto the ground, a dark stain spreading beneath him.

A man stepped out from behind the tree—a man I recognized as one of those to whom I'd been talking in the castle guardroom. He was holding a knife in his hand, and I realized he'd just cut Grimbold's throat. It would have been a nice rescue, except for the fact that—with the death of the person whose orders I was compelled to obey—I was destined to spend the rest of this lifetime as a chicken.

"Don't worry, Princess Janine," my rescuer whis- pered so as not to alert any of the barbarians. "The royal family was willing to leave you here, but we were not."

"Cluck, cluck, cluck," I said: *You stupid idiot, you have lousy timing.*

The man looked startled but nonetheless used his sword to try to pry open a link of my chain. "There are others of us in the woods," he assured me, "so don't worry about the barbarians pursuing."

It wasn't my chief worry.

"Cluck, cluck, cluck," I said: *Look over here, you nitwit,* and I pecked at the dead Grimbold's belt, where the key to my shackle was.

The guard was leaning over Grimbold when a darkness detached itself from the shadows and launched itself at him.

"Cwak!" I squawked: *Wolf!* But the man didn't turn in time, and in an instant my would-be rescuer was dead.

I kept on squawking and flapping my arms, but nobody came; apparently the barbarians had had enough chicken antics for the day.

So it isn't to be orcs eating me after all, I thought as the wolf rounded on me.

But then the wolf did a strange thing; it grew longer, and taller, and less hairy. Then it stood on two legs.

In fact, it turned into Wulfgar, clothes and all.

Wulfgar wasn't raised at the castle, people had kept telling me. No kidding. It was the old cliché, only literally true: He'd been raised by wolves.

But so what if he was a shape-shifting wolf? I was willing not to hold that against him if he'd come to rescue me from becoming orc soup du jour.

But I didn't like the look in his eyes as he picked up

the dead guard's knife and approached me. "Poor Princess Janine," he said with a feral grin. "A shame her gallant band of rescuers didn't arrive in time to keep the barbarians from slitting her throat."

I felt the fizziness start even before the knife touched my skin.

The suggestion from London looked good, but the parts are not available locally and need to be obtained from Pittsburgh. We have chartered a flight, but it is very doubtful this will arrive in time.

We are helpless and dependent on the gamer herself, which is not a comfortable position to be in.

There must be something we can do. Keep thinking. Situation critical.

CHAPTER FIFTEEN

Bright Sword, Dim Brother

W*ell*, I thought as I pulled myself out from under Dusty on the hill that overlooked St. Jehan, *how many more stupid mistakes can I make before my time runs out? I guess that explains what killed me that time in the topiary maze.* People had said the queen was there with Wulfgar, but when I'd seen Kenric, I'd assumed they had gotten the wrong son. Right son, just not human at the moment, thank you very much.

What was going on at the Rasmussem Gaming Center? Were they making any headway in overriding the damaged systems so that they could pull me out? Nigel Rasmussem hadn't sounded as though he thought that was likely. I figured if there had been any real possibility of help from their end, Mr. Rasmussem would have played that up to keep me from panicking.

My optimism didn't improve when I found myself once more standing in front of the statue of Saint Bruce the Warrior Poet, realizing I couldn't remember the poem I'd made up for him.

"An Ode to Saint Bruce," I said, which was *all* that I remembered.

Feordina yawned, loudly, while she waited for me to start.

You'd think someone who's created a poem would be able to remember it.

You'd think.

I recited, "Saint Bruce was a warrior poet..."

That wasn't right.

Too late, I remembered that my former first line had ended with *Bruce*, which rhymed nicely with *loose, juice, puce*—all sorts of possibilities. What did *poet* rhyme with?

"He lived in a cave, don't you know it?"

Was that a little whimper I heard from Feordina?

"He wrote sonnets and verses..."

Hmmm.

"...but never said curses..."

As the moment stretched on and on, I saw Feordina avert her gaze from the sword that hung over me. She began to edge her way toward the cave entrance. No doubt red blood makes a mess of green clothing.

Anything is better than nothing. All in a rush, as though that would prevent Saint Bruce from hearing the way-too-many beats in the line, I finished, "He'll give you one chance—please don't blow it."

I was aware of Feordina hurling herself to the floor, out of the way of both sword and blood splatter.

I was sure the sword wavered in Bruce's hand.

But it didn't come down.

Sounding astonished, Feordina said, "He must be in a good mood. Lucky you; he's accepted your poem."

Saint Bruce, I decided, might have been a mighty warrior, but he couldn't have been much of a poet.

So once again Sir Deming and I were off to the castle, with the ring once more tied to my bodice laces. As we rode I tried to decide what I should do once we got there. *Wulfgar:* Obviously I shouldn't trust a man who had wolf instincts and who had already killed me twice. Who knew what might make him lose his temper with me and cause him to bite off my head—literally? Queen Andreanna kept rebuffing all my attempts to be nice to her, so that left Kenric and Abas. I had chosen Kenric once before, and Mr. Rasmussem had warned me away. "Kenric and Sister Mary Ursula don't work well together," he'd said. That was fine with me; Sister Mary Ursula and *I* didn't work well together. I'd been planning on asking Rawdon to be my counselor, anyway.

Except...

Except, Mr. Rasmussem had given me that warning before I ever met Sister Mary Ursula. Did that mean I was *supposed* to work with her?

But she doesn't like magic, I reminded myself.

Maybe I was supposed to ask her to be my adviser, and then I wasn't supposed to follow her advice.

Mr. Rasmussem could have saved us both a lot of aggravation by talking faster and more clearly, I thought. "Talk to your father before you leave St. Jehan," he could have said. "Choose Abas and Sister Mary Ursula, and..."

And whatever.

However many more chances I had left, I suspected I was going to need every one of them.

In the Great Hall, I called, "Abas!" as Queen Andreanna—yet again—started to walk out in a huff after our family reunion.

"What?" the middle-brother prince demanded, sounding like a petulant second grader, for all that he looked like the "after" picture in an advertisement for expensive home-exercise equipment.

"Nice sword work," I said, "back there while you were menacing me."

"Oh." He sounded both surprised and pleased. *Pleased* won out. "I *am* quite good," he admitted.

His mother didn't wait for him, and his brothers were definitely trying to make it out of the room before bursting into laughter.

Abas whipped his sword out of its sheath and moved its edge to within an inch of my nose.

Now what?

But he didn't slit my throat or give me instant rhinoplasty; he said, "Toledo steel."

And because he sounded proud and cheery, I gathered this was a good thing, and said, "How nice."

He began talking about the wonderfulness of Spanish-crafted swords, and gave me the entire history of the manufacture of blades, making my eyelids grow heavy with terms and phrases like "heat tempered" and "alloy" and "strong but not brittle."

All the while, I kept him moving toward the courtyard, wondering if I'd make it in time to rescue the poacher from the guards, or if I'd collapse in a bored stupor first.

The poacher and I lucked out.

"Prince Abas," the guard I now knew was named Penrod called out, "and, uh, Princess Justine..."

"Janine," I told him.

Captain Penrod shrugged and told Abas, "We caught this boy poaching. He killed a deer. The usual punishment?"

I waited to hear Abas's reaction, just as—that first time—Kenric had waited to hear mine.

"Certainly," Abas said. Then, as the boy was just starting to explain how he'd found the deer dead, Abas eagerly offered, "Shall I?" Once more he brought his sword forth with that metal-on-metal whisper-hiss that gives goose bumps to any sensible person.

"No," I told Abas.

I motioned for the second guard, who'd forced the boy to his knees, to let him up again.

Abas frowned in concentration. "'No'?" he repeated, as though unfamiliar with the word.

"My new reign is starting," I announced to one and all. "This is a time to review the old laws and to reconsider the old punishments."

Abas pouted. "No more beheadings?"

I didn't want to turn him against me, since this was obviously a tradition he cherished. "Not for now, anyway. My first days should be a time of clemency, of people starting anew, with nothing from the past held against them. This might be a way to settle the peasant unrest."

"'Clemency'?" Abas repeated, obviously downhearted. "You mean, no more public hangings?"

"Princess—" Penrod said.

"No," I told Abas.

"Princess," Penrod repeated, "a friendly warning here: The peasants need a firm hand or they will run wild and take advantage."

"'Hand,'" Abas echoed. "Can I at least chop off his hand?"

"No," I told him. To Penrod, I said, "I understand what you're saying. But we will try it this way. If that doesn't work, we can always return to the more severe punishments later."

Reluctantly, Penrod released the boy.

Even as the boy ran away, Abas was asking, "But we can still use the rack and thumbscrews?"

"No," I said.

"*Later* might be too late," Penrod warned.

"That's why I need you to keep an eye on things. For instance"—I was remembering how Grimbold and his barbarians had swarmed into the castle courtyard— "please post more guards on the walls to make sure intruders can't get in."

"Hot coals?" Abas asked.

"No." I turned back to Penrod. "It's not just the peasants I want to make happy. More important is keeping the goodwill of you and your men." I didn't add, *So you don't come up behind me and knife me.* "We will have regularly scheduled meetings where you will be free to give me your opinions. All the men." I smiled at the other guard to show I included him, not just the officers. "How *are* things in my army?" I asked.

"Well..." The guard shuffled his feet.

"Do you get paid enough?"

The two exchanged a does-she-really-want-to-know? look.

In the silence, Abas asked, "Fingernail extractor?"

"No."

The two guards told how Counselor Rawdon, who was in charge of giving them their pay, had lately shorted them.

"I will look into that," I promised. "Meanwhile, please see to it that the castle defenses are fortified immediately."

Both men saluted smartly before leaving.

They might still think me weak, but I doubted they'd kill me while I was promising them money.

Abas poked my arm to get my attention. "Stocks?" he asked. "Dunking in the millpond?"

I was tempted to say, "Only for you," but luckily I didn't have time. I had spotted Sister Mary Ursula, who was standing by the well and had evidently heard much of our conversation.

"Blessed is the way of the One," she said.

Abas gave a groan of dismay. "Oh, not her!"

That was a surprise. So apparently *nobody* got along well with her. Well, come to think of it, that wasn't surprising at all. But it made me wonder what, exactly, Mr. Rasmussem was warning me against when he said that she didn't work well with Kenric.

I figured I needed to be polite but firm. "Hello," I said. "I wish I had more time to talk to you, but I don't."

Sister Mary Ursula couldn't be put off *that* easily. "I guessed you might be One," she said.

"One," I said vaguely, "two..." I was going to say, "What's the difference?" But the pairing of *one* and *two* like that brought to mind something else. "One, two, buckle my shoe," I told her. She wasn't the only one who could be obscure.

"Hmmm," she said. "I surmised you were truly One with the world by how you treated that boy. You recognized his Oneness. Many would not have." She glanced at Abas.

Abas scratched his head and yawned.

"I *did* recognize his Oneness," I said, "and, you know, I'd like to talk to you about your becoming my adviser"—could she *really* be the one the Rasmussem program wanted me to favor?—"but I also need to talk to Sir Deming and Counselor Rawdon. I'd like to meet with the three of you together."

"Rawdon," she said, shaking her head.

Because she looked skeptical, I added, "Four of us—*one* meeting."

"One," she echoed, smiling.

"I'm on my way to see Counselor Rawdon right now." Friendly as the guards seemed at my promise to investigate their salary dispute, the way to really get on their good side was to actually hand over the money due them. I suspected that then they'd be willing to forgive me a lot. So, Rawdon first. I asked Sister Mary Ursula, "Could you please find Sir Deming and invite him to the Great Hall?"

"I am One with your wishes," Sister Mary Ursula said. She bowed, at the same time pinching the bridge of her nose with her thumb and forefinger and making a nasal humming noise.

I didn't know if she expected me to do likewise, but I only said, "Thank you."

Though Abas was looking bored, I wanted to keep him near me in case those barbarians made it past Captain Penrod's increased castle defenses. "So," I said, "Toledo-made swords are the best. But, it takes a master swordsman to use one well..."

Abas flexed his biceps.

"Amazing," I told him. "Tell me about yourself as we walk to Rawdon's quarters, all right?"

Abas didn't need to be asked twice.

Luckily, I found that all I needed to contribute to the conversation was a rapt expression and an occasional "Impressive!" or "My! That's interesting." I didn't have to really listen to a word of his explanations about his workout schedule or his past triumphs.

When we got to Rawdon's room, he wasn't there.

"Excuse me." I interrupted Abas in the middle of recounting how he'd saved the king of a neighboring land, who'd been gored by a charging wild boar. Abas had broken off the beast's tusks with his bare hands, then strangled it—which sounded pretty gross to me.

A servant woman was on her knees in the hall, scrubbing the floor. I asked her, "Have you seen Counselor Rawdon?"

"No, my lady. Sorry."

Abas didn't need me to invite him to resume his story—frothy sweat on the animal's hide, and hot stinking breath, and all.

The servant looked as though she wasn't quite finished with what she'd been saying, so I put my hand on Abas's arm to get him to stop.

He didn't take the hint, and I had to say, "Excuse me," again.

The woman told me, "He was in his room earlier, Princess. But he's not there now. I know because I'd just washed the floor in front of his door; and when he left, I had to clean that part again because he left footprints in the wetness; but luckily, he came this way, and I didn't have to redo the whole hall."

She was only two doors down from Rawdon's room, which couldn't have taken her more than five minutes.

Abas started talking again as we walked to the end of the hall. There I saw steps leading both up and down.

"What's upstairs?" I interrupted Abas.

"Defense battlements. Servants' quarters," by which I took him to mean *minor servants* since Rawdon's room was on the second level, along with the family's apartments. Abas didn't miss a beat and resumed talking about the boar.

I led the way back downstairs and flagged down a servant woman who was going from room to room providing fresh flowers for the vases. She said she had not seen Rawdon.

I poked my head into the Great Hall. Sir Deming was sitting on one of the petitioners' benches that lined the walls. He was definitely drooping, his elbows on his knees, his head resting in his hands while Sister Mary Ursula, sitting next to him, told him, "... and if you acknowledge the cow's Oneness with you, and then ask her politely, she *will* give forth sweeter milk. It's the same with turnips—"

"*There* you are," Deming said, sounding—for this once—happy to see me.

"Sorry," I said. "Not quite ready yet. We haven't been able to find Rawdon."

"I'd be glad to help you look," Deming volunteered. "Maybe Abas..." He glanced from the still-chattering prince to the still-chattering nun, obviously thinking to pair them off.

"Sorry." I backed out, closing the doors. In case of barbarian attack, Abas would be a good man to have by my side. If he *noticed* we were under attack, that is. I couldn't be sure he'd stop bragging about his physical prowess long enough to notice much of anything.

A door opened and a pair of male servants came out, carrying a platter with an entire roast pig, complete with apple. It must be time for the midday meal that I had missed the last time I was here. I realized that the hunger I'd felt in the barbarians' camp had evaporated once the game restarted and set me back down in the morning. But now, as this new day progressed, my stomach was once again rumbling—not that I found a dead porker with fruit in its mouth appetizing.

"Excuse me," I said to the men, "but have either of you seen Rawdon?"

"Not since he stopped by the kitchen asking for field rations," one said.

"'Field rations?'" I repeated. "You mean, like, to take when you're going on a trip?"

The man nodded.

That was odd. Sister Mary Ursula hadn't insulted him in this round of the game, so he had no reason to leave. "Did he say where he was going?"

Both men shook their heads.

I moved out of their way and told Abas, "Let's check with the captain of the guard to see if Rawdon has left yet."

Still talking, Abas followed me outside. While I hadn't been paying attention, he'd shifted to tournaments he had fought in, and the proper technique for splitting a lance, which, apparently, was a desirable thing.

I glanced at the wagon that was still parked by the supply door, even though I assumed the increased guards I'd ordered had prevented any barbarians from sneaking in. I was just turning my eyes away, when I noticed a shadow that moved beneath the wagon.

"Abas, look out!" I shouted. "Behind the wagon!"

There was the hiss of an arrow.

But no *thunk!* of impact.

Abas had caught the arrow midflight.

So maybe there was something to be said for brawn, even unaccompanied by brain.

With a bellow, Abas went tearing behind the wagon before the archer had a chance to notch another arrow.

Hiding didn't seem a kingly thing to do; I might survive the attack, but such obvious cowardice wouldn't win any loyalty from my people. So, fighting my instincts, I ran toward the wagon also, yelling all the while, "Intruder alert! Intruder alert!" which sounded more science fiction than fantasy, but there was no time to worry about vocabulary, and I needed more guards immediately, because I knew from last time that there were three barbarians in the courtyard—and three against one wasn't fair odds, even if the one was used to fighting off wild boar with his bare hands.

On the far side of the wagon, I saw Abas was doing quite well without me. Since he didn't have a bow, he'd simply used his caught arrow as a dagger; it was sticking out of the chest of one of the barbarians, now dead. Abas had kicked the other archer in the face, and while that man rolled on the ground, Abas was engaged in a sword fight with the third man—the man I recognized as King Grimbold.

"Wait—" I started to tell Abas, but in that moment, his sword swept off Grimbold's head.

Was that an *oops!* or not?

Abas turned to the surviving, though injured, man.

"Abas," I said, "put your sword away. He's obviously not going anywhere. I need to ask him a couple questions."

Grumpily, Abas put his sword back in its scabbard.

I was aware of members of the castle guard on the wall, firing arrows over the side into the surrounding woods.

"Four down," Penrod reported to me. "The rest have

escaped into the forest. Do you want us to pursue them, or concentrate on our defenses here?"

Just what I needed—another decision. I didn't yet know if we needed to attack the barbarian camp, but in any case I didn't want to send the majority of my men chasing after a small raiding party, leaving us defenseless; nor did I want a small party of my men stumbling into the barbarian encampment.

"Send two dozen men after them—with clear instructions not to pursue farther than . . ."—I had to estimate what was a good distance—". . . five miles. If they haven't caught the barbarians by then, have them come back."

While Penrod selected which men of the group should go, I turned my attention to the wounded barbarian. He was sitting up now, his back supported by the castle wall, his hands over his bruised and bleeding mouth. No doubt he was missing several teeth from Abas's kick. His voice was slurred because of his injuries, which didn't help his accent. "You be done killing our king," he moaned. "You be done killing King Grimbold."

I knew that already, but everybody else turned to look at the headless corpse.

"You're one of the northern barbarians, aren't you?" I asked.

The man nodded.

"That's one," Abas said.

Of course there was only one barbarian left; we could all see that. Or was Sister Mary Ursula beginning to wear off on him? Ignoring Abas's irrelevant remark, I asked the barbarian, "Why did you come?"

134

"To be kidnapping you, as the new king," he said. "To be forcing you to be handing on the crown of King Brecc the Slayer."

Of course, I knew all this from last time. But I had to ask or I wouldn't be able to explain to anybody *how* I knew. Before I could ask about the location of his camp and the number of people in it—which was what I really wanted to know—Abas announced, "And that's two."

"What—" I started to ask Abas, when he picked up the wagon and brought the back end down on the barbarian's head, like smushing a bug.

For a few seconds, I couldn't even get my mouth to work.

"What?" Abas demanded, seeing my amazed, angry face. "You said not to use my sword."

"I said I wanted to question him."

"You said you wanted to ask him 'a couple of questions.' A *couple* is two." He shook his head as though unused to dealing with such stupidity. "Everybody knows that," he said. "A couple. Two. Same thing. Didn't your foster parents teach you how to count?"

While I was left speechless, he scratched his belly and said, "That roast pig sure looked good to me. Anybody else ready to eat?"

And with that he went back into the castle, the guards following.

CHAPTER SIXTEEN

Lunch

In a moment only Captain Penrod and I remained.

Penrod knelt in the dust at my feet. He took out his sword and handed it up to me on outstretched palms. "Obviously, I didn't post enough guards, Princess Janine. You could have been killed, and it would have been my fault."

Was he officially resigning his post, or did he expect me to punish him by chopping off his head?

I told him, "Take the sword back. We"—I was getting better at remembering that royal *we*—"simply need to be more vigilant from now on. Come on, apparently it's time to eat." I wasn't going to miss lunch again.

Penrod *did* accept the sword back, then started with me toward the Great Hall.

"Speaking of being vigilant," I said, "did your guards see Counselor Rawdon leave?"

Penrod nodded. "He frequently goes to visit his aged mother in the country."

"Very commendable," I said. "But you'd think he could skip it on the day the new king arrives."

"I gather he's her sole support," Penrod said, "and she's the sole support of several grandchildren from Rawdon's two brothers and three sisters, who all died. He brings great bundles of food for them, but seemingly it's never enough. This morning his packhorse was exceptionally laden."

"Sounds like the family has had incredibly bad luck," I said. I got distracted by the thought that I knew all about grandmothers raising kids, but at least my parents were still both alive. "Any idea when he'll be back?"

"He's said she lives in the town of Fairfield, which is two hours' ride off to the west. Usually when he goes, he spends the majority of the day with her."

We arrived at the Hall, where lunch had already started. The two thrones had been pushed against the farthest wall, right to the leaded-glass window. Dozens of long tables had been brought in, at which people sat, evidently divided by rank. The royal family was at one table at the far end of the room, near the thrones, away from the drafts from the doors and from the bustle of servants toting platters of food and refilling people's cups. I couldn't help but notice that they'd started without me and that they'd left no room for me.

Sir Deming and Sister Mary Ursula sat with a group that had to be the queen's ladies-in-waiting, for I recognized Lady Cynthia from a couple games back. Sister Mary Ursula was still talking to Deming, even though he'd arranged to sit two people down from her. Those servants who weren't serving the food were at one cluster of tables, and then there were lots of other tables for the guards, although there were many empty places for those who were away, busy manning the walls or pursuing barbarians. Dogs roamed among the tables, snapping up fallen scraps of food (which would have outraged my grandmother, who believes dogs belong outside, guarding the house or helping the blind).

Penrod hesitated, not knowing whether I was finished with him and if he should go sit with his men.

I couldn't start making decisions if the adviser I was most inclined to speak with wasn't here. I asked Penrod, "Do you think we could send one of your men to fetch Rawdon?"

Penrod immediately tapped one of his men on the shoulder. "Go to Fairfield," he ordered. "The princess commands Rawdon's presence."

The guard stood, shoving a half loaf of bread under his arm and as much food as he could fit into his mouth. I told him, "Be sure to tell Counselor Rawdon he'll be welcome to return to his family in a few more days." Rawdon would be of little use to me if he was ticked off at having his family outing cut short. "Be polite," I called after the man, then remembered to add, "please."

It suddenly occurred to me that for this particular game, the magic-users had not been summoned. "And Captain," I said to Penrod, "please send a message to . . ." Was it Xenos or Uldemar who had the scrying glass? "I'd like to call to the castle those who know magic."

"Orielle, Uldemar, and Xenos," Penrod said. He smacked another of his men on the arm.

"Thank you," I said. "In all haste, please."

Finally I went to the head table.

They were all sitting on benches along one side of the table: Queen Andreanna, Wulfgar, Abas, and Kenric. The queen was making fun of someone I didn't know, an abbot who apparently was very hard of hearing—in fact, practically deaf. Andreanna was imitating this poor guy, saying, "'What did you say? *What?* Oh, you said you couldn't have been the one to murder the blacksmith because you had *no reason* to do it? I thought you said you had *a Norwegian* do it.'"

Very politically incorrect.

The princes were all so engrossed in this merriment that by sheerest coincidence not a one of them noticed me standing there with no place to sit.

They were spread out—four on a bench that looked long enough for six or seven. Their butts weren't *that* big. If they'd all moved over just a bit, there'd have been room for me.

The Hall still buzzed with conversation, but I knew everyone was waiting to see how I would react. Would I be intimidated and slink off to another table? Would I meekly request my family to make space for me? Would I make a scene and *demand* that they make space for me?

I crooked my finger at one of the servants. The noise level was so high, I had to put my mouth to his ear to make sure I was heard. "Get me the king's throne," I ordered.

The servant was aghast. "Surely not for eating in?" Was he worried I'd dribble gravy on the velvet cushion?

He glanced around and pointed out a spare bench, a short one, made for three skinny butts, or two regular-size ones, or one royal one.

Yeah, I thought, *and do what? Set up a TV tray?* "The throne," I repeated.

The conversation abruptly stopped when the servant, with the help of another man, picked up the throne.

Staggering under its weight, they carried it toward where the royal family sat, then saw that—unless the royals moved their bench (and why would they, when they hadn't budged yet?)—there was no room.

I pointed to my feet, to indicate, *Right here.*

The servants came around to where I was, and placed the throne dead center on that side of the table.

I sat down and looked into the startled faces of my family. "There." I smiled brightly and settled my skirt as though it was a voluminous gown, like the queen's. "Isn't this nice?"

And it was, except that the roast pig had been placed before them, so I was looking at his curlicued rear end, not the world's best view.

A servant came rushing up with a bowl of rose-petaled water and a towel, to wash and dry my hands. Other servants provided a dish heaped with slabs of roast pork and luscious fresh fruits, and a cup of mead (which is a sweet beer or wine or something, disgusting in my point of view, and I'm amazed Rasmussem gets away with serving alcohol—even virtual alcohol—to minors).

Kenric leaned forward and told me, "You're sitting on the serving side of the table."

"No," I said firmly, "all of you are."

He considered that for a moment, then gave his extraordinary smile that had caught my notice during the promos.

Wulfgar glared; I was beneath the queen's notice, so she angled herself on the bench to face Wulfgar and began talking to him about the quality of the peaches; and Abas decided I needed an instant replay of his battle against the three barbarians in the courtyard.

I was pleased to note that Wulfgar didn't tear into his meat as a beast would but ate with the same degree of table manners as everybody else. *Those* manners were about equal to what you'd see in an elementary school cafeteria. I could live with that.

"You *were* fantastic," I assured Abas when he paused to take a breath. "One of them mentioned something about a crown—the crown of Brecc." I looked at each of them in turn and was able to tell nothing. "Any of you know anything about that?"

Kenric said, "Father won a crown from one of the barbarian kings."

"Won how? You mean he killed him? Or overcame him in battle? Or he won it in a poker game?" My subconscious tried to warn me the people of this time would not play poker; the phrase *a game of dice* bubbled up.

But the Rasmussem programs are sophisticated enough to ignore most anachronistic phrases and references, otherwise the game would constantly be delayed by the characters saying things like, "*OK?* I do not understand this *OK* of which you speak." Kenric blinked.

Perhaps *his* subconscious—if he had one—told him poker must be some peasant gambling game he'd never heard of before. Or perhaps he just chose to ignore one of the many inane things I'd said. He said, "He won it in a tournament."

Abas interrupted. "I wasn't old enough to participate in that particular tournament except in the capacity of a page helping the squires help the knights get into their armor, but I remember it well. Two years later was my first—"

"In a moment, Abas," I said. "So your father won the tournament, winning the loser's horse and equipment."

"Yes," both Abas and Kenric said. But Abas was inclined to add a blow-by-blow account of the event.

I went ahead and talked right over him. "But if your father won the crown fairly, why do the barbarians feel they have a right to demand it back?"

"Because they *are* barbarians," Abas said.

Which I would have accepted, but Kenric's lips twitched and he chose that moment to lift his cup to his mouth.

"What?" I demanded.

Kenric answered with a question of his own. "Who said anything about winning it fairly?"

"Kenric!" his mother snapped. "That's no way to talk about your father."

From the look he gave her, I gathered he wasn't used to hearing her defend King Cynric's good name.

"Well," Abas admitted, "there *were* certain questions..."

"He cheated," I said. "You're saying he won the

142

crown by cheating. So now the barbarians want the crown back and—in fact—they probably have every right to it."

Kenric shrugged, indicating his indifference to moral nuances.

Abas spoke slowly so I would understand. "No, he won the event, so he won the crown."

Wulfgar was gnawing, with alarming energy, every last bit of meat off a bone, but at least he had the bone raised to his mouth, rather than sinking his face into the pig carcass.

Queen Andreanna was making one of the dogs stand on its hind legs and beg for a strip of meat.

"So where is this crown?" I asked.

"I don't know," Kenric said.

Abas shook his head to indicate he didn't, either.

"Wulfgar?"

"Dunno."

"Your Highness?"

She gave me a blank look. "I'm sorry, what? Were you saying something? I wasn't listening."

Though I'd already seen she had been, I explained, "The crown your late husband won from the barbarian king at the tournament several years back, whatever happened to it?"

"I'm sure I have no idea," she told me.

I summoned one of the servants. "Could you please get that bench"—I indicated the one I had been offered earlier—"and bring it here, then invite Sir Deming and Sister Mary Ursula to join us."

143

"On the serving side of the table?" the servant asked.

"On *this* side of the table," I corrected him.

When the two advisers had sat down, I explained about the crown and asked if they knew where it was.

"Perhaps in the king's treasure room?" Sister Mary Ursula suggested.

Deming shook his head. "He gave it to the dragon."

"What dragon?" I asked.

Deming sniffed at my ignorance. "The one that was ravaging the southern provinces eight years ago, burning fields, scattering livestock, devastating manor houses, demanding maiden sacrifices."

The faintest hint of imposed memory tickled at the edges of my brain. I'd only been six, and the southern provinces were nearly a week's journey from the safety of St. Jehan, but I had heard people talking.

I said, "Excuse me, I don't understand. This dragon was eating cows, horses, and maidens, and then King Cynric bought him off by giving him a crown that had been won at an iffy tournament?"

Deming rolled his eyes, and the queen gave him a sympathetic look like, *I know, I know.* Deming said, "Dragons like gold."

"And a crown," Sister Mary Ursula added, "that would make the dragon feel as One with all the other kings."

OK. I guessed it made sense. "Do we know where this dragon lives?" I asked.

"No," "Nope," "Haven't a clue," they all told me.

"Any idea how we can find out?"

"No," "Nope," "Haven't a clue," they all repeated.

But then Deming speculated, "Maybe one of the magic-users knows something or could find out."

Waiting for the magic-users again. Estimated time of arrival: tomorrow, if I remembered correctly from last time. And I did. I was working on a deadline—never mind the awful pun.

"Oooo, magic," Sister Mary Ursula said. "Nasty stuff. Best to keep away from it."

"As much as possible," I assured her, just to keep her happy.

Deming sighed. "If," he said, sounding as though each moment of speaking politely was an effort, "*if* you're determined to return the crown of the barbarian king, may I point out to you that the king is, in fact, currently separated from his head, thanks to our prince Abas—and I would consider this a serious drawback to the enjoyment of wearing a crown."

"Good point," I said. "We'll send a messenger to the barbarian camp, apologizing for the unfortunate death of their king, which happened by mischance since he did not openly declare himself but led a raiding party into the castle courtyard. As a sign of our goodwill, we will forgive this raid and return the crown to King Grimbold's successor."

Deming pursed his thin lips. "Do you think they'd accept *an apology* for the killing of their brand-new king?"

Andreanna was looking directly at me as she answered, "*I* would. Accidents happen."

I could imagine. I forced a smile at her. To Deming, I said, "It's the best we can do. See to the sending of a messenger. Now, what about the unrest among the peasants?"

"Our laws are too harsh," Sister Mary Ursula said.

"Too lenient," Deming countered.

"I liked the death penalty," Abas said, "before you abolished it. Can we bring it back now?"

We never really came to a conclusion. I felt I didn't know enough to ask the right questions, and nobody volunteered much of interest.

The servants were cleaning up the remains of the meal, and we were the only ones still sitting. The guards I'd sent in pursuit of the barbarian raiding party returned, having lost the trail in the woods. Another set of guards were sent to find the barbarian camp to offer official regrets for Grimbold's death. Meanwhile, I needed to wait for Rawdon's return to make a decision about the peasants, and I needed to wait for the magic-users to do anything about tracking down the dragon who had Brecc the Slayer's crown.

"Well," I said, looking at my filthy sheepherder's dress, "maybe now is the time for me to clean up."

"Oooo," Sister Mary Ursula said, "I have an extra dress you could use."

Since she looked as though she wore Feordina the Knitter's hand-me-downs, I said, "Maybe something from one of the ladies-in-waiting would be more appropriate."

"I can arrange that," she told me.

She showed me to one of the second-floor rooms, but it wasn't Lady Cynthia's. This lady's name was Bliss. One glance told me that if Bliss shopped at the mall, she would need clothes whose size included at least a couple of Xs.

"Oh, this is such an honor!" Bliss giggled, so pleased, her feet practically fluttered off the ground. "Thank you, thank you, thank you for choosing me."

"Well..." I started.

"I have *so many* clothes," she told me, "because"— she leaned forward to whisper as though we shared a secret—"I do have a bit of a weight problem."

OK, I thought. *This might work.*

But as she flung dresses out of her clothes chest onto her bed, I saw that her size varied from big to very big.

"Isn't this a pretty red?" she asked.

"It is," I agreed. I couldn't ask for Lady Cynthia by name because I had never been introduced to her in this lifetime. And I hated to ask for just any other lady, because Bliss was *so* enthusiastic.

Did Rasmussem want me to be nice to her and make her my friend for a particular reason? Or were they only intent on making me look like a fool?

Still, I couldn't look any worse than I did now.

So I chose the red velvet dress, and—after I finally got my bath, and with a lot of tucks and gathers and a belt— eventually got the dress around me. I had just fastened the magic ring around my neck with a length of ribbon when someone knocked at Lady Bliss's door.

"Captain of the guard," Penrod announced from the hallway, "looking for Princess Janine."

Bliss opened the door for him. "And doesn't she look exquisite?" she asked.

I think *clean* was really the best we could say in all honesty, but Penrod didn't have time to quibble. "Bad news, Highness," he announced.

"Regarding the messengers dispatched to try to make peace with the barbarian camp?" I asked, though it seemed too soon for them to have had any result yet.

Penrod shook his head. "Regarding Counselor Rawdon."

Now what?

"The man I sent to Fairfield just returned. He said there is no one in Fairfield answering the description of Penrod's mother."

"But you're sure it was Fairfield that Rawdon said he was going to?" I asked.

"Positive," Penrod said.

I tried to work this out. "Rawdon said Fairfield, and he carried bundles of food for his family..." It suddenly struck me that when I'd asked the servants carrying the pig if they'd seen Rawdon, one of them had said something about Rawdon getting field rations for his trip.

Surely field rations weren't carried in great bundles?

"How long has Rawdon been bringing supplies to his mother?" I asked.

"About three months."

"And how long has it been since you've been having trouble getting paid?"

Slowly, Penrod said, "About three months."

I was beginning to get a sick feeling in the pit of my stomach. "Did I hear somebody say something about the king having a treasure room?" I asked.

Penrod took me there, a locked chamber off the king's own bedroom. Guards had to kick in the door because Rawdon had the key. It was an enormous room, bigger even than the king's bedchamber.

And, of course, the room was totally empty.

CHAPTER SEVENTEEN

Treasure Hunt

The next door we broke down was the one to Rawdon's room. I hoped to find some nice clues indicating where he'd be likely to head now that he'd made off with all the loot from my treasury. But we found nothing—no handy map where *X* marked the spot, no travel brochures from sunny Aruba, no abandoned diary with the crucial page ripped out (but that a clever detective could read by studying the impressions on the page beneath). Rawdon had left behind the rugs on the floors, the tapestries on the walls, and all the furniture; but his clothes were gone and there were no personal items or papers—nothing to show this wasn't simply a spare guest room.

"Any thoughts?" I asked Penrod.

He gestured his men out of the room, then closed the door for privacy. In a low voice he told me, "The news is spreading already—there's no way to contain it."

It took a moment for his meaning to sink in. The guards had not been properly paid for the last couple months, and even now those who knew about the theft were telling the others that the new king had no money left with which to pay them.

"What are the men likely to do?"

"Leave," Penrod said, "most of them. They'll try to find employment elsewhere."

Sure, there was that nice barbarian camp in the vicinity that could probably use some new recruits, being down a few men since morning.

And even if my guards didn't join the barbarians, how long could the castle stand without anyone to defend it?

"I'll stay," Penrod assured me, "of course." It was nice to have him feeling indebted to me. He continued, "I'll try to convince the men to give you a day or two. I'll tell them you're tracking Rawdon down, that it's just a matter of time before you recover the treasury."

"You need to practice saying it with a straight face, or no one will believe you," I warned him. "Where do you think I should start looking?"

Of course it wasn't that easy.

"I don't know, Princess."

Obviously that was part of the fun of the game, figuring that out.

"Maybe I should start in Fairfield," I said. "You said Rawdon always headed off in that direction. Just because the people there never heard of Rawdon's mother, that doesn't mean they didn't see *him*. And wherever Rawdon was taking those bundles of money, it was within a day's journey of here. I'll take men with me, and wagons to carry the money should we recover it." Talk about optimism.

"Do you want me to accompany you or to stay here?" Penrod asked.

He was the only friendly one I'd met—besides Lady Bliss. Well, and Rawdon had been friendly, but now I saw that didn't count. Still, Penrod was more useful here. "Stay," I advised. "Try to talk the men into remaining here. Explain that if they leave now, they've already worked the majority of the month without pay. The worst that can happen if they stay is a couple more days of work without pay. On the other hand, if things work out, they'll get paid when we get back. Bonuses for anyone who stays."

"I'll assign loyal men to accompany you and to guard the treasure on its way back." This time he managed to keep his skepticism from showing on his face.

My good friend, my carefully chosen ally, Abas, refused to come with me, saying if I was just leaving now, I'd be away half the night, and he'd miss his weight-lifting exercises for the evening. But he promised if I *did* get back in time, he'd let me watch.

As for my advisers, Sir Deming told me to ask my officially chosen adviser, and Sister Mary Ursula was going to be busy with her soul-cleansing skinny-dipping-in-the-moonlight routine. As my official adviser, she advised me to join her.

So off I headed to Fairfield.

I rode ahead with five men, leaving the rest of the

squadron to accompany the slower-moving wagons. Guessing I'd need all the time I could get to find Rawdon's stash, I hadn't even bothered to switch out of Bliss's extravagant dress and into more sensible clothes.

Fairfield was much bigger than St. Jehan, which was no surprise: Some of my friends at St. John the Evangelist School have *families* that are bigger than St. Jehan. But Fairfield had a few hundred people, which doesn't sound like much until you begin to think about questioning every one of them.

We arrived at dusk, and our first stop was a tavern. The red dress got a few whistles from having worked its way down so that it revealed more than I wanted revealed, but nobody remembered seeing anyone fitting Rawdon's description.

We stopped at Fairfield's three other taverns. Some of the people had been around that afternoon when my messenger had been looking for Rawdon's mother. They remembered the messenger but not Rawdon. "Isn't there anyone in Fairfield," I asked the tavern keeper at the last place, "who's a bit of a busybody, who sits around watching people, and always likes a bit of gossip?"

"Information costs," the tavern keeper said, "and you and your group haven't spent a penny here yet."

"I'm the new king," I said. "I'm the one who'll be setting your taxes next year—are you sure you want to talk to me about paying for things?"

He directed me to his mother-in-law, who thought she'd seen a man who might have been Rawdon, but she couldn't be sure when or where. She suggested I talk to a friend of hers—a guy who couldn't help but said he got a lot of his news from the goose girl. The goose girl's mother complained that it was past her daughter's bedtime, but she got the child up when one of my men—the only one of us with any cash at all—loaned me a copper penny to pay her if the information was good.

Wiping sleep from her eyes, the eight-year-old assured me that she had seen Rawdon.

"When was the last time?" I asked, suspecting the mother might have coached her so that they could keep the penny.

"Today," she said. "He was carrying big bundles of something or other, bigger than he usually does."

Which was exactly how I had described him to her.

But then she added, "He was looking even more fidgety than usual."

Fidgety. How else would a man who'd just made off with a king's treasury look? Except I hadn't said *who* Rawdon was or why we were searching for him. Still, it could have been clever reasoning on the girl's part. Seeing that we were pursuing someone, she might guess that that someone had been worried about pursuit.

"How do you mean, 'fidgety'?" I asked.

"Looking over his shoulder to see if anybody was watching," the girl said. "Pretending to be just sitting there in the shade, eating his bread and cheese, until no one was looking."

"Except you," I guessed.

She snorted. "Grown-ups don't even *see* children unless we're bothering them."

Well, that was certainly something I'd experienced.

"And then?" I asked. "Once he thought no one was looking?"

"He went into the old church."

Church? A man who was making off with the entire assets of a kingdom?

"What church?" I hadn't seen any church in Fairfield.

"The one the barbarians burned down during the time of my grandmother's grandmother's grandmother."

At least it wasn't anything *I* had caused to happen. "But you said—"

"It's mostly ruins," the girl said. "The timbers burned, and the roof caved in, and the walls collapsed. But the way the stones fell, there are tunnels. And if you can find it, one of the tunnels leads down to the catacombs."

Catacombs might be useful for hiding stuff.

"Have you ever been down to these catacombs?" I asked.

The girl glanced at her mother. "No."

Neither the mother nor I believed her. The mother twisted the little girl's ear until the poor child squealed. The mother said, "I told you to stay away from there. That's no place to be playing—it's too dangerous."

"Yes, Mama," the girl squealed.

"You wait until your father gets home," the mother warned. "You are in *so* much trouble."

"Excuse me," I said. "We're not finished yet. Are you saying children play in the catacombs?"

"No," the girl said, but her mother still had a grip on that ear and warned, "Better not."

"*Other* children," I clarified.

Still, the girl said, "No. It's too scary. We peeked in once or twice. *Ow!* The boys sometimes dare each other to run in, circle the marker, and run back out again. *Ow! Mama!* But they always run as fast as they can, in case of ghosts. Nobody ever goes past the first room. *Ow!*"

"How many rooms are there?"

The girl shook her head that she didn't know. The mother shrugged. "The church is in front of the hill, and the hill is where we buried our dead before we started the cemetery."

I said, "We're willing to pay if you can show us how to get to that first room."

"Pay with what?" the mother asked. "You had to borrow for what you've promised us already. Speaking of which . . ." She held out her hand.

I glanced at the guard to see if he had any more coins with him. He shook his head.

"Can you describe the way to us?" I asked the girl.

She nodded, and I handed over the penny to her mother.

THE GUARDS didn't have any money, but they *did* have the supplies to fashion the torches we'd need if we were going to be exploring underground.

The church was, as the child and her mother had indicated, in ruins. I could see why the mother was frantic to keep her daughter away.

We found the larch tree she said marked the opening that led under the rubble. Crawling in was the tightest squeeze. After that, the pathway, though cramped, was well-worn enough by hands and knees, that we easily found our way through: right turn at the fallen and burned beam; right turn at the darker stone that was shaped like a round loaf of rye bread; ignore the wide way, which looked like where you should go but dead-ended a few feet beyond; left turn under the slab of rock as long and wide as a man.

The biggest danger was crawling while carrying torches—the risk of those in back burning the butts of those in front. Crawling in a dress five sizes too big was no fun, either. I was worried I was going to crawl right out of it.

Suddenly the stone rubble ended and we were on a dirt floor, the ceiling just high enough that the second tallest guard could stand upright. I readjusted my dress the best I could.

I saw the marker the goose girl had talked about the town boys having to circle, if they dared. It looked like a waist-high stone pedestal on which rested a stone coffin. *Was* it just a marker, showing what lay beyond, or was it, in fact, the final resting place of the first dead person?

Too late to be grossed out by that. Beyond the marker, the walls had been scooped out and wooden shelves had been built into them, three high, lining both sides. But these had begun to decay and disintegrate, and many had tipped or collapsed entirely. What the shelves had held was, of course, the stuff and purpose of catacombs: dead bodies. Just within our torchlight, we could see a doorway. Another room. Presumably more bodies. They had been laid head to toe, one after another after another, three tiers and a half-dozen sets of shelves on either side, with just enough room to let pass a small wagon through the center. My feet wobbled on the ruts the wheels had made, carrying generations' worth of Fairfield citizenry to their final rest.

Some of the bundles were wrapped in linen, badly tattered now so that I could glimpse hints of hair and mummified flesh. Other bodies hadn't been wrapped so well, or the shrouds had deteriorated more. There were bones lying on the floor—either flung by the collapse of shelves or scattered by scavenging animals. The place smelled of humans returning to dust: a lung-coating, throat-clogging smell that wasn't the same but reminded me of the nursing-home room where my grandfather had died.

One of the guards stepped forward and shone his smoking torch on the side of the pedestal on which the coffin rested.

Janine de St. Jehan didn't know how to read, but Giannine Bellisario had had enough years of Catholic education to know that *Requiescat pacem* means, "Rest in peace."

The guard knew more than I did. He rattled off the rest of the Latin words then translated: "Rest in peace. Let none but the dead pass through here."

The guards looked spooked.

I was, too. Still, "The dead didn't rest themselves here by themselves," I told them. "It must be safe for living people to *pass through*."

I took the lead, trying to ignore the shadows that my torch sent dancing on the walls.

No sign of treasure, which made sense, since Rawdon wouldn't have risked an especially daring Fairfield child stumbling upon his hoard. It had to be hidden farther in.

We walked through into the second room, which was identical to the first, and then the third. Some of the remains had been scattered at a time when people had still been visiting, for bones were piled up along the sides: the skulls resting on the floor, their empty eye sockets watching us. But that wasn't the important thing about the third room. The important thing about the third room was that there were two doorways leading out of it.

Uh-oh. I shone the torch into the right-hand room. In the gloomy distance, I could make out three doorways.

The guard who had shone his torch into the left-hand room said, "Five."

Five? I looked, just in case he could read Latin but couldn't count. Yup, five. So, eight possible ways to go.

A quick look showed that all the routes had the wagon tracks and footprints of the people—now long dead themselves—who'd brought the bodies in. None of the footprints stood out as being fresher than the rest, so it was impossible to tell which direction Rawdon had taken.

Oh, boy. A maze. And here I'd been hoping the topiary maze was the only one I'd have to deal with.

"All right..." I said. People around here weren't too good at thinking on their own or making suggestions; that was supposed to be my job. "First thing we'll need to do is go back to where the rubble was and get some stones so that we can scratch marks into the doorways. That way we can tell where we've been and not get lost. We'll divide into three pairs. You"—I pointed to Latin boy—"and I will go together. Whenever we have two choices, we'll take the right-hand route, and we'll mark the doorway with an arrow to show which way we passed."

To the second pair, I said, "You two will always take the left-hand route. When you make *your* marks, make two arrows—one on top of the other—so that your mark will be different from ours and we can all immediately see who's passed, going in which direction."

I subdivided the last pair of men. "You will wait in the first room with a supply of torches we can come back for in case we're in here long enough to need them"—*I hope not, I hope not,* I thought—"and in case one of the search parties actually finds the stolen booty." *Please let it be soon.* To the last man, the tall one, I said, "And you will wait outside the church, so you can flag down the wagons when they arrive."

It was, I think, a good plan. The guards didn't disagree with me, but then, they probably wouldn't have, no matter what.

My partner and I went from room to room to room. Rawdon wouldn't have hidden the stolen money one coin at a time on individual corpses. Spreading the treasure out like that would make it too difficult to recover. Or so I told myself so that I wouldn't have to frisk the dead bodies. Already I suspected bugs were gathering on my dragging hem, and I worried about bugs dropping down the front of my dress—bugs that had been crawling on and eating corpses.

And then we came to a room just like all the others, except that there were bodies not only on either side but on the third wall also, the one opposite the doorway by which we'd entered. And there were no other doorways.

Just as I was turning back, convinced we'd reached a dead end, my partner whispered, "What's that?"

And at that moment I, too, caught the flutter of movement just beyond the glow of our torches.

But there was nothing there.

I was leery of approaching, but if something was moving, that might be a sign of a secret doorway. *You HAVE to look,* I thought, and forced myself to lean in close over one of the bodies. I held my breath against the stale, dusty smell, and kept the torch up and away from the cobwebs that hung thickly. *Let it be a current of air,* I hoped, *and not a swarm of maggots.*

Something brushed my arm.

I squealed and just barely managed to keep from dropping the torch onto a corpse.

Cobweb. Just a loose piece of cobweb, despite my precautions.

My partner hadn't fled, but neither had he come closer to make sure I wasn't under attack by Rawdon, the undead, or any other threat.

There were no maggots; there probably couldn't have been on such a long-dead body. Nor was there any breath of air indicating a room beyond, no marks on floor or ceiling where an otherwise hidden door might scrape.

So what had moved?

"Nothing here," I told him. "We have overactive imaginations."

He sighed. I sighed. I realized we'd both been holding our breaths.

We backtracked through the maze, then took the next unexplored path, to begin again.

It didn't get any better. Over and over in various rooms one or the other of us would jump, sure we saw something, sure we felt something brush against us, sure somebody or something was watching. But every time we looked directly, we never saw anything.

Probably nerves, I told myself. Probably a trick of the eyes, where torchlight and shadow met. Probably.

We could also hear what sounded like whispers.

Probably the other team, I told myself. . . .

Until our paths crossed, and with none of the four of us speaking, we once again heard—just at the threshold of sensation—what may or may not have been voices.

No wonder the Fairfield kids were afraid of ghosts.

It must be some strange acoustical property of the interconnecting caves, I thought, *the guard, left behind to make torches, talking to himself to help pass the time.* But when we went back for more torches, I didn't ask him if he was.

The wagons arrived sometime between our second and third torches, and still no sign of Rawdon or the treasure.

I considered whether I should order the rest of the men to join the search but worried that if there were any tracks farther in, they'd get trampled.

Some of the tucks and gathers of my dress had come loose, and I was dragging what felt like yards of velvet brocade along the packed earth path. At one point when I thought I must have picked up about five pounds of dirt, I turned to shake out the dust and saw that I had, in fact, snagged part of somebody's rib cage. I shook it loose and kicked it toward the wall, where I wouldn't step on it on my way back through here.

I was sure we'd been looking for at least the three days of game play.

Even if Rawdon had become worried that we would be on his trail, I assured myself, he couldn't have removed the entire treasury from here and relocated it in the brief half-day he'd had. It *must* still be here.

I *had* to have the treasure to be able to keep the guards working for me, which I obviously needed to do. But I was hot and sweaty despite the chill air, and I was cranky and I was tired and I was hungry.

It was so frustrating, I wanted to bite someone.

And the thought of biting made me think of Wulfgar.

We couldn't see any trace of Rawdon's passing down any of the passages we'd searched. But that didn't mean Rawdon had passed without a trace. Surely someone with wolf-keen senses could smell where a living man had walked among the dead.

Couldn't he?

CHAPTER EIGHTEEN

Calling in the Reinforcements

I didn't want to call off the search entirely, just in case. So I ordered two new pairs of guards to take over while the original searchers rested.

No rest for me, of course. I knew how far I'd get if I sent a messenger to ask Wulfgar—at the crack of dawn, no less—to make the two-hour trip to Fairfield to help me.

So I headed back all by myself. It was eerie, riding my horse across the darkened countryside while the world slept, except for the occasional barking dog and an owl, which swooped so close I almost had a heart attack. The wind whispered in the trees and brushed against my arms, startling me over and over. I arrived at the castle at about the same time as sunrise. I'd made it to the second day. *Hallelujah.*

Penrod must have talked some of the guards into remaining, because two of them guarded the raised drawbridge. The trouble was, they didn't recognize me. They insisted I was a beggar and told me to come back later in the morning when the gates were open.

I argued calmly.

Then forcibly.

Then irritably.

Then I yelled at them, "Get Captain Penrod now! He'll tell you who I am."

"Sorry. No. Can't do that," they said. "Captain's asleep. Come back later."

I was so tired and frustrated and angry, I didn't know what to do. So I screamed. I screamed and screamed and screamed—like a teenage victim in a cheesy horror movie—hoping to wear them down, or to wake up somebody who would verify I was who I said. It sure scared my horse, and the castle's many dogs began to howl.

Screaming continually is actually very tiring, and in less than a minute, my throat was suffering. At about two minutes, I could tell my volume was definitely going down. After three minutes Sister Mary Ursula strolled out from the bushes. She was wrapped in two towels—and only two towels: one around her; the other turban-style around her head. Believe me, under normal circumstances a seventy-year-old nun dressed in two towels is *not* a welcome sight, but I was delighted to see her.

"Such a fuss," she said, shaking her head at me. "If you had cleansed your soul with me this past night, you wouldn't feel this way, I'm sure."

The guards called down to her, "Be careful of the crazy girl, Sister!"

"That's all right," Sister Mary Ursula assured them. "I know her."

So they lowered the drawbridge and let the two of us in.

I glowered at the guards as we passed. People in this world, I was coming to learn, were only able to think for themselves if it inconvenienced me.

As I walked toward the castle, I heard a guard give the order for the bridge to be raised. A few moments later, he repeated the order. And then again.

I went back to see what was the matter.

"It's stuck," the guard manning the mechanism said.

"How's it supposed to work?" I asked.

He showed me the cogwheels and the chain that let the door down so that people could cross over it, and raised it for security at night and when the castle was under attack.

I'm not an engineer, but it was immediately obvious that the drawbridge's natural position was *up* not *down*. The counterweights had to be lifted to lower the bridge so people could get in, which I guess makes sense from a defensive point of view. You don't want the bridge sticking down and open if an invading army is running toward you, screaming and waving weapons. All of which meant the bridge should be easier to raise than to lower—the exact opposite of what seemed to be the case now.

Just what we need, I thought, *with the barbarians on our doorstep.*

"Could it have been sabotaged?" I asked as the guard fiddled with the mechanism.

"I don't see how." He pointed. "Nothing wrong here. The chain is fine. And there's nothing blocking there."

"Except it won't work," I said.

"Except it won't work," he repeated. "It's like something is holding the bridge down."

The trouble was, we could plainly see nothing was.

The bridge wasn't caught on anything, either in the ditch that surrounded the castle, or on the farside, where the drawbridge lay.

Other guards came to see if they could do better, two pulling at a time, though the first guard said it wasn't supposed to be a matter of strength.

"*You* should be able to do it," he said.

He probably meant, "Even a weakling like you," but I said, "Yeah, like King Arthur being the only one who could pull the sword out of the stone."

"What's this Arthur king of?" the guard asked. "And why did he keep his sword in a stone?"

"Never mind," I said. But I tugged, anyway.

And the bridge started to come up. Easily.

Some of the guards who'd come to see and give their advice backed away suspiciously. But most cheered and congratulated me.

Strange, I thought, but since it ended well, I wasn't going to complain.

They took over raising the bridge the rest of the way, having no trouble now, and I went to find Wulfgar.

In the castle the servants were already up and working: preparing breakfast, opening the windows to air out the rooms, heating water for the laundry. The royal family was *not* yet up.

I banged on Wulfgar's door.

No answer.

I banged again.

There was a sleepy mumble—probably he told me to go away.

I kept on banging. The servants who had been in the hall ran for cover.

Wulfgar flung open the door. He had on a nightshirt, and his hair was all askew, and his eyes were still puffy from sleep. *"What,"* he growled, "is the meaning of this?"

"Knocking on a door?" I asked innocently. "That's an ancient custom among many peoples of the world signifying: Please let me in."

Wulfgar drew his lips back from his teeth but retained human form.

"I need your help," I told him, "to get the treasury back."

"Ask *fascinating, remarkable, wow!-imagine-that* Abas."

Was that the way I sounded? "I need you." I could see he was winding himself up for a sarcastic comeback, so I added, "And your special talents."

He raised an eyebrow and waited.

In this lifetime I hadn't seen him turn into a wolf. I said, "I understand you were raised elsewhere."

"Yes." He gave a definitely wolfish grin.

"I need you to track down Rawdon."

"No," he said.

"He stole our treasury."

"Raise our taxes."

168

No time. Plus, of course, that would make the peasants even surlier. "Please," I said.

He closed the door in my face.

I untied the magic ring from its makeshift necklace. I banged on the door some more. This time when it flew open, I said, "Take this ring."

Wulfgar's eyes grew wide and frightened. No doubt he had no desire to take the ring, and yet he found his hand moving to take it. He *knew* he was bespelled.

He took the ring and slipped it onto his finger.

I said, "First, I need you to protect me from harm."

His expression didn't become any less murderous, but I knew that now I was safe from him—and from others while he was beside me.

"Next, I want you to come back to Fairfield with me and help me find where Rawdon has hidden the treasure."

Wulfgar stepped out into the hall.

"You may get dressed first," I told him.

I figured men can always dress faster than women, so there wasn't time for me to get into something more practical, even if I knew where to get it. Sure enough, Wulfgar wasn't long. He wore such a fierce expression that the castle dogs whined and slunk away from us, their tails between their legs.

The guards lowered the drawbridge again for us to cross. I called out for them to keep the bridge up, even during the day, in case of attack. After we'd gone over, I heard the guard yell that we were clear.

No sound of a raising bridge from behind us.

"Raise the bridge!" the guard yelled.

Nothing.

Well, I couldn't close it from this side. Something else for me to look into when I got back.

IN FAIRFIELD, people from the town had gathered at the burned and tumbled remains of the church, drawn by the presence of the wagons and the squad of guards. Seeing that the wagons were empty and the guards were mostly lazing around, I gathered that there still was no sign of the treasure.

I led Wulfgar through the minimaze of rubbled church to the first room of the catacombs. Both pairs of men I had set to search were there, along with the man assigned to make torches. The searchers started explaining—before I said a word—that they'd just come back for replacement torches. I figured I'd returned faster than they anticipated and I'd caught them taking a break. I'd been gone four hours—which was probably about how long their break had lasted.

"That's all right," I said. "Stay here. Prince Wulfgar and I will search now."

Taking a torch, I led Wulfgar through to the third room, the one where the catacomb maze started. "I want you to find Rawdon's trail," I said. "We will go together. Don't try to lose me." I had another thought. "And if we *do* get separated, I want you to come looking for me right away. You are not to let any harm befall me."

"You already said that about no harm," Wulfgar said.

"Just reminding you."

Wulfgar didn't say any magical words that I heard; and I didn't see him make any magical-looking gestures.

He simply suddenly shrank, fell forward, and transformed into a wolf.

Too late it occurred to me that the ring was bound to fall off the toe of his paw. Would that stop the spell? But the ring kept hold, even when Wulfgar padded on all four feet to the left-hand door.

He walked at a steady pace that kept me at a breathless half run.

If you slow down, he'll have to slow down, too, because you commanded him not to lose you, I told myself. But I wouldn't give him the satisfaction of knowing that I couldn't keep up.

There wasn't any pattern to our path, and there were too many intersections, with most of the rooms too similar to be distinctive. Sometimes the dead bodies had mummified; sometimes they were simply bones; sometimes the bones were scattered on the floor; sometimes they were mostly in their carved wall niches. (The wooden shelves were only for those rooms closest to the entrance.) We went through one section where an underground stream must pass near, for several of the rooms were damp, and in two of them we had to wade through puddles that came up to my ankles. There had also been cave-ins in several of the rooms, which I sincerely hoped had happened a long time ago.

Long after I'd given up trying to make sense of our direction, Wulfgar suddenly stopped. He'd slowed down two or three times before, to sniff at the tunnels, but now he suddenly reverted back to human shape.

"What?" I asked.

"Counselor Rawdon," he said.

I lowered my voice to the faintest whisper, just in case Rawdon hadn't heard us coming or seen the light from my torch. "Where?" I asked because there were two possible doorways, plus the one we were closest to, which had collapsed—though surely Rawdon wouldn't have wanted to make his way over that pile each time he came, I thought.

Imitating me, Wulfgar whispered dramatically, "There."

For a moment I thought he meant that Rawdon was in the room beyond the pile of stones and dirt where the doorway had collapsed. But then I saw the foot that was sticking out of the pile, the foot that was neither bone nor mummified flesh. Proof that cave-ins happened as recently as within the last day.

"Do you think he's dead?" I asked.

"No, I think he's napping."

"He could just be injured," I protested.

Without answering, Wulfgar scrambled up the pile of collapsed catacomb, ignoring the body. He had to duck to squeeze through what was left of the opening.

I was going to say, "Not so fast," but when I got to the top, I could see into the next room. Wulfgar hadn't moved on, but stood among dozens of sacks that were stacked on top of one another. Beneath my feet, protruding from this end of the cave-in, was a small hand-pulled cart onto which several of the bundles had been loaded. The force of the cave-in had knocked some of the bags off, and one had split open, scattering gold coins, which glinted in the light of my torch.

"He must have been trying to move the gold out of

here," Wulfgar said. "He might even have been heading for one of the seaports, to hire a boat and leave the country. I'm guessing he rushed too much."

That was my guess, too—that Rawdon had accidentally smacked into the doorway with his overloaded cart, not realizing that this entire area was weakened by the moisture of that nearby water.

That was something for me to remember and be careful of.

"All right," I said. "This time we need to go slowly so that I can make scratches with my stone to mark the way for the guards to find their way here." I'd use double arrows, one after the other, to identify the correct way. "We'll let the men dig this out, gather the money, return it to the castle in the wagons at whatever speed they can make. But the two of us won't wait—we should be getting back as soon as we can to check on the situation with the barbarians."

Wulfgar used the toe of his boot to poke at the stones covering Rawdon. "One of us hasn't had breakfast," he grumbled.

Even with all the trouble Rawdon had caused, I refused to consider letting Wulfgar snack on him. "Neither of us has," I assured him, tugging on his arm. "Don't you dare even think about that."

"Even magic can't control thinking," he said wistfully.

BY THE TIME I had carefully marked out the route and given instructions on how many men to have carrying the treasury out and how many men to have guarding the treasury that had been carried out, so that the people of Fairfield didn't walk off with it, I had a crisis of faith—not over my trailblazing abilities or even my troops' mental abilities, but over how hard it would be for the average guardsman to remain honest in the face of so very much money. They could easily decide that a kingdom's treasury, divided among the fifty of them, was more money per guard than any of them was ever likely to see again.

"Wulfgar," I ordered, "you'll have to stay behind. Keep an eye on the men. Make sure they don't take any of the money for themselves. Then help guard the convoy on the way back."

"I haven't even broken my fast yet," Wulfgar complained again.

Well, none of us had.

"Send a few of the men into town to buy provisions for everyone," I said. I knew Wulfgar was only cooperating because the ring compelled him to, so I specified: "Don't be excessive with spending the money, but pay a fair price. And return to the castle as quickly as you can in safety."

I couldn't think of any loopholes I'd left. Which didn't mean Wulfgar wouldn't find one.

"No plotting against me," I added.

Wulfgar saluted then spat on the ground, just barely missing my toes.

BY THE TIME I made the two-hour trip back home, I had a strong suspicion that lunch was probably over.

I could see that eventually they'd gotten the bridge up without me, though now they had to lower it once more.

Captain Penrod was standing on the castle wall as I approached. I waved and held up the one sack of gold I'd brought with me in case any skeptical guards needed proof that the money *had* been found. Penrod returned my wave, and I heard a cheer from the guards as word of my success was passed.

My horse clattered over the drawbridge, and the eager guards gathered around.

I tossed the bag to Penrod and said, "That's the first of it. The rest is about a half-day behind."

Penrod handed the bag over to one of his lieutenants and helped me dismount. I had a sore butt from all the riding I'd done, Lady Bliss's red gown was stiff and stinky with sweat—not to mention tattered and muddy—and I'd had absolutely no sleep last night and no breakfast this morning.

We watched as the guards were unable to reraise the bridge.

"Any idea what that's all about?" I asked Penrod.

He shook his head. "They say it's as though the bridge is weighted down, but then that weight goes away after a little while."

"That 'little while' could be the death of us in case of enemy attack," I warned. "Can a new mechanism be made?"

Penrod passed that down to his men as an order.

"How are things going?" I asked him.

"Not badly," he answered, but so hesitantly I knew he wasn't telling the truth.

"You might as well tell me now," I said.

"The messengers you sent to find the barbarian camp returned."

Because of his dismal expression, I guessed, "The barbarians didn't accept our offer of peace?"

"The messengers returned without their heads."

That sounded like a definite *no* to me.

Now what?

"All right," I said. "I absolutely need to lie down, just for a bit. I'm so tired I can hardly walk straight, much less think straight."

"Oh," Penrod said.

"'Oh' what?"

"It's just that the meeting has already started."

"What meeting?"

"With the magic-users—Uldemar, Orielle, and Xenos."

I was pleased to hear they'd arrived, but, "Who are they meeting with?" I asked.

"Queen Andreanna," Penrod said.

I guessed there wasn't time for a nap, quick or otherwise.

CHAPTER NINETEEN

Magic Realism (without the Realism)

When I got to the Great Hall, the doors were closed and two guards stood in front, which I gathered was Queen Andreanna's subtle way of letting me know I wasn't invited.

"Make way for the king," I commanded, never acknowledging a *thought* that they wouldn't.

Assertiveness sometimes pays off. The guards were so quick to open the doors that the little guy with the trumpet didn't have a chance to blow a fanfare.

"Oh," Andreanna said as I entered, "look. It's the pig girl."

"Sheep," I corrected automatically.

They were all sitting around one of the dining tables—no serving side this time: the queen, Abas, Kenric, two guys I didn't know, and one woman I didn't know. Actually, the woman wasn't sitting at the table; she was sitting on Kenric's lap, though there was plenty of room on the bench, particularly since I'd left Wulfgar behind in Fairfield. She looked like any teenage boy's fantasy: a Barbie-doll figure that defied gravity, a super-model's face, lustrous black skin, and about fifteen pounds' worth of cornrowed hair fastened off with tiny golden bells. Her outfit was composed exclusively of leather, lace, and strategically placed metal. Wulfgar had said Orielle was better-looking than the other magic-users. I would be willing to bet my college fund that Orielle was better-looking than 99 percent of the world's population.

There was no sign of Sir Deming or Sister Mary Ursula—apparently the queen didn't feel she needed advisers.

"Please send for the royal advisers," I said to the guards.

The queen was making an irritated face, but for once it wasn't about me. "Close the doors, you incompetent fools," she ordered.

I turned and saw that although the guards were tugging on the doors, the doors weren't moving.

The queen sighed.

The page put down his trumpet and joined in the guards' efforts to close the doors. Nothing. Even when all three men concentrated on one door and hurled their weight at it, it wouldn't close.

Don't tell me the castle itself is rebelling against me, I thought.

"Abas, can't you do something?" the queen said.

"I can do lots of things," Abas protested.

The queen sighed again. "Can't you do something about the door?"

The guards moved out of Abas's way. He pushed. Nothing. He pushed harder. Still nothing. He moved around to the other side and pulled. The doorknobs and the ornate metal plates to which they were attached yanked out of the wood. Abas handed them to the guards, then returned to our side of the doors and once again pushed. I saw the muscles on his arms bulge, the muscles on his back ripple, the muscles on his thighs expand like they were about to pop. There was a creaking noise of wood protesting. Then the huge oaken doors cracked, split, and fell in shards. Without the hinges having budged.

What was going on?

"Well, that was quite useful," Kenric said.

Abas shrugged and returned to the table.

The queen gestured for the guards and the page to leave.

As they picked their way through the pile of splintered wood, the page reached behind him—it must have been mindless force of habit—to pull closed the piece of door that was still attached to the hinges. It swung easily.

The people at the table looked at me suspiciously.

Luckily, with such a limited number of them, they couldn't crowd me out this time. I would have preferred to sit on the same side of the table as the any-other-female-would-feel-like-a-poster-child-for-the-criminally-ugly-compared-to-*her* Orielle, so I wouldn't have to look at her; but she was sitting on Kenric's lap, and he was sitting on Andreanna's left, with Abas having returned to Andreanna's right. If I wanted to sit on that side, I would have had to sit directly next to Orielle. There was a space between the two men who sat on the other side of the table, as well as more room at either end of the bench they shared. I decided on the middle seat, to avoid what might be interpreted as favoritism.

"This," Queen Andreanna said in the same tone someone would use to point out a backed-up toilet, "is Princess Janine. Princess Janine"—she managed to look down her nose even though she wasn't quite facing me—"these are Orielle, Uldemar, and Xenos."

"Hello," I said to the wizard on my right, Xenos.

He was dressed in a brown monk's robe, with the hood pulled up around his face.

Shy little guy, I figured. I made a point of smiling at him until he looked up at me. I noticed the pointy, hairy ears about the same time I realized that what he was pulling out of his pocket and popping into his mouth were live centipedes. He glared as though he was sure I was just waiting for the chance to grab his lunch away from him.

I edged toward Uldemar, who announced in a booming voice: "She brings the stench of the dead with her."

Talk about getting personal.

I turned to face him. He was the wizard I'd glimpsed in the coming attraction. I'd noticed that he was very tall and that his head was shaved. But now, close up, I gulped, for I saw what I hadn't had time to see in the promo: His eyes were like Ping-Pong balls—totally white, with no pupils or irises.

Stammering, I said, "I—I've just come back from the catacombs. There *were* dead people there." *Of course there are dead people in the catacombs,* I mentally chided myself. *They know that. Stop blathering.* I said, "I—I've recovered the stolen treasure." I'd kept a handful from the bag I'd given to Penrod, and I placed this on the table to prove my story.

Uldemar sniffed. But when he spoke, his voice—though deep and elegant—was no longer intimidating. "So pleased to meet you," he said.

"Good to see—" I started, my mouth a full syllable ahead of me. How could I be so thoughtless as to bring up *seeing* to a person who was obviously blind? If somebody else had said it, I would have kicked her. I was tempted to kick myself. "I mean," I corrected myself, feeling my face go all hot and red—but his eyes *were* the most disgusting things I'd ever seen, and my stammer came back, "I—I—I—" which I realized sounded like "Eye, eye, eye." For something to do with my hands, which had developed a sudden tendency to flutter, I folded them and went to place them on the table in front of me.

Except that I banged the edge of the table, and when I jerked back, I knocked one of the gold coins onto the floor.

I leaned down to get it, but it was too far under the table, so I pushed the bench back. Wood on stone made a loud screeching like fingernails on blackboard. Xenos leaped to his feet to get away from me, and Uldemar—who couldn't see what I was doing and had felt the bench beneath him move—grabbed for the stability of the table. The bench stopped so suddenly, I nearly slid off.

Again I reached under the table, this time smacking my forehead loudly against the wood. Before my eyes cleared, I accidentally latched onto Xenos's ankle—which was as hairy as his ears.

He shook me loose impatiently.

At last I located the coin, put it back on the pile, and folded my hands on the table in front of me, though at this point the bench was so far back I had to stretch to reach. But I figured I better leave well enough alone. I didn't want to draw any more attention to myself by touching the bump I could feel already swelling over my left eye.

Eye reminded me of Uldemar.

He was still waiting, a pained look on his face.

"Hello," I said.

"Oh, I see what you mean, Kenric." Orielle giggled. "She *is* all that you said."

Well, excuse me. We can't all be naturally gorgeous, polished, and coordinated.

Abas gave a tittery laugh. He was carving his initials into the table with a dagger about the size of a small garden hoe. For all that I had chosen him to be my ally, I was aware that he could just as easily carve his initials into me.

Andreanna sighed. "Well now that *she's* here, I suppose we'd better ask her what she wants to do."

"About what?" I asked, sure I'd come in during the middle of something.

"About new drapes for the windows," Andreanna purred, then snapped, *"About the threats to the kingdom, of course, you absurd little ninny.* Have you been too busy twiddling your thumbs to be aware that the kingdom is in danger on several fronts?"

"No," I said. "I mean, yes. I mean, I *have* been busy, and I *have* been thinking about our problems. I just didn't know what particular problem you were discussing before I came in." *Stop trying to excuse yourself to them,* I told myself. "OK," I said, "what are our problems? First—"

Uldemar interrupted, "You smell of the dead."

"Yes," I said, "I know." I didn't point out that he'd told me so already. "First," I repeated, "the drawbridge."

"What are you talking about?" the queen demanded.

"The drawbridge—it keeps getting stuck on open."

The lovely Orielle said, "It worked when I came through this morning."

Xenos, biting off a centipede's head, grunted and nodded, which I took to mean that he'd had no problem, either.

Abas said, "It worked fine when I went to let in Uldemar."

"It gets stuck," I insisted. "Ask the guards." I sounded pathetic, begging to be believed. "It got stuck when I came in at dawn, and again when I left a little bit later, and just now when I came back. It gets stuck, then it suddenly works again. Just like these doors."

"You mean the Great Hall doors, which worked perfectly well for the rest of us?" Kenric asked.

"You *saw*," I protested. They couldn't deny seeing it, when the broken rubble Abas had generated still cluttered the way. "You saw that the doors wouldn't close."

"I did," Kenric agreed. "I'm just wondering why both the drawbridge and the Great Hall doors stick for you, and only for you."

Uldemar said, "She carries the dead with her."

"Enough already with the dead!" I yelled at him. (All right, all right, I yelled at a blind guy.) "I know I stink. I haven't had a chance to bathe yet. Surely you can put up with it while we discuss more urgent matters."

Uldemar said, "I didn't say that you stink. I said that I could smell the dead about you."

I paused to work this out. "You mean, like..."

"They must have followed you," Uldemar said. "From the catacombs."

So much for assuming I was the victim of an overactive imagination.

Sister Mary Ursula picked that moment to come climbing over the debris of the doors. "Ewww, dead people walking around, following live people. Have you been performing more of your necromancy, Uldemar?"

"Not me," Uldemar said. "Simply ghosts."

"I don't like ghosts," Sister Mary Ursula said. "They hang around watching you when you can't watch them, and they make rude comments. Everybody's fat from the perspective of someone who's been dead a hundred years."

Well, that put a whole new perspective on taking a bath.

Sounding put out, as though I'd invited the ghosts to

follow me specifically to annoy her, Queen Andreanna asked, "How many are there?"

Uldemar leaned closer to me and sniffed. "Several hundred," he estimated.

"Are they dangerous?" I asked.

"If they're all standing on the drawbridge so that it can't be closed while we're under attack, yes," Uldemar said. "Mostly they're annoying—howling at night, rattling chains so that it's impossible to get a good night's sleep. As Sister Mary Ursula pointed out, they do have a tendency to watch when people don't want to be watched, and to make rude remarks. The majority of the living can't hear them unless a whole bunch of ghosts are yelling together, but it isn't fun to know that people— even dead people—are sniggering at you."

As the queen of all sniggerees, I could empathize.

Kenric flashed that distracting smile of his at me. "They do seem to have developed a fondness for you," he pointed out. "If you stay away from the drawbridge so that they don't cluster on it, we should be fine." He gave just the slightest emphasis to his "we." *They* would be fine so long as the ghosts concentrated on harassing me.

"How do we get rid of them?" I asked.

Xenos made a noise halfway between snort and laugh. When he saw me look at him, he pulled his hood down farther over his face, and he jammed a centipede into his mouth to stifle the sound, but I could see his shoulders shaking with his silent glee.

I assumed this did not signify good news.

Uldemar said, "Understand, ghosts get bored. They

don't sleep, they don't eat—day after day, year after year, sometimes century after century. If they've decided that it will be fun to haunt you—"

I squealed as a bony finger that I couldn't see jabbed me in the ribs.

Xenos shook with silent laughter.

Uldemar finished, "—it will be difficult to distract them."

Queen Andreanna said, "We don't have time for this nonsense."

"I once had to do battle with an undead ogre," Abas said, but before he could tell us the details, Sir Deming entered the room.

"What's she done now?" Deming demanded, making a big show of looking at the broken doors—as though I could have knocked them in.

"Ghosts," Orielle told him, and blew him a kiss.

Deming sat down next to her, where he could get a good look down the front of her dress. He said to me, "You didn't need to bring ghosts; I said you could bring the sheep with you if you got lonely."

Deming, I thought, *would make a fine ghost.*

"All right," I said. "Let's get the meeting started. Sister Mary Ursula, why don't you have a seat."

"Ooo, no," she said, shrinking back. "I could never sit down next to a wizard or a necromancer or a witch. They are not One with anybody or anything. They are like buttoning your coat and not noticing till you get to the bottom that you're one button off, or a hot ember that burns your skin, or a piece of doo-doo that you step in while you're wearing sandals."

Xenos pulled back his hood to make kissy-lips at her, and she shrank farther away.

"All right," I said, trying to regain control of the meeting, "we have to decide what to do about the barbarians."

"What about the barbarians?" Uldemar asked.

"I killed three of them," Abas said. "First—"

"Abas," I interrupted, "later." To the three magic-users, I explained, "The barbarians sent a raiding party into the courtyard, and Abas did kill three of them."

"Saving your life," Abas emphasized.

"Saving my life," I agreed. "Before the last one died, he said that one of the others had been their king, and that the reason they were attacking was because King Cynric had taken a crown made for their first chieftain, Brecc the Slayer."

"*Won* the crown," Abas corrected. "You're not very good at telling stories."

I ignored his criticism and turned to Xenos. "Did you make that crown?"

Xenos spoke for the first time, his voice as sweet and melodious as the sound you get when you accidentally telephone a fax number. "Yes," he said.

"The barbarians want that crown back," I said. "And I'm told Cynric gave it to a dragon who was ravaging the south."

Rather than replying, Xenos popped another cen-tipede into his mouth.

"We sent messengers to the barbarian camp to let them know we were willing to return the crown if we could get it, but the barbarians killed the messengers."

Andreanna turned to Abas and whispered loudly, "Big surprise."

"I wasn't surprised," Abas said. "If I was a barbarian, I would have killed the messengers, too."

"I think," I said, "that we are in imminent danger of the entire barbarian camp attacking." I looked at my advisers. "Any thoughts?"

Sister Mary Ursula said, "To forgive and to be forgiven are two sides of the coin of Harmony."

When it became clear she had no more to say, I said, "Yes, well, anybody else?"

Deming said, "Though yesterday's raiding party was small, they *did* bring an entire armed camp into our lands. Presumably that was in case the smaller group did not succeed. If they were willing to wage war to get the crown, I can't believe they'll forgive the killing of their king—regardless of how many sides of coins forgiveness covers."

I said, "So you're saying to forget retrieving the crown, to concentrate on defending the castle."

Deming nodded.

"Still..." I said. I had to believe that if Rasmussem included a dragon, I was supposed to have *something* to do with it. "How difficult would it be to track down this dragon?"

Uldemar said, "I could find him in my scrying glass."

The blind guy, I thought.

"Sure," I told him.

Uldemar was wearing a pendant that he took off from around his neck and laid on the table. It looked like a slice of onyx—flat and about the circumference of a cross section of a baseball—in a gilt frame.

I bent closer. It *might* have been glass, but it was totally black. I could see myself and part of the room reflected in it.

Uldemar arranged his hands so that all ten of his fingers rested on the edge of his scrying glass, which left only a small area open in the middle.

As I watched that space, a swirl formed beneath the surface, as though thick black liquid were being stirred. But the swirling got lighter, as though the invisible stirrer were adding a lighter substance, like someone adding cream to melted licorice. Then more and more cream. I glanced up at Uldemar and almost squealed. The exact opposite was happening to his eyes: His white eyes were aswirl with darkness.

A bony finger jabbed me in the side, and I came close to becoming airborne. But it wasn't one of the ghosts; it was just Xenos, who was so pleased with himself for startling me that he practically choked up a piece of centipede.

Still, Andreanna found fault with me rather than Xenos. "If Cynric hadn't been so fevered and delirious when he was dying," she announced to all, "he never would have chosen her."

Finally, Uldemar's eyes and the scrying glass were reversed: The glass was smooth as white porcelain, and Uldemar's eyes were totally black, without any definition or detail at all. Unsettling as it was, I couldn't look away. After several long moments, Uldemar closed his eyes, probably for about five seconds. When he opened them, they were once more featureless white. The scrying glass had resumed its former blackness.

He said, "The dragon is in the southern province, in a cave on a mountaintop known as the Old Hag."

Andreanna said, "How is this little sheep-tending person going to overcome a dragon?"

I glanced at my good old ally Abas, who could—single-handed—overcome wild boars, undead ogres, and princess-kidnapping barbarians.

"I don't do dragons," he said.

Of course not. Since it was *my* game, naturally *I* would be the one to have to do it.

Orielle said, "If you can get close enough to the creature, I could give you a potion that would poison it."

"Wonderful." Xenos chortled so hard I expected to see centipedes come flying out of his nose. "She could present the dragon with a doctored ham-and-cheese sandwich: 'Here, Dragon, why don't you eat this before you eat me?' Fast-acting is this potion? Or did you have in mind something that would be absorbed through its skin? 'Care for a massage before I die, Dragon?'"

Orielle smiled as though she found his comments amusing even though they were derisive. Then she gestured with her finger, and Xenos's ear fell off.

It sat, hairy and warty, on the table.

"Put it back," he screamed at her. "Put it back now."

"What?" She tapped her own delicately shaped ear. "Can't hear you."

"Stop fighting," I told both of them. "We need to stick together or we're likely to all die together."

Orielle sulked but made a dismissive gesture to the hairy ear. Xenos snatched it up and slapped it against the side of his head. It stuck immediately, and I figured it was best not to mention that he'd put it on upside down.

"Uldemar," I said, "do you have any ideas on how to overcome the dragon and regain the crown?"

"No," he said. "I'm mostly a finder."

"Yeah," Xenos complained. "And mostly he's good at finding dead bodies. That's probably how he found the dragon—by the leftover bits and pieces of those who went before you to kill it."

"That's true," Uldemar admitted.

I rubbed my hand over my face. I was having trouble concentrating when I was so tired and no one was cooperating. "There has to be some way," I said. "But I haven't slept or eaten in ages, and I can't think straight. I'm going to take a nap and..."

What was all that racket coming from down the hall? *Probably the ghosts,* I thought, *already practicing sleep prevention.*

But it wasn't.

A guard came scrambling over the debris of the broken door. "Attack!" he yelled. "We're under attack!"

These readouts are alarming. G. B. doesn't have much time left. Premature disconnection may be the only option, and the technologists warn this could result in severe brain damage likely to leave G. B. in an irreversible vegetative state.

***The translation software garbled Japan's last message. Japan, please have something for us. Reword and resend ASAP.

CHAPTER TWENTY

Siege

Kenric, Abas, and Xenos were fastest. I was right behind them as we ran down the hallway. From outside I could hear yelling, but when I reached the doorway to the courtyard, I could see the drawbridge was up, which was a pleasant surprise. A flaming arrow hit the doorframe inches from Xenos's head. He yelped and went into reverse, treading my toes.

"Never mind," he muttered, slinking past me, past Andreanna and Deming, who were on my heels, back into the safety of the hallway. Orielle had stopped far enough back to be out of danger of stray arrows, and Sister Mary Ursula had just rounded the corner, huffing as she waddled in our direction. We'd forgotten poor Uldemar back at the table.

Just as I was about to peek out of the doorway, Kenric and Abas came racing back from outside. I stepped out of their way barely in time to avoid a collision. Abas paused only long enough to grab the burning arrow out of the wooden doorframe and fling it to the ground, where it would burn out harmlessly. Kenric threw open a side door, and both brothers dashed up a steep spiral staircase.

I took a moment to see what was going on in the courtyard. Some of our guards were there, lugging buckets of water to put out fires that had caught in the thatched roofs of the surrounding outbuildings—like the barracks and the well housing. But most of the guards were up on the walls. Assuming that was where the stairs led, I followed after Abas and Kenric.

The noise of men shouting became louder.

I came out onto the wall that surrounded both castle and courtyard. I know I'd been over it when the barbarians had carried me, but at that time, I hadn't been in any condition to notice much. Now I saw that the walls were wide enough to accommodate men running back and forth, trying to defend the castle. There was no safety rail on the castle side—which made my twenty-first-century self cringe at the possibility of injuries and subsequent lawsuits—but the side that faced out had that typical solid-then-open pattern, like a jack-o'-lantern smile with every other tooth missing, that my medieval self recognized as battlements. The guards could hide behind the upright sections, the *merlons,* then shoot arrows through the openings, or *crenellations*. The trouble was that *enemy* arrows also could fly through the openings. Dead and wounded men lay where they dropped, stepped over by guards intent on keeping the barbarians from scaling the walls.

When I'd been in the barbarian camp, I'd had the impression that there were a lot of them. They looked like even more now that they were running toward the castle waving their swords, firing their arrows, and battering at the upright drawbridge with a tree trunk long enough to reach over the ditch. They had catapults, too. I was just in time to see the first bombardment, huge rocks wrapped with rags that had been soaked in something flammable. Two of the rocks landed in the courtyard, where they didn't inflict much damage; but the third landed on the battlement itself, crushing one man and burning those who tried to go to his rescue.

Abas and Kenric had taken up bows and were firing into the advancing crowd of barbarians. I hovered uselessly, worrying that the ghosts that had followed me from the catacombs might find it amusing to give me a little shove while I was standing in this precarious place. The smells of blood and pitch were making me woozy, and the smoke stung my eyes.

"Princess Janine!" one of the guards called above the screams of men, some attacking, some dying. "Lady, this is a dangerous place for one not trained in war craft. Best for you to find a more secure position within."

He was right. Even if my personality had provided me with the inclination to participate, Rasmussem had not provided me with the skill for fighting. But I couldn't believe my role in this battle was merely to seek a suitable hiding place—even though that *was* my inclination.

I had to fight every instinct I had. "What can I do to help?" I shouted back.

For one who had been so concerned about getting me to safety, he was quick enough to point to one of the pages who was dumping a basketful of arrows to replenish the stock the archers were using. "Show the princess where the supplies are kept," the guard ordered the page.

And so I started running up and down the stairs, bringing load after load of arrows to the archers, delivering them to different stations on the wall to make sure nobody ran out. Apparently the ghosts were diverted enough by all the activity that they didn't feel called on to trip me or knock me down.

Despite my ongoing terror, things went well until I dropped a basket of arrows between Abas and Kenric. The area was slick from water used to douse some burning debris, and as I turned, one of my feet slipped. No amount of frantic arm-waving was enough to regain my balance. I could tell I was sliding toward the edge, like an out-of-control skater. I had time to ask myself, *Can I possibly survive a fall from this height?* and to answer myself, *Not likely,* before my right foot cleared the edge, then my left—and then someone had hold of me around my waist and hauled me back up onto the wall.

That someone was Kenric. I saw the surprise on his face as he took in my damp, sooty appearance and recognized me, and then he gave that grin that—even under the best of circumstances—made my knees weak. "Thank you," I managed to whisper.

"You're welcome."

Too bad he was my half brother. Too bad he wasn't real.

Behind him a barbarian who had shimmied up a rope anchored by a grappling hook cleared the top of the wall, and Abas took his head off with a swipe of his sword, then he sliced through the rope to prevent anyone else from climbing up.

I looked down the dizzying height and saw a cluster of barbarians holding their shields above the heads of other men to protect them from the arrows our archers were raining down on them. "What are they doing?" I asked.

"Sapping," Kenric told me.

My Rasmussem-provided subconscious told me that meant they were digging a tunnel so that section of wall would collapse.

"Are we in danger?" I asked.

"Not imminent danger. It will be worse at night, when we can't see them so well. Meanwhile..." He nodded beyond me, and I saw that Captain Penrod and some of his men had emerged from a nearby doorway, carrying a huge cauldron that I could only assume held something hot and nasty.

The barbarians must have had a lookout for just such a thing, for as our men tipped the cauldron, a trumpet or horn sounded, and the barbarian sappers ran from their place by the wall so that the burning oil spilled only on the slowest of them.

Then suddenly their horn sounded again, and all the barbarians fell back.

"What's that all about?" Kenric asked suspiciously.

"Dunno," Abas answered. "No reason for a retreat."

197

Back and back the barbarians pulled, until they were out of range of our archers. Then one man, bearing a white flag, approached on horseback.

"Surely they're not surrendering?" I said, though I very much hoped they were.

"Parley," Captain Penrod told me. "They want to talk—though I don't know why. They weren't winning, but neither were they losing."

Watching with barely suppressed strain as the barbarian messenger approached, the castle guards waited, their arrows notched and trained on him.

Finally within shouting range, the barbarian reined in his horse and called up to us, "Return that which is being ours or we will be killing you all."

Kenric, Abas, Penrod—everyone—was looking at me.

Oh, my turn again to do something?

I stepped closer to the edge of the battlements. Clutching the upright merlon to steady myself, I scanned the ground below, deserted now except for the bodies of the dead and wounded. If a ghost tickled or shoved now, I was a goner. If one of the supposedly dead barbarians below was faking, I was an open target. Still, I raised my arm so the messenger could see me, and I shouted down to him, "That offer was made to you already. You returned our envoys without their heads. If you killed them before they spoke, this is what they were sent to say: We don't have the crown of Brecc, but we are willing to help you find and reclaim it."

The messenger said, "That is being well and good. But firstest you must be turning over to us that one of you which is being responsible for the death of our good king Grimbold. Otherwise we will never-ever be giving up until everly one of you is being dead."

Everyone was looking in our direction.

I reassured Abas, "Don't worry. I would never turn you over to them."

Kenric made a sound, which, after a moment, I realized was a stifled laugh. Abas scratched his head, obviously confused by what I'd just said.

What? I thought.

Captain Penrod shuffled his feet and told me, "The ranking officer is responsible for the actions of all in his or her command."

For a second I thought *he* was taking responsibility. But he didn't outrank Abas. I did.

"Oh," I said. *I* was responsible for Abas? And Andreanna? And Kenric and Wulfgar? That hardly seemed fair when they were so intent on killing me off.

There was a *whizz* and a *thunk,* which I figured was that hypothetical decoy left on the field to pretend he was dead until he got a clear shot at me.

But it wasn't. It was one of our men, shooting down toward the barbarian. The arrow had struck about a handspan in front of the horse and stood quivering in the ground while the rider tried to control his mount, which was rearing in fright.

Lucky he didn't hit him, I thought, for surely breaking a truce by murdering an unarmed messenger was not right. But before I could take responsibility for my men and yell, "Don't kill him!" another arrow flew from the battlements and struck the ground inches from the horse's leg. And then another. And another. And another. And not a one hit horse or man. Their feathered shafts formed a line in the dirt between him and us.

Despite the threat of death, my men were saying they would not turn me over.

Which was a big relief to me.

The horse was turning in tight circles, but at least he was no longer rearing. The envoy spat on the ground and yelled, "Then be preparing to being dead!" and he spurred his horse back in the direction of his own lines.

"Janine! Janine!" my men began chanting, sounding for all the world like fans cheering their favorite baseball player. For a delicious moment, I forgot this was all make-believe and that my life was in danger—not from barbarian invaders but from computer overload. For a moment I knew what it was like to be popular. Then I remembered that this was merely one step toward surviving this game.

Captain Penrod was saying, "The men are with you because of your courage."

Courage? I'd been scared stiff every moment I'd been up here.

Penrod must have known what I was thinking. He said, "You stayed. You helped. You did what you could."

"Well," I said, "so did all of you."

"The queen didn't," Penrod pointed out.

Abas and Kenric shared a sour look over that rebuff to the royal family name.

By then the barbarian messenger had made it back to

his own lines. The rest of the barbarians gave a great yell and shook their swords and spears and bows in our direction.

I expected them to storm the castle, but they didn't. In fact, they seemed to be settling down where they were.

"They'll wait till nightfall," Penrod said. "They'll be able to accomplish more under cover of dark. Still, we'll need to keep alert in case of raiding parties."

Could I be crowned as king tomorrow if we were still under siege? It didn't seem likely. I couldn't believe I was just supposed to wait until we wore the barbarians down or the barbarians wore us down. I would have asked Kenric and Abas their thoughts, but they had melted into the crowd, and there was no sign of them.

Penrod was ordering his men: "We must tend to our injured during this respite. Sergeants, count up the casualties so that we can set up a schedule for resting and watching."

"I'll be back," I promised Penrod.

I felt the presence of the catacomb ghosts crowding me as I went down the narrow stairway back to the Great Hall. Apparently the other times they had stayed on the battlements, watching the attack. But now that there was a lull, they wanted to hang around me some more. *Oh boy.*

We climbed over the broken doors of the Great Hall and had another meeting. Uldemar had fallen asleep and had to be nudged awake.

"I," Queen Andreanna announced as she walked into the room, "was seeing about provisions for our men.

There was no need to be making unfounded speculations about my courage."

Well, someone had run to Mama fast with news of all that was said.

And I didn't believe her excuse, either. How long does it take to run down to the kitchen and tell the cooks, "We're under attack, so prepare portable food"? But I didn't point that out. I just said, "Good. Thank you. That's one thing less for me to have to worry about." *One VERY SMALL thing...*

We didn't wait for Sister Mary Ursula, whose size and age pretty generally made her the last to arrive. Eventually she would catch up.

"Any thoughts?" I asked.

"You could sacrifice yourself for the good of the many," Andreanna suggested.

Of all people, it was Sir Deming who came to my defense. "The way the barbarians would see it is that if we're weak enough to offer up our king, we're weak enough to be conquered. They would not be satisfied with just her death."

"It was only a suggestion," Andreanna pouted.

"How vulnerable are we?" I asked.

Kenric said, "We have enough food to last for two weeks, longer on half rations. The well is supplied by groundwater springs—no way they can befoul that—so, an unlimited supply."

Which would have been good news if *I* didn't have only until tomorrow to settle this.

"The sappers?"

Abas answered, "If the guards are alert, the sappers can be kept at bay." He cracked his knuckles, which—if it was meant to show how tough he was—didn't impress me.

"Any back way I should know about?" I asked. "Secret passages into the castle?"

Deming rolled his eyes. "What's the purpose of fortified walls and a drawbridge if you're going to have a little door marked SECRET ENTRANCE—ATTACKERS PLEASE STAY OUT?"

"Is that a *yes* or a *no*?" I pressed.

"No," he said. "No secret ways in."

"OK," I said. "So, for the moment we're in no immediate danger. Is there anything we can do besides having our archers pick them off one by one?"

"You mean by magic?" Uldemar asked, his eyes as blank and disconcerting as ever.

"That would be a possibility," I said. "What can you do?"

"I can smell the ghosts you brought with you," Uldemar said. "I can use my scrying glass to find people or other living creatures. I can transform my shape, and I can reanimate the dead."

"Reanimate the dead?" Finally this was sounding like good news. "You mean you can bring back our men that were killed during the attack?"

Uldemar was nodding, but Orielle said, "But they'll still be dead, and they'll keep on decomposing, which, personally, I find disagreeable in someone I'm trying to carry on a conversation with."

It did sound like a serious drawback. "What do *you* do, Orielle?" I asked.

She smiled, showing off perfect teeth that I would bet never had an overbite or suffered from tartar buildup. "My specialty is potions," she said. "I have one that will give a man, or a woman, great strength and stamina. If you'd like, I could mix up a batch for all the guards, so each man could fight as though he were two."

"Sort of like an Abas clone," I said, wondering if she'd given some of her potion to my middle half-brother, or if he'd come by his strength solely through diligent self-absorption.

Orielle blinked and processed my anachronistic statement and said, "Like a miniature Abas, yes."

"Except," Xenos said, obviously delighted to be the bearer of bad news, "for that slight little complication."

Orielle made a bad-smell face.

Of course Xenos would find the flaw in anything. "What complication?" I asked.

"It only lasts one hour," Orielle admitted, "so you'd have to calculate exactly when would be the best time to administer it to the men."

"And . . ." Xenos prompted.

Peeved, Orielle pointed out to him, "Your ear's on upside down." Sullenly, she admitted to me, "After it wears off, the person will be so weak, he won't even be able to stand up. That stage lasts two hours."

Not a good thing if the battle isn't quite over on schedule.

Xenos was tugging his ear and frowning, so Uldemar

had a chance to say, "Hardly better than one of my dead people, eh?"

I asked, "Xenos, what do you do?"

Now he was ticked off, too. "Apparently I sit here all afternoon with my ear on upside down, and nobody tells me."

"Can you fix it magically?" I asked, trying to be helpful, as well as trying to get a feel for what he was capable of.

"You ignorant little nobody, you," he snapped. "I make artifacts. Like crowns that get stolen away from perfectly nice barbarian kings by unscrupulous civilized kings and then stupidly given to nasty dragons." He jumped to his feet. "So I, for one, have no need to worry about the barbarians tearing down your walls or starving you out, for they hold me in high esteem and will let me pass without harm."

"Perhaps," I told him. "But unfortunately we won't be able to lower the drawbridge to let you out—"

"I don't need you"—he glanced around the room to include all of us—"or your drawbridge." He muttered something I couldn't make out, then walked through the wall with as much ease as someone walking from sunlight through shadow.

"Now you've done it," Uldemar said. "Now you've really irked him."

I guessed so. Annoying as the beastly little guy could be, I asked, "Can you stop him?" because I might need him later on in the game.

"I can only try." Uldemar reached into his robes and

pulled out a vial from which he poured a powder into his palm. This he tossed into the air in front of himself. As soon as the powder touched him, he transformed into a bat. Either that, or he disappeared and the powder itself transformed into a bat—it happened too fast to be sure of anything, except that it was one of the scenes from Rasmussem's promo. Only then it had been an eagle. With a cry disconcertingly like a squeal, the bat flew out the window.

Queen Andreanna said to me, "Well, you've gotten rid of two out of three of the people most likely to help us out of this disaster you've caused. What are you going to do next?"

I caused this? What about Abas's input into the situation?

Luckily, I didn't have to answer, because at that moment Sister Mary Ursula entered the room.

Unluckily, what she said was, "Bad, bad, bad news. Bad news. Prince Wulfgar and the squadron accompanying him and the treasury are now One with the barbarians."

CHAPTER TWENTY-ONE

Back to the Battlements

Queen Andreanna screamed and threw herself backward like a Victorian lady having the vapors. But I figured it was calculated drama, for she didn't lose herself to the moment enough to fall off the back of the bench.

Orielle rushed to her side to fan her and to say, "There, there," which might have meant that Orielle was easily fooled, or—more likely—that she was smart enough to *pretend* she was easily fooled.

"What happened?" I asked Sister Mary Ursula.

"Wulfgar was returning from Fairfield, leading the wagons bearing the recovered gold," Sister Mary Ursula said. She paused and considered. "Gold..." She shook her head disapprovingly. "True, it is of the earth and comes from the earth, but if ever there was a thing which caused more division rather than Oneness—"

"Sister Mary Ursula!" Andreanna bellowed, having recovered, at least, the strength of her voice. "Get on with what's happened to my son!"

"He must have been feeling a certain sense of One-ness," Sister Mary Ursula said, refusing to be put entirely off, "for he didn't send scouts ahead, and so he stumbled into the barbarian camp and was captured."

"*I* would have sent scouts," Abas grumbled, "no matter how *One* I felt."

"Yes, dear," Andreanna said, "but that's you."

I was thinking that Wulfgar, being what he was, should have had a certain advantage in a surprise attack. Not sure how many people knew of his ability to transform into a wolf, and not wanting to give away anything that I shouldn't, I said, "Perhaps Wulfgar, being the clever person he is, might have managed to escape..."

Sister Mary Ursula asked, "You mean by turning into a wolf?"—which goes to show that not every situation calls for subtlety. "No, the barbarian messenger specifically said that didn't work."

"'Messenger'?" I echoed. "The barbarians sent a messenger?"

"Well, of course there's a messenger. How else would I know what had happened? Captain Penrod sent me to ask you to come up to the north battlement."

Again my brothers moved faster than I could—one of the disadvantages of wearing a dress, particularly a dress that's five sizes too big. But I was ahead of Andreanna, Deming, and Orielle, and way ahead of Sister Mary Ursula and, once again, Uldemar.

Looking over the parapet, I saw the barbarian messenger had walked this time, and he had one of our guards as prisoner. The guard was holding a sack, and a pile of gold was poured out at his feet—proof that the man was not a simple deserter but one of the group that had been accompanying the gold.

I called down, "If you think *that's* Prince Wulfgar, you're mistaken."

The barbarian spat. People in this world seemed fond of spitting. He said, "Wulfgar is being the one what can be changing his self into a wolf. He is being our captive."

"We take your word for that?" I asked.

The barbarian gave his prisoner a shake. "Tell," he commanded.

The guard was nodding. "The prince is alive," he assured us. "He was asleep in one of the wagons when the barbarians surrounded us. He changed into a wolf but was struck in the shoulder by an arrow. Though he's injured, he will recover."

Sure, one of us got some rest, I thought grumpily, though it was hardly a fair grievance considering that now he was captive and wounded. I also thought, *Am I the only one in this kingdom who DIDN'T know Wulfgar could take on the shape of a wolf?*

Meanwhile, I called down to the barbarian, "What are you offering?"

"The life of the prince for the life of the princess."

To my surprise—and gratification—there was a roar of protest from my men on the battlements.

Before I could get too smug, Abas, sentimental softy that he was, nudged me and said, "Ask if that trade includes the gold, too."

Deming said, "The situation is more emotionally

209

wrenching than before, but we cannot give in to their demands."

Thank you, Deming.

I was glad to have a refusal that sounded like a political stance rather than cowardice. I yelled down, "We do not bargain with extortioners. But remember this: Harm Wulfgar and you lose any chance to negotiate later."

The barbarian spat—which came as no surprise—and slit the throat of his hostage—which *was* a surprise.

Our men released a flurry of arrows, deeming he had broken the truce first, but he was at the border of their range and quickly sprinted back to his own lines.

Andreanna said to me, "That's what they'll do to Wulfgar, too. And it's all your fault."

I half expected her to spit, too, but fortunately she didn't. She turned and headed for the stairs. "Out of my way, you old fool," I heard her say.

Sister Mary Ursula hefted herself up the last step, huffing like a beached whale. Andreanna pushed past her, and Abas and Kenric followed, with Orielle close behind, and Deming behind her. Sister Mary Ursula asked, "Did I miss anything?"

I ignored her and asked Penrod, "Did you see Xenos come walking out of the castle—through the walls—a short while ago?"

Though that should have been hard to miss, he said, "'Through the walls,' Princess?" and shook his head. "No, Princess."

"Or did you notice a bat, maybe?"

"A..."—Penrod hesitated—"bat?"

I waved my arms to indicate flapping wings.

210

"Hard to say, Princess," Penrod said. "Usually bats don't come out till dusk."

It didn't make any difference. I doubted Uldemar could get Xenos to return—even if, as a bat using his sonar sense instead of eyes, Uldemar could find him.

Perhaps thinking I'd become mentally unbalanced, Penrod said, "You should take what rest you can now, Princess. When the sun sets, they will resume their attack."

Would a two-hour nap make me feel like a new person, or would it just give all my overworked muscles time to stiffen? Better, I thought, to stay in the guards' view, helping—getting their attention in a good way lest they reconsider how much they had to gain by turning me over to the barbarians.

"Let's get these men fed," I told Penrod. "There'll be little enough time for that later."

Sister Mary Ursula said, "Oh no, not the stairs again."

"Sorry," I told her. I tried to think of something useful to occupy her. "Could you organize the ladies into making bandages?"

"I am One with the chickadee," she answered. "I am mother and sister and child of the deer the moment before the hunter's arrow pierces its heart."

I had no idea if that meant yes or no, or if she was simply declaring that she was a vegetarian.

THE GUARDS stayed on the walls, in case the barbarian attack came sooner than we expected, so their food had to be brought up to them.

I tried to help the pages, but frankly I was more bother than benefit because I had to hold my skirts up out of the way going up those stairs—and that's hard to do while carrying a heavy tray of food—and because the ghosts kept getting in everybody's way in the crowded stairwell.

"Maybe," the head page suggested, "it would be best if you stayed up here, helping to distribute the food."

I ended up doling out the mead, which had to be the best job I could have to make them appreciate me, for they seemed to like drinking better than eating.

But all the while, the shadows were lengthening and the edge of the sky got pink, and the pages scurried to clean up before the battle began and the trays and barrels and dishes became a hazard to the men who would be defending our lives.

I pounded the lid back onto the barrel of mead with the butt of a knife one of the men loaned me for that purpose.

"And did *you* take time to eat?" someone asked from behind me.

I turned to see Kenric, but my happiness at his concern was diminished by the sight of Orielle standing by him. He was carrying a huge wicker laundry basket filled with rags, and he put this down by my feet.

Ah, I thought, *Sister Mary Ursula's bandage brigade has been at work.*

Kenric said, "Orielle, go fetch Janine something to eat before they bring everything back to the kitchen, will you?"

I thought she might bristle at being spoken to as though she were a servant, but she only said, "Certainly," and went to intercept one of the pages.

Kenric nodded toward the bandages and said, "Orielle has doused these in a potion that will help promote healing."

"That was kind of her," I said.

Kenric grinned. "Orielle doesn't do things out of kindness," he said. "She works for pay."

Well. So maybe the two of them weren't as cozy as I'd thought.

Orielle came back bearing a bowl of stew and a hunk of bread. "You aren't being very kind," she complained to Kenric. "I don't *always* demand to be paid." She handed me the bowl. "I very much admire how you're handling yourself," she told me. "To go from the quiet life you've been used to...I can't imagine. My father ran out on us when I was born with the witch mark on me." *Another no-account father,* I thought as she held up her palm, showing a pentagram that seemed etched into her skin. "My mother tried to drown me when I was seven, and I was raised in the gutter. I'm used to betrayal and deception and people trying to use me. But you're doing this all on your own, not needing anybody, not having to play *men's* games..." She drifted off, and I knew she meant "not having to flirt and act sexy," which I figured I couldn't have done, anyway, but I didn't think she was putting me down for not looking like a cover girl. It didn't sound as though her fabulous looks had given her a happy life. In fact, she said, "I envy you *so* much."

Somebody who looked like Orielle envied *me*?

"I've got an idea," Orielle said. "How about if we send Kenric away, and then we can discuss what's wrong with men and the way they run the world?"

"I beg your pardon," Kenric said. "What's wrong with men?"

"Nothing," Orielle said. "Nothing is ever wrong with a man—it's always someone else's fault."

"That's a stereotype," Kenric pointed out.

It was, but I couldn't help throwing in a joke I'd heard: "If a man is all alone in the forest with no one to hear him...is he still wrong?"

Orielle laughed.

"So," Kenric said, "should I just leave the two of you on your own, then?"

We waved him away and sat down on the battlement. "This stew," I said, "is the best thing I've eaten all day."

"It's the *only* thing you've eaten all day," she pointed out.

It was venison, which I wouldn't have chosen even before Sister Mary Ursula's comment about poor hunted deer. But I was hungry enough that I was willing to eat Bambi's mother.

Watching Kenric, who had gone to stand by Abas, Orielle said, "I'll admit those three are good-looking..."

"They are that," I agreed.

"But if I hear Abas brag one more time about how many roast ducks he can eat in one sitting or how many cows he can lift with one arm..."

I said, "Do the words *Spanish steel* mean anything to you?"

In unison and with a great deal of pomposity we both said, "Toledo," then giggled as though we were safe in a school cafeteria.

Orielle said, "And, of course, you can't trust Kenric."

214

"So I've heard," I said, thinking of Nigel Rasmussem's warning.

"And Wulfgar—come the full moon and he's impossible."

"I can imagine."

Orielle sighed. "But their looks *are* distracting."

I nodded, but I shifted uncomfortably. The stew seemed to be sitting in a lump somewhere between my throat and my stomach.

"Is something wrong?" Orielle asked.

I set down the bowl of stew. "I think I ate too fast after not eating for so long." I tugged on the neckline of my dress. "And I really should change out of this velvet monstrosity. I'm *so* hot." The day was ending. Shouldn't it be cooling off? My lips felt parched, and I went to lick them, but my tongue was so dry and heavy, I couldn't move it. I tried to say, "Isn't it getting awfully hot?" but my voice came out thick and garbled. Besides, I could see that it wasn't hot. Some of the men had put on cloaks against the evening chill.

Though my body was still hot, my heart went cold.

It's not fair! I thought. *I'm doing well. I'm going to finish this game in this lifetime.*

But I'd taken too long to get here.

The damaged Rasmussem computers were overloading my brain. I was beginning to die.

"No!" I tried to cry defiantly, but it was little more than a moan.

"Let me get you something to drink," Orielle offered.

I saw her stand, but I felt as though I were looking through the wrong end of a telescope. And either she

215

was tipping, or I was. *Must be me,* I reasoned, for the parapet was at an odd angle, too.

Kenric came up to Orielle and put his arm around her waist. "Not feeling well, is she?" he asked.

"Fevered," Orielle said, "and delirious."

"Ah, what a pity," Kenric said, not looking or sounding the least bit pitying.

Neither did Orielle, come to think of it.

Captain Penrod came rushing over. *He* did look distressed. "Princess!" he cried. He took hold of me and sat me up straight—I know only because I could see him do it. I couldn't feel his hands on my arms. My neck was no longer strong enough to hold my head up.

I couldn't feel anything, and I told myself, *Don't panic. It could be worse. Not feeling anything is better than feeling pain.* But that didn't truly help.

Abas must have joined the group. "What's the matter with *her*?" I heard him ask.

"Fevered and delirious," Kenric said.

"Just like Father," Abas commented dryly.

"Just like Father," Kenric echoed.

And then I *did* feel something. I felt fizziness engulf my body.

CHAPTER TWENTY-TWO

Did Someone Say Déjà Vu?

They'd *poisoned* me, dammit. Probably to trade my dead body to the barbarians for Wulfgar's safe return. Or maybe just for the fun of it. Both Sir Deming and Queen Andreanna had insisted King Cynric had been fevered and delirious before he died. They'd brought it up as a rationale for why the king had named me his heir, but now I wondered what had killed *him*.

And Kenric. Deming had declared him much too interested in magic. Yeah, right. Much too interested in a certain user of magic. I should have asked Orielle *why* her mother had tried to drown her.

I stood up on the hillside overlooking St. Jehan and screamed in frustration—which scared Dusty, though she still came up to me, just slower than usual, her tail giving a tentative little wag. I was glad that I wasn't being deep-fried by the computer, but I *would be* if I didn't figure my way out of this convoluted, backstabbing, mean-spirited game.

"Is everything all right, dear?" my mother asked when I got to the bottom of the hill.

"I am One with the morning," I told her. "And my chosen adviser knows her meats."

"That's nice," my mother said, and she introduced me to Sir Deming, and I met my father—who was my favorite person in this game—and I went to the shrine of Saint Bruce the Warrior Poet.

I spent my travel time working on remembering the poem I'd recited last time. I was beginning to suspect that Saint Bruce would accept any poem a player made up, but I knew for a fact that he had accepted "An Ode to Saint Bruce." *I* didn't think it was good poetry, but who was I to argue with a saint with a sword in his hand? So I recited it again:

> *"Saint Bruce was a warrior poet.*
> *He lived in a cave, don't you know it?*
> *He wrote sonnets and verses,*
> *But never said curses.*
> *He'll give you one chance—please don't blow it."*

Feordina whimpered and flung herself out of the way, but then she always did.

I was waiting for her to say, "He must be in a good mood. Lucky you; he's accepted your poem," when I saw the sword begin its fatal swing down.

Our numbers concur with Japan's:
Giannine may or may not have time
to complete one more lifetime. There
definitely won't be another chance.

She is making a valiant effort but may
not be able to make up for time lost in
her initial attempts to break through
level 1.

Medical personnel standing by.

Members of the press are aware that
there is a situation but do not have
details. Please remain calm and refer
all questions to Jim in PR, who is
preparing a statement.

I will try to remain calm, too, but I
am sick at heart.

CHAPTER TWENTY-THREE

Will the Guilty Party Please Step Forward?

O K, so apparently when Feordina warned that Saint Bruce had a good memory, she didn't just mean he would recognize published poetry—apparently she meant a player had to make up a new poem each time.

Thanks a lot, Nigel Rasmussem.

OK: hill, Deming, Dad, shrine...The next time I stood in front of the statue, I recited:

> *"A poem in a cave:*
> *Offering up all my hopes*
> *On butterfly wings."*

Feordina didn't wince and duck. She smiled and said, "Haiku."

"Yes," I said.

"Saint Bruce likes haiku."

"Well, good."

"Except..."

How had I known there'd be an "Except..."?

"Except, haiku's so *very* short..."

"Succinct," I corrected.

"Good word," she told me. "Haiku's so *very* short that if a poet offers up haiku poetry, Bruce *does* like two." She smiled her brown-toothed smile at me.

A *second* poem?

"Did I mention the time limit?"

So, on the spot, I made up another haiku:

> *"The statue of Bruce,*
> *Silent but waiting to strike:*
> *Poem, do not fail me."*

Feordina and I watched the sword.

"Not quite as good as the first one," she said. "But he must be in a good mood. Lucky you."

If I were lucky, my father would have forgotten my birthday.

But apparently, I thought as I hid the ring in my bodice, I had to make my own luck one step at a time.

So when, at the castle, Rawdon introduced himself, I wouldn't let him go. "No, you come into the Great Hall with me," I told him.

"Oh, but you're meeting your family for the first time," he said. "This should be a joyous private occasion."

I could have said, "Yeah, well, we both know it's not going to be and, anyway, I know where you're off to, you larcenous little weasel, you." But I didn't. I just said, pleasantly, "I insist. As your new king."

The royal family didn't care that I brought a witness with me; they were just as irritable and snide as ever.

I'd been thinking about which family member I needed to choose as an ally. They'd each had a crack at

221

killing me: Abas had taken my head off in this very room; Wulfgar, in his wolf shape, had killed me both in the to-piary maze and in the barbarian camp; and I was sure Kenric had arranged for me to be poisoned—whether or not he was also behind the death of King Cynric.

So, who to choose this time?

Wulfgar was unpredictable unless I used the ring on him; so if I needed the ring later on, I'd be out of luck.

Abas had prevented the barbarians from kidnapping me—which I had to believe was a good thing—except that, in saving me, he had killed King Grimbold, which the barbarians seemed exceptionally reluctant to forgive. Was there a way to get Abas to fight off the barbarians more...gently?

"Abas" and "gently" in the same sentence: *Right.*

Bringing me back to Kenric, who had been my first choice all those tries ago, based on his good looks—which were, come to think of it, what had gotten me into this game to begin with. *Kenric.* Well, Mr. Rasmussem had warned me away from him. Or maybe not. "Kenric and Sister Mary Ursula don't work well together," he'd said. Maybe all he had meant was that that pairing needed extra work.

How many more times could I afford to be wrong?

"Kenric," I called as the royals dispersed. "May Counselor Rawdon and I walk with you?"

At which point Rawdon said, "You know what would be nice? Why don't the two of you have a cozy little chat—"

"No, no." I linked arms with both him and Kenric.

"Let's all three of us walk together and get to know one another. Tell me, each of you, your impressions of King Cynric."

They both looked startled and maybe a bit worried at that thought.

I said, "Rawdon, you first."

"Oh," Rawdon blustered. "Well. Ah. What do you mean?"

"I haven't had a chance to know my father. It's very difficult to grow up without a father, you know. So many things make no sense if you don't have your dad— those mushy Father's Day cards every June, Father Christmas, 'Our Father who art in heaven...'"

They were looking at me as though my brain were dribbling out of my nose.

"Not that I'm bitter or anything. Was he a good man? Fair? Did he have any faults, like, was he overly trusting, perhaps?"

By then we were out in the courtyard. There was the supply wagon, though no barbarians were lurking behind it for the moment. And there were Captain Penrod and the other guard, yet again dragging the poacher boy between them.

"Oh, look," I said. "I wonder if this is something we need to make a decision about. Hello, Captain. I'm Princess Janine. What's happened here?"

Penrod said, "We caught this boy poaching. He killed a deer. The usual punishment?"

Before Kenric could ask me what I thought, I turned to Rawdon and asked, "What do *you* advise, Counselor?

223

Are you an advocate of strict interpretation of severe laws to deter crime?"

I saw Rawdon gulp. His voice faint and maybe wobbling just the slightest bit, he said, "The law is the law."

The boy sniveled, "No. I didn't do nothing. I found 'im dead already. I was dressing 'im down so's the meat wouldn't go to waste, but I didn't kill 'im."

I pressed Rawdon. "So there's no room for compassion for one who has foolishly done wrong, then come to sincerely regret his crime?"

"I wouldn't say that," Rawdon whispered.

No, I wouldn't think you would.

I saw that Kenric was watching Rawdon appraisingly, no doubt wondering what had rattled him. I said, "Of course, in this case, we don't even know for sure that the accused is guilty. Or do we?" I turned to Penrod. "Did any witness actually see him kill the deer?"

"No witnesses," Penrod admitted. "But look at his hands."

I said, "Good point. But then, he admitted he was dressing down the deer once it was already dead. This is a difficult decision without witnesses. Do we know for a fact how the deer died, and how long it had been dead?"

"There was an arrow in its gut," Penrod said. "And the body was still warm."

"You're very good at details," I told him. His manner was friendlier, too, once I didn't simply dismiss him and declare him wrong and the boy free. "Was the boy carrying a bow?"

"Yes," Penrod said.

The boy hastily said, "I found it. It was just layin'

there, like, on the ground, at the edge of the clearing. And I, uh, picked it up before I started in on the deer. Which was dead already. Killed by someone else. Who probably heard me comin', and thought it was you, and fled before I got there. Before *you* got there, too."

"That's not a very likely story," I told him. "But on the other hand, I don't see any way to disprove it." I looked at the men around me, none of whom was saying anything. I said, "I'm inclined to say that—since we can't avow that this boy is the culprit—it is better to err on the side of compassion."

Penrod looked about to object, so I added, "But neither can we be seen to let people flaunt the law. Still, killing the boy serves no purpose. The deer is already dead, whether by his doing or another's—and his death will not bring the deer back. Cutting the boy's hand off will only make him unlikely to find gainful employment, and he'll become a drain on society. If we jail him, we have to feed him and take guards off their regular duty in order to watch him. I think the best solution is to put him to work—for a period of...a month?" I looked at Rawdon. "What do you think?"

"That sounds fair to me," Rawdon said weakly.

"Interesting," Kenric said, whether at my line of reasoning or at Rawdon's response.

"Captain, you decide what chores you think would be best to set for this boy. Keep in mind his age and his strength, but assign him whatever duties you see fit."

Penrod nodded. He ordered the other guard, "Bring him to the crew that's fixing the smithy roof."

"Meanwhile," I said to Penrod as the second guard

led the boy away, "I want you to come to me if there are any problems you or the other guards have with the way anything is done here."

"Yes, Princess," Penrod said.

"Anything," I repeated. "You and your men are the backbone of this castle. The work you do is invaluable, and I see that you run things smoothly, efficiently, and fairly, and I want you to know how much I appreciate that."

"Thank you, Princess," Penrod said.

"You know what?" I turned to Rawdon. "Here we are starting a new kingship, with a new way of interpreting the laws, and I think something else we need to do is give a better salary to our hardworking guards. What do you think?"

"Well," Rawdon huffed, but that was all he could get out.

I smiled at Penrod. "How much and how often do you get paid?"

"Actually," he said, "there seems to have been a problem with that lately. We've been shorted several times the last months, and we haven't yet been paid for the past fortnight."

"Really?" I said. Kenric was already looking at Rawdon, so I turned to him, too. "Who's in charge of the men's pay?" I demanded.

"You see," Rawdon told me, "as the king was getting weaker these past weeks, I began to worry that someone might take advantage of the situation, and once the king named you his heir, I thought, *Well, but the king's wife and her sons might refuse to acknowledge the king's wishes,* and I thought, *If they have access to the king's treasury, there's no telling—*"

Kenric took hold of Rawdon by the scruff of his neck. "Have you done something with the treasury?"

"No," Rawdon said. "That is, I just moved it—for safekeeping."

"Where?" Kenric demanded.

"I didn't mean that I mistrusted *you*," Rawdon assured Kenric. "Of course, I knew *you* wouldn't try to make off with the money, but sometimes your brothers—"

Kenric gave him a shake.

"Fairfield," Rawdon admitted.

Kenric shook him even harder.

"How much did you steal?" I asked, because in this lifetime there was no way for me to know. "All of it?"

"No," he said as though that thought was ridiculous. "Just some. Just a little."

"Uh-huh," I said. "You've seen my mercy with the boy accused of poaching. I will spare your life, too, if you show us where you've hidden the treasury. You will be dismissed as counselor and instead will be put in charge of..." What was something bad, but not so horrible he'd rebel? I thought of our neighbors in St. Jehan and finished, "...in charge of raising the pigs."

Rawdon dropped to his knees, kissed my hand, and said, "Thank you, Your Gracious Highness."

"Good job, Princess," Captain Penrod said to me.

"Yes," Kenric acknowledged. Was he actually looking at me with respect? Yes, I was pretty sure he was. *Surprised* respect, but still...

I said, "Penrod, you take Rawdon and keep him

under guard, while Kenric and I determine how much of the treasury is gone."

Penrod saluted, while Kenric held his hand out for Rawdon's keys.

I said, "And, Penrod, the queen mentioned the possibility of barbarian unrest. My instincts tell me this is a very serious danger. Double the guards around the castle wall, and make sure everyone is alert."

"Yes, Princess."

As Kenric and I turned back to the castle, I just barely caught a glimpse of Sister Mary Ursula as she reentered ahead of us. Apparently, if I didn't simply let the poacher go, she didn't approach me. Either that, or the fact that I was with Kenric kept her away.

"Who was that?" I asked since, in this lifetime, I hadn't met her.

"That is the singular Sister Mary Ursula," Kenric told me.

I let it go at that.

Naturally, when we got to the treasury room, there was quite a bit more than "some" of it missing. All that was left was what he would have made off with this day. "The first thing I think we should do is put Sir Deming in charge of counting out exactly how much is left," I said. Obnoxious irritant that he was, I had no reason to doubt his honesty; and Sister Mary Ursula had made clear her distrust of and disliking for gold. For all I knew, she might toss what was left into the lake to make the gold One with the water. "Then I want the guards paid, and I want them to get a bonus for their salaries being late, because the last thing we need is to lose credibility with them. Then we'll need to get wagons and guards to travel to Fairfield to retrieve the money."

"How many?" Kenric asked.

"I'll leave that up to you," I said, to make him feel I valued his opinion. If he suggested something significantly different from what Penrod had in the previous game, I could always overrule him.

"And will you go to Fairfield yourself," Kenric asked, "or will you send a representative?"

"What do you suggest?" I asked.

"*I* don't care."

OK. "Well, then," I told him, "probably I'll go." I didn't think anything was scheduled to happen at the castle in the afternoon that I would miss. All I'd done the previous time was get cleaned up and fitted with that awful red dress. Then I'd lost a lot of time searching in the catacombs, running back and forth to the castle....

Oh, yeah, the catacombs. I suddenly remembered the ghosts. If I *didn't* go, the ghosts wouldn't be able to follow me—surely a good thing. But I worried that, without me, the game would arrange for *something* to happen so that whomever I sent wouldn't be able to find the money.

We went back down to the courtyard to assure Penrod there was enough left in the treasury to pay the back salaries. Though I could see the extra guards posted, I remained alert for barbarians, glancing back and forth and over my shoulder—for I was fairly certain Rasmussem would have them get in even if I ordered *all* the guards out.

Kenric finally asked, "Is something wrong? You seem to be doing an awful lot of twitching."

I couldn't admit what I knew, so I said, "Fleas."

"Charming." Kenric sighed.

Sure enough, when we got to the wagon, I saw a shadow that shouldn't be there. I shoved Kenric out of the way, hit the ground rolling, and yelled, "Attack! We're under attack!"

CHAPTER TWENTY-FOUR

Fast Forward

An arrow whizzed through the air where a moment earlier Kenric and I had been standing.

"Attempt to take prisoners!" I shouted. I kept rolling, reversing direction, this way and that, trying to make myself an unlikely target for the barbarian archers.

Our guards manning the walls fired a flurry of arrows into the area behind the wagon. They were also firing over the wall—which must have meant that the rest of the raiding party had come out of hiding when they realized their compatriots in the castle compound were in trouble.

I stopped rolling, figuring that the three barbarians who were behind the wagon had enough other worries that they were unlikely to be concentrating on me. Besides, if nobody was shooting at me, I must look incredibly silly rolling all over the courtyard.

Some of the guards went behind the wagon, and they

dragged out two bodies and led out a prisoner. For the moment, I was too dizzy to focus on his face.

Kenric helped me to my feet and held on to me as I staggered toward the wagon. The survivor *was* King Grimbold. I sighed heavily, and Kenric tightened his grip, no doubt convinced I was about to faint. Penrod was on my other side, though I'd been unaware when he'd joined us. One of the guards on the wall yelled down, "Captain, about a half-dozen barbarians took off into the woods."

"Should we pursue them?" Penrod asked me.

"No," I said. "We'll question this man first." I gave my most regal look down my nose—though I was no competition for Queen Andreanna and her *what*-is-that-bad-smell? glare—and I demanded, "Who are you? And why did you sneak over our walls and attempt to do harm to me and my men?"

Grimbold spat—big surprise—and announced, "I am being Grimbold, King of the North, and I have comed here to claim that which is being mine that has been stoled."

I gave just the hint of a bow of my head—only enough to acknowledge his status as a king. "King Grimbold, I am Princess Janine de St. Jehan, due to be crowned as the new Shelban king in two days' time. I wish that we could have met under better circumstances. Surely this"—I waved my hand in the direction of his two dead compatriots and all my guards with bows still trained on him—"this is not the way for neighbors to meet."

The fact that I was speaking calmly, without threats, had a positive effect on the captive king.

"My peoples," he explained, "have never been having good luck speaking to your peoples."

"I am sorry to hear that," I assured him. I gestured for our guards to put their weapons away. There was little Grimbold could do to harm me unless he made a suicidal leap forward to throttle me, and my show of good faith could only make him obligated to me. "What is this item of yours that you believe we have?"

"The crown of our firstest chieftain, Brecc the Slayer, made for him by the wizard Xenos."

"Do we have such a thing?" I asked those around me.

"Yes," Kenric admitted.

"We *stole* it?" I tried to sound as appalled, as though I were only hearing it for the first time.

"Not exactly."

"I think," I said in my best Solomon voice, "we need to settle this immediately. King Grimbold, I regret the death of your companions. I wish that you had known me well enough to have felt you could approach openly."

He inclined his head, which I very much hoped meant he was taking responsibility for the death of his own men.

"Meanwhile," I said, "let us discuss this matter indoors. Shouldn't it be almost time to eat?"

There were lots of enthusiastic nods from my men.

"Then let us go in."

Neither those guards who were scheduled to eat at that time nor Grimbold waited to be invited twice, leaving me alone with Captain Penrod and Kenric.

Penrod dropped to his knees and offered me his sword. "Obviously, I didn't post enough guards, Princess

Janine. You could have been killed, and it would have been my fault."

"No." I shook my head for emphasis and refused to take the sword. "They were determined and would have gotten in no matter what. I have the utmost trust in you."

He bowed, with a murmured, "I am indebted to you."

Kenric said, "As am I. I owe my life to your vigilance."

"To my fleas," I corrected, "that made me restless."

Kenric smiled. "Nevertheless..." he said, and took my arm again—this time not to steady me, but to escort me into the Great Hall.

When I entered the room on Kenric's arm, Queen Andreanna wore an expression as though she'd just put a pickled eyeball into her mouth. Kenric ignored his mother's scowl and smacked Abas on the arm, indicating for him to move in closer to Wulfgar, so that I could sit at the high table with them.

"We need room for King Grimbold, too," I said.

Abas had already gotten as close to Wulfgar as comfort would allow, but neither Wulfgar nor Andreanna budged.

"That is being all right," Grimbold announced. "I will be seating myself here, next to this handsome woman." And with that he plunked himself down on the edge of the bench beyond Andreanna, which—under normal circumstances—would have accommodated only the tiniest of persons. Grimbold wasn't tiny.

Andreanna scooted closer to Wulfgar faster than I'd ever seen her move.

"Hello, there, my lovely," Grimbold said to the queen. "I be guessing you still being fit enough to be breeding children."

"I beg your pardon!" Andreanna was practically on Wulfgar's lap, trying to gain more distance from Grimbold.

Grimbold, who hadn't spoken quietly before, now shouted, "I said, 'I be guessing you still being fit enough to be breeding children!'"

"King Grimbold," I said by way of introduction, "this is Queen Andreanna, the widow of King Cynric. Queen Andreanna, this is King Grimbold, whom I have invited to dine with us while we discuss matters of state."

"Ah!" Grimbold shouted the length of the table down to me. "The queen, is she? Probably one of them delicate sorts—is that what you be telling me?"

I nodded.

He turned his attention back to Andreanna. "All right, then," he assured her, "I be acting refined around you." He nudged her in the ribs with his elbow and winked. "I don't be believing in making my women skittish."

For just this once, things only got better.

Grimbold explained that King Cynric had taken the crown that rightfully belonged to him and his people.

Abas explained that his father had won it in a tournament.

Grimbold and Abas debated the finer points of tournament rules till the rest of us were just about facedown asleep in our bowls of leek soup before Abas conceded that perhaps his father had been a bit overly lenient in his interpretation of what was and was not allowed.

Queen Andreanna protested, "He won it fairly!"

Grimbold said, "I be liking a woman what defends her man."

Next I asked where the crown was likely to be—of

course, nobody knew—and we invited Sir Deming and Sister Mary Ursula to join us. Grimbold moved in even closer to Andreanna and said to Sister Mary Ursula, "Come over here and sit next to me, you sweet young thing," though she had to be thirty years older than he was.

Sister Mary Ursula giggled like a sixth grader.

Once again Deming remembered that King Cynric had given the crown to the dragon, and once again he speculated that one of the magic-users might know how to find the dragon.

I gave orders for the magic-users to be sent for, despite Sister Mary Ursula's warning that magic was nasty.

Grimbold assured her that he would protect her from any of magic's nastiness.

She giggled some more.

Grimbold said he would send word to his people that I was working on reclaiming the crown and that they should postpone attacking the castle.

"Give me three days," I told him, knowing I had only two days, at the most, before the game would end—with or without my having recovered the crown.

"One," Grimbold said, a hard bargainer despite the fact that he'd just eaten close to an entire roast pig at my table.

"Two," I countered, and he spat on the floor and slapped his palm on the table, which seemed to mean we had an agreement.

Queen Andreanna left the table before the pastries were served, murmuring something about having to watch her figure, despite Grimbold's assurance that he liked his women substantial enough to grab hold of.

In fact, we all left the table before Grimbold had finished eating.

I had decided it was safest if I accompanied Rawdon and the guards on the expedition to Fairfield, just in case of complications. I hoped that, with Rawdon leading us through the catacombs directly to where he had hidden the gold, I might avoid picking up any ghosts. But, just in case, I decided I'd better take a quick bath now and choose what clothes to wear. Who knew when the next time would be I could do so without witnesses?

I told Sir Deming I'd chosen him to be in charge of the treasury—what was left of it, plus what we recovered—and that made him almost pleasant. What he said was, "Good decision."

"Can you suggest someone I might borrow clothes from?" I asked, sending mental vibrations his way that said, *Not Lady Bliss, not Lady Bliss*.

Deming looked at me appraisingly, and I was sure he was about to make a disparaging remark. Instead, he said, "If you're going to be running around the countryside digging up treasure, you might do well to borrow one of the page's uniforms."

It struck me as a good idea, too.

After bathing and changing, and making a twine necklace to hold the ring, and handing out to the guards their back salaries and their bonuses, it was time to set off for Fairfield. This time we brought provisions in case we were there long enough to get hungry. I left Kenric in charge of the castle because that seemed a good show of trust in him at a time when, in fact, I was fairly confident nothing much would be going on. I brought Captain Penrod with me, since the castle was no longer in danger of barbarian attack.

Rawdon didn't cause any trouble on the way, being so relieved not to have received a death sentence that he kept trying to kiss my hand. Who would have guessed that such a thing could become excessive?

In the catacombs I still caught glimpses of things that weren't there and heard echoes of whispers that had never been spoken.

I didn't have high hopes for not accumulating ghosts.

It *was* much easier crawling around tunnels and exploring catacombs while wearing a page's tunic and breeches than it was wearing a red velvet gown made for a woman of the kind Grimbold would definitely have found substantial.

Rawdon led us to his hiding place. Despite all the trouble he'd caused, I even warned him that the doorway looked rather punky and that it needed to be shored up so it wouldn't collapse.

I stayed while the guards brought load after load of gold to the waiting wagons; but if any ghosts had attached themselves to me, and if they *were* going to make sleeping difficult, I knew I should probably get a head start home. Leaving Captain Penrod in charge of escorting the convoy home, I made it back to the castle at about midnight.

The guards recognized me this time—as well they

should, since I was the one who'd given them their money—so they readily let me in. As I walked to the castle, I heard them having trouble raising the drawbridge.

"Hello, ghosts," I muttered.

One of them poked me in the ribs, while another pulled my hair.

The good times were over.

CHAPTER TWENTY-FIVE

Morning Comes Early
When There's No Snooze Button

Just as I had been warned, the ghosts proved to be a nuisance all night long.

They moaned.

They wailed.

They rattled the window shutters.

They set the castle hounds to howling.

It wasn't that their noise was continuous. No, you can get used to just about any sound that *never* stops. Instead, they periodically grew quiet, giving the impression that they had worn themselves out or gotten bored or taken pity on the castle's inhabitants. I would start to doze. Then a door would slam. A long-dead person would scream. Cobwebby fingers would brush my face.

My brain knew that my body was lying on a total immersion couch at a Rasmussem Gaming Center, and that probably less than an hour had passed since I'd gotten there on a Saturday afternoon. Try to tell *that* to the body

I felt I was wearing, which was convinced it had been tossing and turning all night.

I gave up around dawn. A servant had left a bedpan, and a pitcher of water to clean up with. I used both beneath the cover of my blanket, and I dressed under there.

Despite these precautions, I was pretty sure I heard ghostly laughter.

While I'd been away at Fairfield, someone had left an elegant gown for today's use, but I once again chose the page's outfit. The way this game had shown a tendency to go—breeches and tunic were a more practical choice than a dress.

I stuck my head out the door to see if anybody else was up yet. In the hallway, bleary-eyed servants stumbled about their early-morning tasks. And Sister Mary Ursula, wearing her fetching two-towels outfit, was just returning from her skinny-dipping trip. "My soul is refreshed, and I am One with the world," she announced.

"Congratulations," I mumbled. "Do we go to the Great Hall for breakfast, or is it brought up to our rooms?"

"Whatever you decree, dear," Sister Mary Ursula said. "You *are* our next king."

"In my room would be nice," I said, heading back to bed, too exhausted to check whether she or any of the servants had heard.

Apparently the ghosts had truly quit come sunrise. I awoke at a slightly more reasonable hour when a sleep-deprived servant came in carrying breakfast. Buttered chocolate Pop-Tarts would have been nice, but I made do with fresh bread and honey.

"Could you ask Sister Mary Ursula and Sir Deming to meet me in the solar when they finish their breakfasts?" I said.

The servant, yawning, nodded and shuffled her weary way out.

I fought the inclination to put my head back down. Surely someone who hoped to be crowned the following day had more important things to do than sleep—no matter how tired I was. There would be time to catch up *after* I was king.

I knocked on Kenric's door. Though he was dressed, I wouldn't have sworn he was truly awake. "Somehow or other we seem to have picked up ghosts," he told me.

I didn't tell him how or who. I said, "We recovered the gold."

He nodded. "I heard the wagons come in some time between the banshee wailing and the chain dragging."

So had I. I'd figured if there was any problem, Captain Penrod would have sent for me, despite the hour. In fact, I suspected that the guards who had fetched the gold had an easier night than those of us in our beds in the castle.

"I'm going to interview the advisers," I told him, "to see which one to name my official appointee. Any suggestions?"

As I reflected on past games, I saw that Sister Mary Ursula did sometimes give good advice, as when she had warned against trusting Rawdon or eating the venison stew. The trouble was, most often I couldn't tell what she was saying until after the disaster struck. Of course, she had clearly cautioned me regarding magic and Kenric, but I was willing to ignore that. So I thought for a change I'd ask Deming, whom I'd already placed in charge of the treasury. I was pretty sure Kenric would pick him, too—considering that Mr. Rasmussem had warned against choosing both Kenric and Sister Mary Ursula—and that would give me the chance to seem like I was seeking out his advice while I was, in fact, doing what I wanted.

Kenric said, "All things considered, Rawdon wouldn't be my first choice—though he was my father's counselor. And Sister Mary Ursula is a bit..."—he paused and then came up with—"mystical...for my taste. Deming is a bit of an obsequious toady, but on the whole he's steady."

Obsequious? Doesn't that mean the kind of person who says, "Yes, sir. No, sir. Please let me grovel at your feet, sir"? Maybe he was obsequious to some of us in the royal family...

I tried to look thoughtful as I said, "Deming. Hmm."

Kenric was probably waiting for me to go so he could lay his head down for a few more minutes, so I took pity on him and left.

In the solar, Sister Mary Ursula was doing tai chi exercises: those slow-motion, almost dancelike stretches. She had changed out of her towels to another outfit; the accent pieces looked like stuff that was either left on the beach by high tide or blown by the wind against a fence. Sir Deming wasn't there yet.

"Hello," I said. "We haven't had much of a chance to

talk." We hadn't—not in this lifetime. Of course, I *had* been actively avoiding her.

She didn't stop her exercises, but she said, "I am One with my body."

"Well, that's good," I told her. "Meanwhile, I was hoping that you might stay while Sir Deming and I discuss matters of state—"

"Oh no, no." This time she *did* stop. "Oh dear, no. One counselor is all you need. A unicorn only needs one horn to be a unicorn and not a horse or a goat. A blank sheet of parchment only needs one drop of ink before it is no longer blank. A pretty girl only needs one wart on the end of her nose before she doesn't want to leave her house. One counselor is enough, my dear."

I really liked the idea of getting multiple possibilities laid out before me, so I pointed out, "Only if the counselor is the right counselor. I want to be One with wisdom."

Sister Mary Ursula said, "Don't we all?" and resumed her exercises.

Sir Deming came in then. He raised one eyebrow in surprised disapproval at my boys' clothing. "Didn't Lady Patrice bring a dress for you?" He looked ready to turn right around and search for Lady Patrice to complain that I was dressed inappropriately.

"Yes," I told him. "But this seemed better suited to me."

"Oh," he said. I was surprised he could speak at all with his lip so curled in superior disdain. "This is a fashion statement rather than an oversight. I see."

"Good. Because my wardrobe is not what I'm seeking advice on." I smiled to show I was joking. Yeah, right. "But I *do* need advice on just about everything else."

We discussed every detail I could think of concerning the running of my kingdom. We started with taxes: how much the people were charged, how often they paid, what services were provided in return for payment. (Sister Mary Ursula, despite her contention that I didn't need her advice, gave a very loud *Hmph!* when I didn't abolish the tax system.) We discussed every single law on the books. (Though Deming pursed his lips disapprovingly and said I was asking for anarchy, Sister Mary Ursula hummed approvingly when I abolished capital punishment in favor of fines and community service.) We made plans for the improving of roads and the establishing of schools (who could have ever guessed I'd end up in favor of schools?) and the forming of a trade fair to be held every autumn in the town of Fairfield. I called for riders to announce the proclamations from town to town, hoping that my new way of running things would settle the peasant unrest.

Deming and I had our midday meal in the solar since we didn't want to stop in the middle of things. That, and I was worried about the ghosts, who were periodically knocking over piles of paper and had already spilled one jar of ink. If they messed up our notes or walked off with something we'd been working on, I was sure we'd never be able to get it right again afterward.

Sister Mary Ursula had gotten bored and left while we'd been discussing gross national product—which sounds like it means something interesting, but I'd learned in Participation in Government class that it simply means how much, totally, a country owns and produces.

Deming and I were just finishing when Kenric came by.

"I thought you'd like to know," he said, "that the magic-users have all arrived, and Mother is even now meeting with them."

"Well, how kind of her to ask you to tell me about it," I said, knowing—even before his grin—that she had not. "Sir Deming, would you please find Sister Mary Ursula? I'd like the two of you to attend with me. Tell her I know she mistrusts magic, but I would very much appreciate her counsel. And Captain Penrod, too."

Deming nodded, and I went with Kenric to the Great Hall.

CHAPTER TWENTY-SIX

Keeping Everybody (But Me) Happy

The guards in front of the Great Hall doors didn't wait for me to order them to let us in—which might have had more to do with Kenric than me. Whatever. They saluted and opened the door, and the page blew the trumpet to announce us.

"Oh," Andreanna said as I entered, "look. Someone has hired a stunted, shoddy little page to help us out. Oh dear; my mistake. It's only Janine."

Abas gave his surprisingly tittery laugh.

I asked, "Has lack of sleep made some of us cranky?" though I knew she could sleep as long as Rip van Winkle and still wake up grouchy.

As last time Xenos and Uldemar sat on one side of the table. The queen, Abas, and Wulfgar sat across from them. This time Orielle was sitting on Wulfgar's lap. I wondered if she had moved to him when Kenric left to fetch me, or if she had only chosen Kenric last time because

Wulfgar hadn't been there. I liked to think that Kenric was her first choice but he had told her, "No way. I'm looking for Janine instead of you."

Uh-huh.

Not that I would sit on his lap. Not unless, of course, he asked me.

Andreanna ignored my superior comeback to her ill-tempered jibe and turned her sour face to the guards, ordering, "Close the doors, you incompetent fools."

"Just leave it for a few moments," I recommended to the men who were pushing, pulling, and throwing their weight against the unmoving doors.

Now, if you were a castle guard, who would you be more afraid of: me or Queen Andreanna? The guards continued trying to close the door.

I went to the table and introduced myself. "Hello, I'm Princess Janine. I'm guessing you're Orielle." Orielle gave a dazzling smile that was sure to melt the heart of any young man and to make just about any female want an appointment with a plastic surgeon. I turned to the two men. "And Uldemar and Xenos."

Uldemar nodded at his name, though Xenos was hiding in his monk's cowl.

"Welcome," I told all of them. I realized I hadn't properly greeted them last time. "Thank you for coming on such short notice. I truly appreciate your willingness to help."

My words must have made Xenos feel at home, for he reached into his pocket and tossed a centipede into his mouth.

Kenric sat down next to Abas, making sure that there was enough room for me to sit beside him.

At the other end of the room, the ghosts must have finished squeezing through the doorway, for the guards were suddenly able to shut the doors—which slammed with two solid thuds.

Uldemar took the opportunity to announce, "She brings the stench of the dead with her."

Because we had all been kept up all night, Andreanna knew exactly what he meant. "Oh, you're the one who let the ghosts in, are you?"

"Yes," I said. "I'll tell you my plan for them later." Of course, I had no plan, but suggesting I did *might* be a way to get the queen off my back.

She gave a suspicious, "Likely, I'm sure!" but didn't demand details.

One of the ghosts, however, poked me in the ribs.

It's hard to look self-assured and in command when you've just given a sudden squeal and jumped about a foot out of your seat. "If we're quite ready to settle down..." I said. Nothing from the ghosts, but Sir Deming chose that moment to come in.

"Sorry to interrupt." Instead of sitting, he cleared his throat. Twice. He had either developed a twitch, or he was trying to signal me about *something,* giving his head a sideways jerk toward Queen Andreanna. But when she noticed, he immediately stopped and pretended to be scratching his neck.

Andreanna snapped, "I hope she hasn't brought lice, as well as ghosts."

Deming, practicing his obsequious toady manner, said, "No, I'm sure not. Sorry. Just a crick in my neck."

Andreanna glowered as though the fact that he didn't have lice was a personal affront to her.

I asked, "Will Captain Penrod and Sister Mary Ursula be joining us?"

Deming sat down—how could any male resist?—next to Orielle. He told me, "Captain Penrod said that as a simple military man, he could not possibly attend a state meeting. He assures you that he will steadfastly follow and defend whatever policies you set."

Meaning: "I can carry out instructions, but I can't make suggestions." Silly me.

"And Sister Mary Ursula..."—Deming sneaked a glance at Andreanna, saw that she wasn't at the moment looking at him, and gave me that look-over-*here* nod that signified I-had-no-idea-what—"Sister Mary Ursula is on her way." Nod, nod. Seeing both my baffled expression and Andreanna's increasingly impatient one, Deming shrugged.

Probably just another disaster, I told myself. "OK," I said slowly, "well, then, why don't we get started? I've asked all of you here so we can have a chance to get to know one another, but most pressingly because of the problem with the barbarians."

"Excuse me," a familiar voice interrupted from the doorway, "but it is not *we* that are being the problem."

I looked up and saw that King Grimbold had arrived, with Sister Mary Ursula on his arm.

Oh, so that's what Deming was trying to warn me

about: Queen Andreanna's new beau had invited himself.

"I'm sorry," I said. "Terrible wording on my part. The problem is not you and your people; the problem is how to win the friendship and gain the trust of you and your people by recovering that which has been taken from you."

Grimbold gave a solemn bow to indicate he accepted my explanation.

"Please have a seat." I gestured to the bench across the table, where only Xenos and Uldemar sat.

But Grimbold squeezed himself in between Abas and Andreanna. "Have you been missing me as muchly as I have been missing you, you delectable woman you?" he asked Andreanna.

"Wulfgar," Andreanna demanded from between clenched teeth, "*do* something."

Trying valiantly to swallow a grin, Wulfgar said, "Sorry, my hands are full."

She-with-whom-Wulfgar's-hands-were-full winked and blew a kiss to Grimbold.

The barbarian king smiled and said, "Hello, young lass," but his attention was all for Andreanna.

"Sister Mary Ursula," I said, "have a seat anywhere."

"Oh dear, no," she said. "The room is One with ghosts, necromancers, wizards, and witches. No, no, I couldn't possibly sit down, no."

I wasn't sure how standing made the situation better for her, but I wasn't going to argue. I said, "I thank you for coming despite your dislike of magic."

"Well, you asked so nicely," Sister Mary Ursula said.

Score one for being polite.

I said, "Xenos, my understanding is that you made a crown for the first chieftain of Grimbold's people."

"Yes," Xenos said in his fingernails-on-blackboard voice.

"Brecc the Slayer," King Grimbold reminded us.

"And then King Cynric..." I hesitated and Queen Andreanna said emphatically, "Won," and King Grimbold corrected, "Stoled, my turtledove," and I compromised with, "*got* that crown from King Grimbold's father." Nobody argued, so I went on, "Then King Cynric gave the crown to a dragon who was ravaging the south, though we don't know where that dragon is now."

Sure enough Uldemar leaped in, offering, "I could find him in my scrying glass."

The process was no less disconcerting for knowing what to expect. After Uldemar cast his spell on the black glass, he announced as he had before, "The dragon is in the southern province, in a cave on a mountaintop known as the Old Hag."

Andreanna started, "How—"

And I interrupted, asking, "How far away is this mountain?"

"A week's journey," Andreanna said, obviously delighting in the bad news.

A week? When I only had this day and the next? If I was lucky. "Isn't there any shortcut?"

I looked at each of them in turn. From Deming's, "Nope. Sorry," to Andreanna's self-satisfied smirk to Kenric's gloomy shake of the head, there was no hope from my side of the table. Uldemar was checking his scrying glass again, but he, too, was shaking his head.

Xenos, however, had sunk so deep into his monk's robes that he was in danger of disappearing under the table. He looked, I thought, exactly like a kid mentally begging the teacher not to call on him.

"Xenos?" I said.

"No," he mumbled. "No shortcut." He popped a centipede into his mouth.

"Any idea how to get from here to there and back to here in, oh, let's say a day and a half?"

"Theoretically or actually?" Xenos asked.

Uldemar said, "Come to think of it, how did *you* get here so soon, Xenos? When I contacted you through the scrying glass, you were at least two days' journey away."

"I walk fast," Xenos said.

"He's got boots!" Sister Mary Ursula cried. "That is *so* like a wizard! You are so not One with the world!"

"'Boots'?" I repeated.

"Seven-league boots," Kenric interpreted for me.

"Ah!" I looked under the table. Xenos tried to cover his boots with his robe. "May I borrow those?" I asked.

"And am I supposed to go barefoot meanwhile?"

"I'm sure we can get you some nice slippers to use," I said. "And there's a boy working for us who's interested in wildlife"—I didn't explain about his being a poacher— "and if you'd like, I would put him in charge of finding all the centipedes you could possibly want the entire time I'm away."

Xenos considered for a moment. "I like spiders once in a while, too."

"Certainly."

"Chocolate covered?"

I forced myself not to shudder. "However."

Xenos took off the boots. "They work as regular boots unless you say, 'Seven leagues.' Then they'll take you one step. If you want to go another seven leagues, you have to say, 'Seven leagues' again."

"Gotcha," I said. "Thank you."

Andreanna said, "And I don't suppose you're even going to fumigate them before putting them on."

I took off my shoes and put on the boots, which were green leather and knee-high and *did* give off a smell like the school's locker room on a bad day. But at least they fit.

Andreanna curled her lip at me. "All those hideous boots are going to do is get you there and then—once you see how truly terrible the dragon is—get you out of there quickly. That's *if* you're lucky enough to see the dragon before it sees you. Of course, if *we're* lucky, you'll get up such a momentum of seven-leaguing, you'll walk right by us and get lost in the wilds of the north."

Grimbold patted her arm and said, "Now, my precious, you should na be speaking so harshly to the princess. She be doing her best."

I smiled to show I appreciated the thought. "Does anyone have any dragon-slaying ideas?"

Orielle said, "I could give you a potion that would poison him, if you can get close enough to him."

Xenos started chortling, but before he could go too far, I asked, "What other kinds of potions do you have?" I knew, but not in *this* lifetime.

"I have one that will increase a person's strength and stamina—giving him, or her, the ability to fight as two, or to work for twice as long."

"Any drawbacks?" I asked before Xenos could get a word in.

"It lasts only one hour."

"That's not so bad," I said, which made her admit, reluctantly, "And ... after it wears off, the person will be so weak, he won't even be able to stand up. That stage lasts two hours."

"Very useful," Xenos taunted.

Before Orielle had a chance to turn on him, I pretended his words had been meant earnestly. "Yes, it might be, if I time things perfectly. Please mix me up a batch, Orielle, just in case. What's the price?"

Orielle paused to consider. "The hand of Wulfgar in marriage."

"What?" Andreanna screeched.

"Just the hand?" Xenos asked innocently.

Wulfgar, I saw, did not look displeased. "Wulfgar?" I asked.

He didn't need long to think it over. "Yes," he said.

So, "Agreed," I told Orielle.

"You ..." Andreanna sputtered, "you ... you ..."

Grimbold patted her hand again. "They be making a mostest attractive couple," he said trying to calm her. He nudged her and winked. "Just like us."

Andreanna leaped to her feet to get away from him. "How dare you give away my son?" she shouted at me.

"She asked," I explained, "he agreed."

Grimbold tugged on her arm. "Sit down, sweetest, before you be hurting yourself," he advised.

Andreanna sat down because there really was nothing she could do.

Sister Mary Ursula clapped her hands in glee. "Oh, I love weddings: two people becoming One. And it gives all of us the chance to wear our best clothes."

In her case, I could only imagine.

Still, none of it *really* helped. Was I supposed to take Xenos's boots to get to Old Hag Mountain, then use Orielle's potion to make me strong enough to fight the dragon? I wasn't a fighter, and I couldn't imagine how I could succeed in killing the dragon when trained knights had failed. I was sure—or, at least, I was hoping—this situation called for thinking, not brute strength. I asked, "What weaknesses does this dragon have?"

"None," Andreanna snapped. "It's big, and it's fierce, and it's ruthless. Only my husband stood between it and destruction of our entire kingdom when it began raiding the towns and villages eight years ago. It would have killed us all if Cynric hadn't faced it down, then convinced it to take the crown and leave." She turned on her sons. "Perhaps you were too young to remember when it came to our very walls and we were within one dragon's breath of dying."

"I remember," Wulfgar said.

"And now you, you foolish little would-be king, you want to take that crown back?"

Well, I thought, maybe I *wasn't* supposed to get the crown. I asked Grimbold, "You have to have *that particular crown* back?"

"Yes," he said.

"You wouldn't accept anything else?"

"No," he said.

I looked at Wulfgar and Orielle. I looked at Grimbold and Andreanna. I said to Grimbold, "Like, perhaps, the hand of—"

Queen Andreanna interrupted, "Don't you dare even suggest that."

"Tempting as the offer is being," Grimbold told me, "I have been telling my people I would be returning our crown to us." He kissed Andreanna's hand. "Forgive me, my pumpkin."

She wiped her hand on her gown as though removing something very foul and very sticky.

I could give him the ring and compel him to accept Andreanna in trade for the crown. But I had the feeling that solution would cause more problems than it solved.

I was going to have to face the dragon.

CHAPTER TWENTY-SEVEN

Preparations for a Journey

I declared the meeting at an end. "I will leave as soon as Orielle provides me with the strength potion," I announced.

"Good riddance," Andreanna said, which I gathered was the closest she would come to wishing me luck. She stalked out of the Great Hall in a huff.

Grimbold, poor lovesick puppy, followed.

Orielle needed to gather some herbs from the garden; and Wulfgar—another lovesick puppy—went with her.

Abas said, "Past time for my aerobics."

And Xenos announced he was going to look for those slippers I'd promised him, and then he was going to find that centipede-catching boy.

"I'll help you," Deming said. "As for you," he told me, "now that King Grimbold is gone, let me be more free in my advice."

"Yes. Please. Thank you," I said.

"You'll never succeed in killing the dragon," Deming said. "Kill Grimbold instead, then have our army take on the barbarian army."

"But I promised. And he's our guest. And that's just so . . . so . . . dishonorable and underhanded."

"Hey," Deming said, "you pay me for my advice. Take it or leave it." He followed Xenos.

"Sister Mary Ursula?" I asked. "What do you think?"

She pinched the bridge of her nose and hummed. "I think I will check if my blue dress with the pieces of rose quartz sewn around the neckline and the shedded-yak-hair cuffs is clean enough to wear. It's a bit warm for summer but very slimming."

That left just Kenric and Uldemar. Uldemar, I saw, had fallen asleep.

"Any advice?" I asked Kenric.

"You have advisers for that," he told me.

Yeah, except neither of them had any useful advice.

Except, I suddenly remembered, except I *did* have three advisers.

"I think," I said, "I'll see what ex-Counselor Rawdon has to say."

Kenric and I found him sitting on the wooden fence of the pigpen, tossing vegetables that were past their prime to the pigs.

"Princess Janine"—he jumped off the fence to kneel at my feet—"thank you for sparing my life."

"Everyone makes mistakes, Rawdon," I said, "and mistakes need to be paid for. But if I ordered your death, that would be *my* mistake. Do well here, and eventually you may once again work your way up to your old position." *Minus the treasury key,* I mentally added.

He bowed to indicate he accepted my words.

"Rawdon," I said, quite loudly because the pigs were making complaining noises that their feeding had stopped, "as the late king's official adviser, you might have information that would help the kingdom."

"What would you like to know?" he asked.

That was the problem: I didn't know what I needed to know. At least he hadn't answered, "Fat chance I'd do anything for *you.*"

I said, "Do you know anything about the dragon to whom King Cynric gave the crown from the barbarian king?"

Rawdon nodded. "After threatening to wipe out the entire castle eight years ago, it was . . . let's say *turned back* by King Cynric, and it swore never to visit these lands again. It resides in the south, somewhere. I'm not sure exactly where."

Kenric said, "Uldemar says it's at Old Hag Mountain."

Rawdon nodded. "Then what's the question?"

I told him, "Xenos gave me seven-league boots to get there, and Orielle is mixing up a potion to make me stronger. Do you think that's the best way, trying to physically overpower the dragon?"

One of the catacomb ghosts tossed a head of lettuce into the pigpen, bouncing it off the head of one of the pigs, but the pigs didn't seem to mind the manner in which the food was delivered.

Rawdon said, "You are aware that this dragon is

something on the order of ten times as tall as you? And that it breathes fire? And that it will not readily give up one iota of gold? Dragons *love* gold."

"Yeah," I said.

"I'm glad it's not me," Rawdon said.

"I'm glad it's not me," Kenric echoed.

I'd known better than to even ask him.

"What do you suggest?" I asked Rawdon.

"You said Xenos is here?"

I nodded.

"You know that he puts magic into items, such as those seven-league boots."

It suddenly occurred to me where Cynric had gotten that ring I currently had tucked beneath my tunic.

"Xenos has other such items," Rawdon told me. "I'm guessing he probably has something that would be useful to you in this situation. It's just that he doesn't like to part with them, so you may have to twist his arm a bit."

"Thank you," I said. "That was very helpful. I'm going to recommend an immediate promotion for you." I asked Kenric, "What's one step up from tending pigs?"

"Tending chickens?" Kenric suggested.

"Would you prefer that?" I asked Rawdon. When he nodded, I promised, "I'll see to it."

As we left, he once again sat on the rail and began tossing produce to the pigs.

KENRIC AND I found Xenos in the barracks, describing to the poacher boy the attributes of prime centipedes.

I waved the boy away.

"Are you still here?" Xenos demanded.

"As you see. I understand that your specialty is magical artifacts?"

"I already gave you the boots," he complained.

"Yes, and I'm very grateful. But I was just thinking: If I'm wearing them when the dragon steps on me or eats me, you won't get them back."

"You could take them off," he suggested. "Before you go into the dragon's lair."

"But I'll be alone," I pointed out, "since obviously nobody would be able to keep up with me while I'm wearing them. So there won't be anyone around to return them to you."

Xenos pouted.

"Do you have anything else I could use that would help me survive my encounter with the dragon, so I could come back here and return your boots to you?"

"You're trying to trick me." Xenos folded his arms across his chest. "You're a tricky talker, just like your father."

I needed a moment to remember he was talking about Cynric and not Dexter the peat cutter or my own dad back in Rochester, New York.

"I'm not trying to be tricky," I assured him. "If, for example, you have a second pair of seven-league boots and you want to come with me so that you could bring the first pair back..."

"No," Xenos admitted sullenly.

"Or something else to help me defeat the dragon?"

"No," he repeated, but I didn't believe him.

"OK, then. Well, thanks for the boots." I held one foot

up admiringly. "Maybe, somehow, they'll get back to you. Come on, Kenric, let's see if Orielle's potion is ready."

"All right, all right," Xenos said. "I know of something that may be able to help you. But I don't *have* it. I was telling the truth when I said I didn't *have* anything to help you. My father has it."

His father? When he'd been around to make the crown for the first barbarian king? How old could this father be?

"What is it?" I asked.

"A hat."

"What kind of hat?"

"A hat that lets you slip between the moments of time."

Kenric and I exchanged a puzzled glance.

"Excuse me?" I said.

Xenos explained, "You can keep on moving, but all around you everyone and everything else stays at the moment when you first put the hat on."

"It stops time?" I asked incredulously.

"Obviously, you don't understand the concept at all," Xenos scoffed. "It only *feels* as though you've stopped time. You're slipping through the time stream." He shook his head and muttered in disgust, "Amateurs."

"This sounds like it would be very helpful," I said.

"I should think so," Xenos sneered.

"And all I need to do is go to your father and ask him for the hat, and he'll give it to me?"

"Yes."

Somehow I doubted it would be that simple. Somehow I suspected that Xenos knew something—in fact, probably a lot of somethings—I didn't.

While I was worrying about that, I had a sudden inspiration. I said, "That crown you made: Is that magical, too?"

"Maybe," Xenos said.

"Do you want me to shake him a bit?" Kenric offered, sounding for a moment like his brother Abas.

"It grants the Midas touch," Xenos said.

"You mean whoever wears it can turn things to gold?"

"Thing," Xenos corrected. "It only works one time for each owner. The barbarian kings have slowly been building their wealth. King Cynric, of course, thought big. King Cynric used it on the tallest tree in the forest."

I finished, "But once he'd used up his 'once,' he gave it to the dragon."

Kenric said, "The fact that the dragon was about to make dinner out of all of us would have helped in that decision."

So much for Andreanna's claim that Cynric had scared off the dragon—he'd *bribed* it. This also explained why Grimbold wasn't willing to accept Andreanna in exchange for the crown.

"Do we know what the dragon used the crown on?" I asked. "Or if, in fact, he's used it yet?"

"Don't know and don't know," Xenos said. "But even if he's used it, he *still* won't be willing to give it up. Dragons love gold."

"So I've been told," I said.

ORIELLE MET US back in the Great Hall, where she handed me an earthenware vial about as big as a medium-priced bottle of perfume. "It isn't my best-tasting potion," she apologized.

Naturally.

She said, "But I added mint to make it more palatable."

I wondered if that was just coincidence, or if somehow the people at Rasmussem knew that I hate mint. But I thanked her, even so.

"One hour," she reminded me.

Uldemar woke up then and asked, "Have you thought of any way I can help you?"

"You've been a help already," I said, "contacting everyone for me, and finding the dragon."

"Still . . ." he said.

"And Xenos has me going to his father to pick up a magical hat that will help me."

"Well, then, let me bring you to his father."

"I have the seven-league boots," I reminded him.

"But what if his father doesn't live seven leagues away?"

"Excuse me?"

Uldemar explained, "The boots take seven-league steps. No more, no less."

Seven leagues, I calculated—no doubt helped by Rasmussem's subliminals—was about twenty-five miles. "You mean I can't take, like, a half step? Maybe if I only wore one boot?"

"I'm afraid not," Uldemar said. He had taken out his scrying glass, and he set it on the table. He cast his magic spell and said, "I see he lives beyond Fairfield. I could take you there; then once you have what you need, I can calculate exactly how to get you to Old Hag Mountain in seven-league increments."

"All right," I said. "Thank you. How can you get me to Xenos's father's place?"

"I can turn into a horse and carry you."

"That would be wonderful." I thought about it for a moment. "Ahm, I hate to be rude or anything...but when you transform into an animal...ahm, does that mean you can...ahm..."

"I'll still be blind," he said. "You'll have to guide me."

Well, maybe *wonderful* had been a slight overstatement. Maybe this would be... *OK*, I hoped. "And what payment do you want?"

"Well, I certainly don't want to eat centipedes or to wed any of the queen's remaining sons. How about twenty-five gold pieces?"

It was expensive, but I said, "Yes."

We packed some food, since I'd seen that these things always took longer than I guessed.

"Good-bye," Kenric told me. "Good luck."

"Keep everybody out of trouble while I'm away," I said to him.

Uldemar turned into a handsome bay horse, already saddled. His eyes were still disconcertingly blank.

I climbed on and blew kisses to those who came to see me off, which was Kenric, Orielle and Wulfgar, King Grimbold, and Captain Penrod.

We rode over the drawbridge, and—after we'd passed—I heard the guard order the bridge to be taken up.

Nothing.

Oh boy. The ghosts were coming with us.

CHAPTER TWENTY-EIGHT

Xenos's Dad

Actually, Uldemar was very surefooted; and if we didn't make as good time as I had with the horse I'd ridden last night, we made better time than I would have walking.

"Let me know when you get tired," I told him.

He threw his head and whinnied.

We rode through Fairfield at a time my subconscious insisted was between midafternoon and vespers, though I would have called it somewhere around five-thirty of a summer afternoon.

For a blind guy, Uldemar was certainly good about landmarks. Periodically he would return to his own shape to say something like, "We should be coming upon a pond ahead and to our right." And, "We'll be going through some scraggly trees, but there's a meadow beyond." And, "As soon as we reach the stream, we'll turn to travel into the sun."

"Have you been here before?" I asked.

"No," he answered. "I saw it all in my scrying glass."

It took about an hour beyond Fairfield before Uldemar said, "The house is on a hill after the lightning-struck elm. It isn't," he added, "much of a hill."

And there it finally was, a neat little house with a little garden around it, all on top of a grass-covered hill.

Reverting to human shape, Uldemar put his hands to the small of his back and stretched. "Does it look promising?" he asked.

"Hard to say." I turned him so he was facing in the right direction.

The hill was about fifteen or twenty feet tall, steeply inclined except in front of the house, where it sloped more gently and there was a flagstone walk.

"There's a path," I told Uldemar.

"Lead on."

I took one step onto the walk.

And couldn't take a second.

I could lift my foot up, but I couldn't put it down. I felt like a mime walking into a giant wind. Something I couldn't see was keeping me from moving my foot forward.

"Princess Janine," Uldemar said, "there appears to be something in my way."

"There appears to be something in *my* way, too," I said. "But I can't see what it is."

"Drat! Has it gotten to be night already?" Uldemar asked.

"No. I can see perfectly well, but when I try to move

my foot..." I still couldn't move it forward. I tried to one side. I tried to the other.

The other worked.

"Oh," I said. "Here we go." I took another step forward. But then I was blocked again. "No, wait," I said.

I looked down at the walk. Each flagstone was big enough to accommodate a person's foot. They were various colors, set in what appeared to be a random pattern: a heathery blue, rose, gray, black, and cream. I was currently standing on a rose-colored stone, and the stone behind me was rose, too. The one directly behind that was cream, but the one I had crossed over from was another rose. I took a step to the left, onto another rose stone. "I think this path is color-coded," I said.

"Lucky me," Uldemar said.

There wasn't another rose touching the one I was on, but there was one two over. I stretched my leg and stepped onto the new stone.

"It seems," I said, "as though we can only step on the rose-colored stones." But then I looked back and saw that he was on a gray one. "Or maybe not. Uldemar, can you take a step, not exactly to your right, but halfway between forward and right?"

He did, and he was able to move.

I revised my analysis of the situation. "It seems as though whatever stone we first step on, after that, that's the only color we can step on."

Uldemar went back to his original stone, then backed off the path entirely. "I'm going to let you handle this," he said.

"OK." I made my way more or less forward for about a dozen more easy steps. The path even let me jump over three stones to get to one that was rose. But when I tried to leap over four stones, I bounced back as though a rubber band attached me to the previous rose-colored stone. There were no other rose ones to step on from where I was, so I had to back up and find my way down another pathway. After following that for a bit, I once again came to a place from which I couldn't step or jump to another rose stone. From where I was, I looked toward the doorway of the house. All the stones near the stoop were cream, black, or gray. No wonder I wasn't getting anywhere on the rose path. I made my way back to the start.

Uldemar was sitting on the lawn. "Back already?" he asked. "Did you get the hat?"

"Not yet," I told him, and started again, this time using the gray stones.

But no matter how I tried, there was one stretch I couldn't get beyond—where there were too many rose, blue, cream, and black stones in between the grays.

Again I made my way back.

Again Uldemar turned his face expectantly in my direction.

"I'm trying the cream ones now," I explained before he could ask.

What was it with the Rasmussem people and mazes?

But this time, eventually, I made it to the front stoop. "I'll be back as soon as I can," I called to Uldemar.

He waved cheerily.

I knocked on the door.

A little boy answered.

I realized I didn't know Xenos's father's name, so I was left to say, "I'm looking for Xenos's father."

"That's me," the kid said. He looked about five.

"Not Xenos's child," I said, creepy as that idea was. "Xenos's father."

"That's me," the kid repeated.

Cute. Like when people let their toddlers record the message for their answering machines. I hate that, too. "Is there an adult home?" I asked.

"Look, honey," the kid said, "if I gotta tell you one more time, I'm going to slam the door in your face and go back to smoking my cigar in peace: Xenos's father—that's me."

He *was* holding a cigar in his pudgy little hand, I noticed.

OK.

"I'm sorry," I said. "You took me by surprise. Xenos said to go to his father—that would be you, I see now—to get the hat that allows the wearer to step out of the time stream. Or was it step *into* the time stream?" I tried to remember what Xenos had said. "Something like that. It doesn't stop time, but it makes it *seem* as though time has stopped. To an amateur."

"Honey," Xenos's father said, "you've got to learn to stop dithering. I know what hat you mean." He held the door open for me, and I stepped into a tidy hallway. There was a hat rack with an assortment of hats on it, and I was already sure the one I was going to get was the ugly pink faux fur with the rhinestones and the ratty peacock feather.

"Stand here," Xenos's father said. He pointed to a spot where there was a big red X on the floor.

"Why?" I asked suspiciously.

"I'm bored," he said. "Humor me."

I stood on the center of the X.

"Now I'm going to ask you three riddles," he said. "If you answer them correctly, I'll give you the hat."

"And if I don't answer correctly," I guessed, "that coatrack is going to come over here and beat me to death."

Xenos's father shook his head in obvious distaste. "You have an unhealthy imagination, young lady—anybody ever tell you that? No, if you don't answer correctly, you get another chance."

"One chance?" I asked.

"As many as you want."

My suspicion must have shown on my face.

"I'm an old man," Xenos's father said, despite his appearance. "Nobody ever comes to visit *me*. Everybody comes because they need to pick up something Xenos promised them." He gave a baby-toothed grin. "Humor me," he said again.

Well, I could just give him the ring and demand the hat, but what if I needed that ring later?

"All right. What's the first riddle?"

"The first riddle is this: You see those woods outside this window?"

I nodded.

"That part wasn't the riddle," Xenos's father explained.

"I already guessed that," I said.

"Kids today. Anyway, you see the woods. My question is this: How far can you walk into those woods?"

I had no real sense of where I was, much less how big the woods were. And what did he mean, how far could

I walk into those woods? Was there something blocking the way, a river or a cliff, something or someone dangerous? Or did he mean how far could I walk before I tired out? Or how far in one day?

I decided it was time to clarify the rules. "I don't have just one guess?"

Xenos's father smacked his palm against his forehead. "If I was a stickler, I would call that your answer. Once the riddle is asked, you aren't supposed to say *anything* except the answer to the riddle. Haven't you ever done this before? You're lucky I'm a patient man. And I already told you, you can try as many times as you want. Now: How far can you walk into those woods?"

Anything I said would be just a guess. So, remembering my boots, I answered, "Seven leagues?"

The floor opened under me, and I went flying down the fastest, slickest slide I'd ever been on, through a black tunnel, popping out a hole at the bottom of the far side of the hill the house stood on. Several of the catacomb ghosts had been caught at the same time I was and had made the trip down with me. *They* liked it—I could tell, picking up their excited psychic energy. *They* didn't have to worry about concussions or contusions.

I rubbed my bruised elbows and said the kind of words my grandmother grounds me for. Shakily, I got to my feet and walked back around to the front of the house.

Uldemar asked, "Got the hat?"

"Not yet. Xenos's father likes riddles. He wants to know about these woods here. Do you have any idea how big they are?"

"Square acreage?" Uldemar said, and I realized that

would be no help at all, because the woods could be long and skinny, or a square, or who-knew-what? "Do you want me to check my scrying glass?"

"No," I said sulkily.

"What, exactly, did he say?"

"He said, 'How far can you walk into those woods?' And the trouble is, I don't know these woods."

"The trouble is," Uldemar corrected me, "he's not asking you a question; he's asking you a riddle."

I thought about it and groaned. I went back to the flagstone path and once more picked a way, using only cream-colored stones, to the front stoop. It was faster this time than last, but I still had several dead ends and reversals. I banged on the door.

Xenos's father opened it. "Hello," he said. "Care to play a riddle game?"

I followed him indoors, and he once again positioned me on the X.

Looking satisfied with himself, Xenos's father once more said, "The first riddle is this: How far can you walk into those woods?"

"Halfway," I answered. "After that I would be walking *out* of the woods, not into them."

"Very good!" Xenos's father cried. "See, you aren't hopeless after all. All right, the second riddle is this: Two great armies are about to do battle, the Great Army of the North and the Great Army of the South, and they meet exactly on the equator. After the battle is over, the bodies are too mangled to identify. Where do the survivors get buried?"

"Well," I said, "but which army won the battle?"

Too late I remembered his warning that I wasn't supposed to say *anything* except the answer to the riddle. The floor disappeared from under me. I tried to grab for the edge, but I was already going down that slide so fast it felt as though my butt was about to catch fire. This time, I could definitely hear a whispery ghostly, "Whee!"

After I hit the ground and the dizziness passed, I went back around to the front of the hill. Uldemar was sitting on the lawn, trying to make music with a blade of grass. I said to him, "Two armies meet at the equator and fight a great battle. After it's over, where..." I sighed, having caught up to myself. "Never mind." The ghosts could have told me that one.

Once again, I picked my way up the front walk and knocked on Xenos's father's door. I was beginning to get faster at this. "Are you enjoying yourself?" I asked.

"Immensely," he admitted.

He stood me on the great red X and said the long sad story again: "The second riddle is this: Two great armies are about to do battle, the Great Army of the North and the Great Army of the South, and they meet exactly on the equator. After the battle is over, the bodies are too mangled to identify. Where do the survivors get buried?"

I said, "The survivors don't get buried."

Xenos's father gave a great drag on his cigar. He said, "I haven't had this much fun since Xenos had a cold and was sneezing centipedes. All right, here's the third riddle: Where was Moses when the lights went out?"

That one I knew. "In the dark."

"There. See," Xenos's father said. "I don't know what you were worried about."

I said, "Those riddles were hardly the quality of the riddle of the Sphinx."

Xenos's father shrugged. "Egyptian humor. Personally, I don't get it. Now for your hat." Sure enough, he picked up the awful pink one. But then he reached into the crown of the hat, and pulled out another, a crumpled knitted ski cap the color of March slush. "So, I'm assuming Xenos told you all about this. Don't bother answering; that's what's known in the business as sarcasm, dearie. The hat lets you keep moving when all about you is still—that part he told you, I'm sure. What he probably left out is that once you put the hat on, whatever you're doing—whether it's stealing money from the poor box in church, or spying on the boyfriend when he's out without you, or sneaking back into the house so your parents don't know you climbed out the bedroom window—"

I interrupted. "Those are pretty lame reasons to be using a hat that lets you avoid the time stream."

"Do I criticize you when you're giving examples? All I'm saying is that whatever you're doing, you only have a limited time to do it. Ironic, isn't it? Get it? Time/time?" He shook his head. "You don't get it."

"I get it," I assured him. "How long do I have?"

"If you count like this," he said at a leisurely pace, "one Rasmussem Enterprises, two Rasmussem Enterprises, three Rasmussem Enterprises . . . then you'd get to three hundred Rasmussem Enterprises, and the hat comes back here."

Nothing like a little bit of blatant self-endorsement. And what he was saying was that I had five minutes. Five minutes.

"The hat..." I said.

"Comes back here," he finished.

"With me?"

He shook his head.

"Leaving me..."

"With your hand in the poor box, or your face pressed up against somebody else's window, or climbing up the stairs to the second floor while your father's sitting there watching you."

Or, in my case, face-to-face with the dragon.

"Yeah," Xenos's father said, taking another drag on the cigar. "I didn't think he'd told you. Any questions?"

I sighed, but said, "No."

Yet again the floor swallowed me, and I went skittering down that slide through the hill and out the other side. Luckily, I managed to keep hold of the hat. But I was going to be a mass of bruises even before meeting the dragon. More and more ghosts were joining me for each ride.

I picked myself off the ground and yelled up to the house, "Ever wonder *why* nobody ever comes to visit you?"

Still staggering, I rejoined Uldemar. "Got it," I told him.

He had the decency not to say, "About time."

CHAPTER TWENTY-NINE

A Journey
of a Thousand Miles
Begins with a Single Step
(and Other Trite Nonsense)

Sitting at the bottom of Xenos's father's hill, Uldemar did his calculations of exactly where I had to step to have the seven-league boots take me to Old Hag Mountain. The trouble was that the direct route was not divisible by the seven leagues each step would take me, so I had to head off southwest to a certain point, then turn and head due east. There was also a minor detour to avoid a step that would have landed me directly in someone's kitchen.

"That's not a physical problem," Uldemar told me. "As you're moving, the boots pass through solid objects." Which explained how, in the previous game, Xenos had walked through the wall but then was not seen by Penrod's men outside. Uldemar continued, "But it would be unsettling to those seeing you. Out of fear, they might harm you."

"What if I land inside a tree?"

"You can't. You'd land on top of it. I'll try to keep you away from trees."

We decided it would be best not to have the boots take me directly into the dragon's cave. If the creature was home, it might kill me before I had a chance to get my bearings.

"This route will take you to a flattened area between the summit and the base of the mountain," Uldemar said. "It should be climbable."

Should be. Don't you love it?

It was getting to be dusk, but I decided to start, anyway. Once I got to the mountain, I could make up my mind if it would be better to continue up at night or wait there till morning. Dragons, Uldemar told me, were like cats, taking a lot of little naps throughout the day and night so no time was better than others to try sneaking up on it.

I tucked the hat I had riddled for into the bag that held my evening meal and Orielle's potion, and I looped the bag over my belt.

"Good luck," Uldemar said. "Remember to always walk straight in the direction you're facing." He'd already said that about seven times. "Don't try to take big strides—just walk normally. The boots will take care of themselves." *That* he'd said about nine times.

"Will you be all right?" I asked him. Maybe I'd asked him once or twice before but I felt guilty leaving him.

"I'll be fine," Uldemar assured me.

So I took a deep breath, said, "Seven leagues," and put my right foot forward.

When I'd tried to make too big a jump on Xenos's father's front walk, I'd felt as though a rubber band had yanked me back. Now I felt like the rubber band itself, all stretched out, with my vision a meaningless blur and an awful rushing-of-air sound so intense I was sure my eardrums were about to burst. I was tempted to bring that right foot back, canceling the seven-league step so that I could try again later. But I knew it wasn't going to get better. I moved my left foot forward.

And found myself in a totally different place from where I'd just been.

Instead of Xenos's father's hill on an otherwise flat area bordered by woods, I saw gently rolling hills coming down to an immense lake.

Thank you for not landing me in the lake, I thought to Uldemar.

I took another step and found myself in yet another landscape: farm country, with fields of barley and rutabaga.

And another, this time landing in a rocky, desolate place. That was where I was supposed to turn ninety degrees to the left to avoid the unpredictable kitchen. I stepped onto a seashore.

Step after step I took until finally, as the sky turned dramatically pink, I found myself partway up what had to be Old Hag Mountain.

Amazing! I had never, in my heart, actually believed it would be so easy.

I left a whole bunch of broken sticks so I would be sure—if I survived my encounter with the dragon—to be able to start my return trip from the exact right spot.

Next was climbing up.

It should be climbable.

Yeah, right.

I had to find handholds and toeholds and trust my life to an anemic tree that didn't have the sense to grow out of horizontal ground.

This would be a lot easier, I told myself as my arms began to ache, *if I was stronger.*

Which was when I remembered Orielle's potion.

One hour of being as strong as Abas, followed by two of being as weak as Dusty at her arthritic worst.

Should I take it now? I looked up the remainder of the way I had to go. It was getting dark, so I wasn't able to see clearly. I *thought* that if I was stronger I could make it up in less than an hour—if I didn't fall off the mountain first from not being able to see. But what then? Then, with night coming on, I would have to find my way into the lair, avoid the dragon, locate the crown, and hope that my two hours of total helplessness didn't strike while I was still in there. It was the same thing I would have to do if I waited until morning, but my chances had to be better if I could see what I was doing.

I found a cozy little crack in the stone, and I settled in for the night, hoping the catacomb ghosts wouldn't think it a good joke to roll me out and over the side while I slept. Thinking about the ghosts, I suddenly realized I had no sensation of them around me. *They weren't able to keep up to those seven-league steps,* I thought. *Ha!*

They were probably still at Xenos's father's house, riding down that slide. *Double ha!*

I ate my meal of bread, cheese, and cold mutton, with an apple tart the castle cook had packed for dessert. For drink, I had warm water from a clay jar. I was happy for the tart, but a double-cheese pizza and a milk shake would have been even nicer.

I HEARD the dragon several times during the night, moving about, snoring occasionally, once singing—I *think* it was singing—in its dragon language. To me it sounded like a recording of a cough, played backward at slow speed.

Once it got to be light—my third day in this adventure (my, how time flies when you're having fun)—I ate the last of my bread and drank almost all of my water, saving a bit for just-in-case.

I started climbing back up that mountain, but it wasn't any easier today than it had been last night. When I almost fell because my fingers cramped, I realized it was time to try Orielle's potion. Pressing myself onto a ledge big enough for about half of one foot, I got out the vial, took out the stopper, and downed the whole thing in one excruciating gulp. Not one of her best-tasting potions had Orielle said? Imagine a ninety-five-degree August day, and a construction worker slaving away on the melting asphalt. Then imagine licking toothpaste out of his armpit.

But a moment later, that didn't matter. I had a hot flash that caused a tremor in the leg on which I was balancing all my weight. In another moment that was gone, leaving a warm, tingly glow all over, from toes to fingertips. That, and the foul taste in my mouth.

I reached for a handhold, and pulled myself up as easily as an Olympic gymnast doing a chin-up.

Up and up and up I went, so easily that I asked myself why I hadn't taken the potion earlier.

Then I remembered why, for I'd come to right below the ledge of the opening to the cave where Uldemar's scrying glass showed the dragon lived.

When I was securely positioned, I got out the hat so that I could slap it on my head at a moment's notice. I held it in my teeth, so that it wouldn't accidentally brush off as I swung myself up onto the ledge.

Then I swung myself up onto the ledge.

There, close enough to spit on—if I'd been a barbarian and inclined to spit—was the dragon.

CHAPTER THIRTY

Dead Oxen and Gold

Andreanna and Rawdon had been right: The dragon was enormous. Even though I'd been prepared for its size to stun me, its size still stunned me.

The creature had its head on its paws, and its eyes were closed—which meant that it was either sleeping or trying to lull me into believing that it was sleeping, at which point it would jump on me and either eat me in one quick swallow (I could only hope it would be one) or incinerate me or squeeze the life out of me.

I fought the inclination to seven-league my way straight out of there. I fought the inclination to slap Xenos's magic hat on my head and make time stop moving for the dragon.

I knew both inclinations were stupid. After determining that I *had* to get the crown and struggling my way up that mountainside—what would running accomplish? If I didn't succeed in this, I would stay hooked up to Rasmussem's computer equipment until my brain fried. That made getting fried by a dragon look slightly...well, not better, just less bad.

And what if I put on the hat while the dragon was asleep? That would waste its power.

Anyway, why would the dragon pretend to be asleep? If it saw me, wouldn't it simply kill me right away?

Except I remembered Uldemar explaining how dragons napped like cats. What if, like cats, they also played with their prey?

But could the dragon have kept a straight face if it saw me, a girl dressed as a page, walking on the tips of my toes, looking as though I was about to eat a ski cap? I wondered if dragons shot flames out of their mouths when they laughed.

The dragon didn't twitch.

Scattered about this area were various bones. There was a gnawed-on ox over to one side, which explained that the awful smell was not entirely dragon bad breath. But not all the bones were animals—some still had scraps of clothing attached. I kept on moving. There was a second, bigger, cave beyond, and I could see the glitter of gold.

Luckily, there was room to circle behind the dragon without having to climb onto it. I nervously kept my attention on the creature's eyelids until I realized I was endangering myself by walking backward. I could easily trip or knock something over, and the noise would surely awaken a catnapper.

I turned my full attention to the piles of treasure.

The piles and piles of treasure.

The piles and piles and piles of treasure.

How could I ever find one crown amid all that glittering hoard?

I started pawing through mounds of gold. There were coins, there was jewelry, there were boxes, baskets, combs, and plaques. There were eating utensils, musical instruments, tools, toys, knickknacks, figurines, and a bigger-than-life statue of a Greek hero. (I could tell he was Greek, because he didn't have any clothes on, the way Greek statues never do.) There were even a pair of robes woven entirely of spun gold.

But was there a barbarian crown? Not that I could see.

I started unloading one of the overflowing treasure chests—there were seven or eight, probably more buried in that one corner where the gold was piled to within inches of the cave's ceiling.

It can't be there, I tried to convince myself. *THAT pile's been accumulating for generations, and King Cynric gave the dragon the crown only eight years ago.*

Unless, of course, the dragon had been moving things around, shifting stuff from one pile to another, handling the gold while gloating over it—and why bother amassing gold if you aren't going to gloat over it? Maybe the crown had been buried.

No, I told myself. This was a crown that could turn things into gold. Surely that would gain it a special place. Or at least not a place at the bottom of a pile.

I was putting things from the chest onto the floor so that I could get to the bottom, and there, finally, beneath a golden serving tray, was the crown.

Oops, no, wait. Wrong crown.

During our lunch King Grimbold had described his people's crown, and this wasn't it.

Maybe, over the passage of years since his father had lost the thing, *maybe* Grimbold hadn't remembered correctly?

Not likely, I knew.

I set the crown on the head of a waist-high statue of a monkey. If I couldn't find the right crown, maybe Grimbold could be appeased by this one, along with whatever other trinkets I could stuff into my now-empty provision bag. And Andreanna. I very much hoped I could give away Andreanna.

My teeth were sore from holding the hat for so long. I took it out to work my jaw. A watch would have been nice about now, to know how long since I'd taken Orielle's potion. My guess was about a half hour. I wondered if I'd have any warning, any sense of weakening, or if I'd just keel over.

I went to put the hat back in my mouth and somehow brushed against the monkey statue. The thing must have been hollow for it wobbled. I grabbed it just in time to keep it from going over.

But the crown fell off the back of its head.

A golden crown hitting a cave floor doesn't make all that much noise.

But enough.

The dragon was awake and on its feet in less time than it took me to glance in its direction.

For the moment, as I crouched beside the chest with the monkey statue between us, the dragon couldn't see me. But I could see it. I could see its nostrils dilate as it sniffed. *Sniff, sniff.* It took a step toward me, its massive belly dragging on the floor. *Sniff, sniff.* For a creature that slept next to an ox carcass that was at least a couple days old, surely it couldn't have a very well developed sense of smell. Another step. And then its huge head swiveled, and it was looking directly at me.

I jammed the hat onto my head, pulling it so low it stretched beyond my earlobes. I felt no change, but the dragon wasn't moving. Was it?

I peeked an eye open.

No, the dragon wasn't moving.

Slowly I got to my feet. I moved cautiously to the left.

Its glittering eyes didn't follow me.

I started breathing again. Then I started counting, "One Rasmussem Enterprises, two Rasmussem Enterprises, three..." I kept on counting as I hurled golden objects out of the chest, no longer needing to be quiet.

At "fifteen Rasmussem Enterprises," I got to the bottom of the chest, and there was no other crown. I moved to another chest. That took me to "sixty Rasmussem Enterprises," with no sign of a crown. Four minutes left—less, because I hadn't started right away. *Three hundred Rasmussem Enterprises* was looming close.

I kicked at a heap of gold sitting on the floor, scattering coins. A crown rolled out. I snatched it up. Then threw it down in frustration. Still not the right one.

The next chest was a big one with clumsily shaped heavy objects I had to lift out one by one, and it took me to "one hundred forty-four Rasmussem Enterprises" to find there was no barbarian crown in there.

There was a chest about the size of a two-drawer filing cabinet on its side. With my added strength coupled with the adrenaline of desperation, I held it upside down, scattering its contents on the floor. I threw the chest behind me and lunged for the crown I glimpsed, but it was the same one that had fallen off the monkey statue before. "One hundred sixty-seven Rasmussem Enterprises," and I was already looking twice in the same place.

Ignoring the other chests, I began pawing through the huge pile, convinced the crown had to be in the single hardest place to get to.

"Two hundred fourteen Rasmussem Enterprises... two hundred twenty-five Rasmussem Enterprises... two hundred thirty-seven Rasmussem Enterprises..." I kicked the Greek hero in frustration and glanced back at the dragon.

Not moving yet, but it would be soon. How many "Rasmussem Enterprises" had I lost while shivering under the unseeing gaze of the time-stopped dragon? Five? Six?

And what was the matter with me? I should have known better than to think other numbers while I was trying to count. Had I actually counted to "two hundred forty-five Rasmussem Enterprises," or had I skipped numbers because I'd been thinking the number five? I didn't actually remember saying, "forty-two," "forty-three," or "forty-four Rasmussem Enterprises," but maybe I had, and meanwhile, trying to figure it out, I'd lost more time.

Where was I? Never mind. I gave up counting entirely.

Once again I looked at the dragon. I had to get out of there, save myself now, try coming back later, with a better plan.

Yeah, right. If I was capable of thinking up a better plan, I wouldn't be here now.

That wasn't the same as being willing to let the dragon lunch on me.

I ran past the huge beast, back out onto the ledge, to the very edge overlooking the steep cliff with hand- and toeholds. I was going to have to go racing down there?... with my strength about to give out probably a few minutes after the hat spell gave out?... with a dragon sniffing after me?

The other choice was to hang around and wait for the dragon to gnaw on me like it had been gnawing on that ox.

I saw the gashes on the stone from the dragon's talons. I also saw two globs of gold on the ledge and realized what the dragon had done with its Midas touch—it had tried to turn Old Hag Mountain to gold, but instead had only gotten two golden rocks. No doubt it had been plenty ticked off.

Just like it's going to be now, I thought, suddenly aware of the breeze in my hair: *Good-bye, hat. Hello, dragon.*

I turned back to meet my fate.

The dragon was in the inner cave, facing the way it had been when, from its perspective, I'd disappeared. But now that I was on the ledge facing this direction, I saw what I hadn't seen before. The crown. Out here. The dragon had been sleeping with it tucked safely in the crook of its elbow, like a kid with a teddy bear.

I dove for the crown just as the dragon turned. A blast of flame frizzled the air at my back. I grabbed up the crown like an oversized bangle bracelet on my arm and looked over the nearest edge, which wasn't even the way I'd come up. How could I ever make it down onto flat ground with the dragon so close behind? Even now I could hear the grate of its scales as it heaved its massive body back out onto the ledge.

Without even turning back to look, I said, "Seven leagues," and stepped forward, though the ground was a mountain's height below me—hoping the boots worked in thin air.

CHAPTER THIRTY-ONE

Home Sweet Home
(Or Not)

I found myself on someone's thatched roof. I turned hurriedly, said, "Seven leagues" hurriedly, and stepped hurriedly, because my foot felt about to go through. Now I was in the middle of a field of something-or-other—I didn't take the time to make out what. I turned, said, "Seven leagues," and took another step. Now I was in a wooded area, having just missed a tree, which was good, because I was in no mood to have to climb down.

I'd just completed three sides of a square. One more and I'd be stepping back onto the mountain ledge I'd just stepped off of. Where the dragon might or might not still be sniffing around for the one who'd made off with its favorite crown. And even if the dragon had flown off, I'd have to climb back down. If my strength gave out while I was hanging from that cliff face, that would be the end of me. Instead I tried to estimate how to walk, in regular steps, to a point where after I turned and "seven-leagued," I'd be at the foot of Old Hag Mountain.

But landing on iffy ground was a danger. I'd do best to walk farther than I thought I had to. So I walked and walked and walked. And then all of a sudden I collapsed.

Oh, I realized, *the potion must have worn off.* I couldn't even move my legs to a more comfortable sprawl. My left arm, the one on which I'd been carrying the crown, was under me, and the tines of the crown were sticking into me, but there was nothing I could do. I did finally summon the energy to close my eyes.

I felt sweat trickle down my sides, I felt bugs crawl on me, I felt that miserable crown sticking into my rib cage.

I...felt...two...hours...pass...one...moment...at...a...time....

And then suddenly my right arm worked. I'd been concentrating on getting my hand to move—it only needed to cover about two inches before it could reach to wipe the sweat from dribbling into my eyes—and suddenly there it was, behaving like a perfectly normal arm with a perfectly normal hand attached to it, a hand whose fingers flicked away a drop of sweat that was about to roll into my eye and make it sting.

I sat up. There was no lingering weakness. I wiped my face with my sleeve and loosened my belt in an attempt to get some airflow under my clothes.

The crown was only slightly out of shape from my lying on top of it. I put it in the empty food bag tied to my belt.

I walked some more, until the sun was close to

overhead, maybe eleven or even eleven-thirty where people had normal clocks instead of canonical hours based on monasteries' prayer times. I turned. I took a deep breath, said, "Seven leagues," and stepped.

I was—at least I hoped I was—in the correct vicinity. There were mountains in the distance that I *thought* were the group of which Old Hag was one.

I did an about-face and tried to retrace the directions Uldemar had given me: so many steps straight ahead, turn (remembering to turn the opposite direction as I had coming here yesterday), some more steps, another turn. I knew I wasn't directly on course since I hadn't started from the place I had ended yesterday, and it was hard to tell if any of it looked familiar, though from a different angle, or if that was just wishful thinking.

Another step and I found myself treading water. Could this be the lake I'd seen after my first step? What would have been nice was if I could swim to the shore and walk a bit so that I could take one more step and find myself at Xenos's father's house. Of course, that all hinged on *if I could swim*. Which I can't. "Seven leagues," I managed to get out, in between taking in great mouthfuls of water. I moved my feet and found myself perched on top of a tree.

Luckily, it wasn't much of a tree, so I realized I wouldn't have a hard climb to get down. But I didn't even have to do that. While I was still busy coughing up water, there was a loud crack, and the branch I was on fell to the ground, taking me with it.

I lay dazed and bruised, looking up at the tree, vaguely wondering why it was in such sad shape that it broke under my weight. More exactly, I was wondering if it was in bad enough shape that it might fall on me as I lay there, helpless, with the wind knocked out of me.

The branches had no leaves, and the trunk was black, as though it had been through a fire. *Lightning struck*, I thought.

And then I remembered there had been a lightning-struck tree that had been the last landmark before Xenos's father's house.

I hiked and hiked and hiked, and just as I was telling myself that surely there were plenty of lightning-struck trees in the kingdom, there was the hill with Xenos's father's house perched atop it.

"Uldemar!" I called, seeing him, in horse form, grazing.

He had turned back to human by the time I reached his side. "I was beginning to worry," he said.

"Me, too," I admitted. "But I have it."

"Good for you!" he told me. "We should probably head back immediately."

Before I even had a chance to agree, the front door of the house opened. Xenos's father threw an old shoe at us and hollered, "And this time take your stinking ghosts with you!"

IT WAS PROBABLY after three in the afternoon, and we were almost back to the castle. I felt the press of ghosts around us, but for the moment they weren't poking, or pulling my hair, or otherwise being a nuisance.

We rounded a bend in the woods that bordered the castle lands, and there blocking our way were several woodsmen.

Now where have I seen these guys before? I wondered. Then I noticed their bows, and I remembered. *These are the poacher boy's friends or relatives.* The guys who had killed me in these woods once before.

For the moment their bows were at their sides, not up and pointed. Still, I dug my feet into Uldemar's sides. I wanted to yell, "Run them down," but they were sure to take offense at that. *No, no, no, no!* I was so close to the end; it was almost the close of the last day. All I had to do was hand over the crown to Grimbold, wish him and his people luck, and invite him to my coronation. This was no time to be running into surly woodsmen.

But Uldemar only made a hey-what's-with-those-feet? expression, and he stopped.

The thought flickered through my mind that I could jump to the ground, say, "Seven leagues," and be out of there. But I was sure Rasmussem would penalize me heavily if I abandoned Uldemar.

"Princess Janine," said the man whom I believed to be the poacher's father.

I figured it wouldn't do any good to claim he was mistaken—*See these clothes, I'm just a poor page out for a ride on a simple blind horse*—and besides, the man had, surprisingly, given a slight bow as he said my name.

"Yes," I admitted.

"You have my son in your custody at the castle."

"He was caught poaching," I said. "Under my new laws, he must work off the price of a deer, which is set at one month's labor. That means he has twenty-eight more days to his sentence." Under the circumstances, I was willing to consider this a thirty-day month rather than thirty-one.

The man did not rant or rave or demand an early release for his son. "I am indebted to you for changing the laws in time to spare my son's life."

"Oh." I had been expecting an argument. "You're welcome."

"The boy is wild," the man said. "His mother spoils him. I was sure he was going to be the death of all of us. I believe a month of hard labor—not backbreaking labor, understand, but hard, honest work—will benefit him."

"Hard, honest work it is," I assured him. "I hope it will benefit all." I gave Uldemar just the tiniest nudge to let him know I believed the conversation to be closed.

Uldemar took the hint, but the man shifted to remain in our way. "Princess Janine..." He licked his lips. "Don't go to the castle. Some of the peasants—*not us*," he hastened to clarify, "but some troublemakers from the east—are planning to seize the castle."

"What?"

"They set out when they had news that old King Cynric was ailing. They believe it's time to live without a king."

Not during my reign, I thought indignantly.

The woodsman continued, "They don't know you, Princess. We tried to tell them about the new laws, but they've been on the road for three days. They don't dare return home empty-handed."

"I appreciate the warning," I said. "I truly do. But I *must* return. I can't let my people suffer a siege without me." *For one thing, they don't seem capable of tying their boot-laces without me there to tell them.* But I didn't say that, and the men finally moved out of my way.

"Good luck, Princess Janine," the man called after me.

In any case Uldemar had taken off at a gallop, aimed straight for a tree, and all my concentration was on holding on and directing him so that he wouldn't kill us both.

"Left!" I yelled. "Right! Left again! Duck!" Actually, if *he* had to duck, I would have been in serious trouble, but we both ducked, and we made it beneath a low-hanging branch.

As we got closer, I became aware of other people in the woods, also traveling swiftly toward the castle. A moment later we broke through the trees along with the first of them and could see the castle walls. We were in the front line of the invasion. All around us men were charging the clearing, waving bows and swords and knives as well as homemade pikes and staffs and clubs.

The guards manning the walls started raising the drawbridge. But then someone must have recognized me, and the bridge went down again.

The peasants were on foot, and Uldemar quickly outdistanced them. I rode low, for minimal wind resistance and to make myself a small target. An arrow flew close by my ear, and we weren't yet near enough to get covering fire from the castle.

And then suddenly Uldemar stumbled. I looked and saw a gash across his rump. But the arrow had only grazed him, and in a moment he took up his stride again, and after that we were beyond the range of the peasants.

"Drawbridge!" I warned Uldemar, and moments later, we clattered full speed across it.

"Raise the bridge!" I heard Captain Penrod yell from the battlements.

I reined Uldemar in, but I wasn't saying, "Whoa." I was saying another of those words that would get me in trouble with my grandmother.

"Raise the bridge!" Penrod repeated more urgently.

"You!" I yelled to one of the guards in the courtyard. "Tend Uldemar." I threw the reins in his direction and ran up one of the sets of stairs to the battlements.

Other men had taken up Penrod's cry of "Raise the bridge!" but we all knew it wasn't going to budge until those catacomb ghosts had finished crossing.

From the battlements, I could see the peasants were almost in range of my archers. There was no way the ghosts would be out of the way before the peasants reached the bridge.

"Men, ready your weapons," Penrod commanded.

All along the walls, guards raised their bows.

"No!" I shouted. "I can't begin my kingship with a slaughter of my people." *Even if they ARE ungrateful rebels.*

King Grimbold was in the courtyard and he shouted up to me, "My men are being just beyond the stream over there." Now that he pointed, I could make out their banners. "If you be having the crown, pull it out and hold it up for my men to be seeing. Then they be killing these peasants for you, and there be no need of yourself to be getting their bloodses on your hands."

"It's just the same," I protested. "I can't let your men kill them for me."

"Princess!" Penrod shouted, directing my attention to the peasants. In another few seconds they would reach the drawbridge, which was still held down by the weight of the ghosts. "Do we let them come in and kill us all?" Penrod asked.

"Ghosts!" I screamed. "Ghosts, listen to me! You're going to get us all killed."

Well, obviously, these guys wouldn't find that a particularly compelling argument.

I tried again. "Ghosts, you're from Fairfield. That's where your families still live—your children and your children's children. These peasants from the east will destroy not only this castle but Fairfield, taking over the fields you tilled, tearing down what you built. You heard my plans for an annual fair. That fair would make Fairfield a prosperous town. These men will prevent that from happening. All memory of you will die out with the slaughter and enslavement of your descendants—your children and your children's children. At best they will suffer and remain poor because of you." I was running out of things to say. "Rise up. Rise up and protect what's yours!" I wished I'd paid more attention to some of those patriotic speeches we'd read in school.

The fastest of the peasant army had reached the drawbridge. Their boots clattered on the wood. Momentarily. Then the men fell off on either side into the ditch.

But more men were coming up fast. Then they went into the ditch also. Their weapons rose up into the air and began beating them about the heads and shoulders.

Seeing this, the men behind began to slow down. Fruit seemed to suddenly fall off the trees in the castle garden—or to be plucked off by invisible hands—then those fruits sailed through the air to pelt the men still in the ditch. A banshee wailed, dogs began to bark, the peasants who were still on their feet backed away. Those in the ditch had a hard time getting out, with the ghosts harassing them.

But eventually, one by one, they managed to crawl out, to make their way across the clearing back into the woods.

We could hear them crashing through the trees, the ghosts still pursuing. If we were very lucky, the ghosts would be permanently distracted from us. And for once in this game, I truly did feel lucky.

Our men set up a cheer.

Grimbold's men began to approach.

I stepped out from behind the protection of the upright merlons and held up Brecc the Slayer's crown, and they, too, began to cheer.

Then somebody from within the castle courtyard screamed.

I could see one of the servants backed up against the wall of the castle, cringing and pointing up into the sky behind me.

I turned and saw the dragon.

CHAPTER THIRTY-TWO

The End

There wasn't time to run.

Not that running would have helped.

But *run?*—I couldn't even *duck*. I was frozen with fear. It was as though the strength potion had run out again, only this time leaving me standing, like a statue of a basketball player about to make a free throw.

The dragon had looked enormous in its lair. Now, with its wings outstretched and its taloned claws coming straight at me, I knew what *enormous* really meant.

I figured I also knew what *about to get her heart ripped out of her chest* really meant.

But at the last moment, the dragon pulled up short, landing on the parapet, its feet on two of the merlons right above where I stood. Standing upright, it breathed flame out over the courtyard—a warning shot over our heads, we would say in my regular era. But that warning shot had fire licking at the walls of the castle, a good hundred yards away, and the heat was enough to singe my eyebrows. Then the creature sniffed the air.

A moment later its face was a foot away from my face.

I realized the stench of its lair couldn't *all* be blamed on that ox carcass.

The dragon didn't breathe flame on me. It said, in a harsh, sibilant voice, "Seven-league boots are *not* impossible to track."

Oops.

"You have broken the covenant I made with King Cynric. Now I will take back that which is mine. Then I will kill you all." Its amber eyes blinked, slowly, like a lizard's. Then it said, "But I will eat *you* first."

For once I was hoping for the fizziness that signified Rasmussem's version of dying. I didn't want to feel a moment of that awful heat or those teeth ripping into me.

Idiot, I called myself as the dragon caught me up in one taloned claw and I suddenly realized what I should have done back at the creature's lair. "Dragon, take this ring," I said.

Would the compelling spell work with the ring hidden from sight beneath my tunic for safekeeping?

Apparently not.

The dragon continued to bring me toward its mouth—its mouth with its many, many sharp teeth— and I closed my eyes, not wanting to see my own end coming. *Three days. I had made it three days.* How many more chances could I possibly get?

And then I thought, *I don't NEED any more chances.* With my eyes still closed, I plunked the crown of Brecc the Slayer onto my head and pressed my free hand against the claw that held me.

I could feel the dragon stop moving.

I slitted one eye open a crack. Brightness nearly blinded me, and I shut that eye quickly, sure the dragon had tricked me into looking just as it was shooting flame out of its mouth.

But I didn't feel anything, heat or fizziness, and now my people were cheering, which I was fairly certain they wouldn't do if I was about to become a flame-broiled McNugget.

I peeked again.

That wasn't fire; that was the glint of sun off gold.

A lot of gold.

The dragon had turned into gold, a victim of my Midas touch.

Then began the rescue operation. With grappling hooks and small pikes, my guards were scaling the dragon's body to help get me loose of the golden statue's grip. It took a lot of undignified squirming and leg pulling and calls to suck in my stomach, but finally I popped free. Luckily, Captain Penrod had a good hold on me, or I would have dropped a hundred feet to the ground.

I took the crown off and handed it to Grimbold. His men were cheering like crazy. "Be careful with this," I warned.

He gave a look at the huge golden dragon perched on our battlements and said, "You been doing good."

"I been doing lucky," I corrected him.

People were coming up and giving me congratulatory slaps on the arms or rubbing my head for luck. Kenric gave me a hug, which was better than either. Even Andreanna had a kind word for me. She said: "I never thought we'd see *you* again."

I thought of how I'd set off with such low expectations with Uldemar...

"Uldemar!" I said. I searched for him in the crowd, but he was right beside me, and he took my arm, saying, "Well done, Princess!"

"You were injured," I said.

Putting his hand to his rear end he said, "Mostly in dignity."

Sir Deming, standing below in the courtyard, cupped his hand to his mouth and yelled up, "Why don't we take the celebration inside, where there isn't so much danger of someone taking a flying leap off the battlements?"

It sounded like fine advice to me.

"Head for the Great Hall," Deming shouted.

So I did, with my people clustering just as close about me as the ghosts used to do.

In the Great Hall, the tables were heaped with all sorts of delicious-looking food, including a huge cake shaped like the castle. The smell of roasting meat, of fresh peaches, of just-baked bread—it would have been irresistible even if I wasn't half starved.

"What's all this?" I asked.

"Your coronation feast," Kenric told me. He indicated the throne at the head of the room—presumably they'd put the second one in storage—and I saw a crown waiting for me on the velvet seat.

Queen Andreanna sidled up to me and said, "And you're late—what a surprise."

But she didn't have time to waste belittling me. She caught sight of Grimbold, who'd somehow or other gotten hold of a satin pillow and was walking around with the pillow on his arm, displaying his newly recovered crown, so that he looked like a hairy ring bearer at a giant's wedding feast. "Grimbold," Andreanna said with enough enthusiasm to indicate she'd been waiting all her life to greet him. She caught hold of his arm and looked into his eyes with newly established fascination. As she led him away, I heard her saying, "What a lovely crown! You know, my deceased husband never told me..."

I waved to Orielle and Wulfgar across the room. Orielle waved back, but Wulfgar had his attention captured by Abas, who was demonstrating one-armed push-ups.

Xenos came up to me, but only long enough to say, "Remember, those are *my* boots."

I wiped my brow with my sleeve and realized how dirty, hot, and tired I truly was. I blew loose the hair that was sticking to my forehead. "Should I change into something more regal?" I asked Kenric. A three-hour soak would have been nice, but I didn't know how long I had.

"Whatever you want." Kenric handed me a goblet. "You look hot."

"I don't really like mead," I said.

"I remembered. This is honey water."

It was overly sweet, but at least it was wet.

Sister Mary Ursula, wearing the most extravagant— and ridiculous—dress I'd ever seen, said, "I am One with happy endings," before the crowd carried her away.

In fact, the crowd, noisy and jostling, was beginning to get on my nerves, making me feel claustrophobic.

"Maybe," I told Kenric, "I should sit down."

I took two steps before my knees gave out. Fireworks seemed to be going off behind my eyeballs, the sound exploding inside my skull.

Stupid! Stupid! Stupid! How could I have accepted a drink from someone who had already poisoned me once?

Kenric knelt down beside me.

"How could you?" I asked, my voice a weak and raw whisper.

"What?" he asked.

"What did I do wrong?" I demanded. "Didn't I do everything I was supposed to? I can't go through all this again."

"You didn't do anything wrong," Kenric said, which I took to mean that my choices as would-be king were fine with him—he just wanted to be king himself. "I don't understand what you're saying."

It wasn't fair. I'd lived the entire three days. I'd saved the kingdom from barbarians, peasants, and dragon. And I had no idea what to do differently next time. If there was a next time. I winced against the sparks going off in my brain. "I trusted you. How could you poison me?"

Kenric protested, "I didn't."

To my embarrassment, I found that tears were leaking out of my eyes and rolling down the sides of my face.

"Janine," Kenric said, enunciating each word slowly and carefully, *"I did not poison you."*

If Kenric hadn't poisoned me, maybe this wasn't game

death. Maybe this was, finally, the long-anticipated brain overload. That would explain the fireworks.

I was aware that Kenric was holding me, cradling my head, while the crowd had pulled back to give me room.

I could barely get my mouth to work. "I don't know what to do," I said, aware that I sounded as though I had a mouthful of oatmeal.

"Give my mother the ring," Kenric said.

How did he know about the ring?

I saw Andreanna hovering with the crowd. I managed to get the piece of twine showing, and Kenric slipped it over my head. "Andreanna, take the ring," I mumbled.

Andreanna took the ring.

"Tell her to treat you fairly and not to incite her sons to rebel against you," Kenric told me.

"Treat me fairly..."—I licked my parched lips, and Kenric brushed my hair off my cheeks while I got up the energy to finish—"and don't incite your sons to rebel against me."

While Andreanna nodded, Kenric said, "Ask for the crown."

"Crown," I echoed.

Kenric forced me to sit up a bit more, and Sir Deming placed the crown on my head. "Long live King Janine," Deming proclaimed.

The world dissolved in a shower of glitters.

CHAPTER THIRTY-THREE

Satisfaction Guaranteed,
Or Your Money Cheerfully Refunded

Despite the special effects, I knew I hadn't gotten out of the game because I could feel that Kenric was still holding me.

On the other hand I was suddenly also feeling much better—I wasn't burning with fever, my head didn't ache, and the internal fireworks had stopped.

I could also smell popcorn, which struck me—in a vague, detached way—as odd.

Something, however, nearly ripped the skin off my head at my temples, and off either side of my neck, and off various other sites on my body.

"Got it," a female voice announced.

I opened my eyes and saw that the Rasmussem receptionist was leaning over me, holding a bunch of wires with suction cups at their ends—the wires that had formerly connected me to the Rasmussem computer.

"Are you here, too?" I asked, thinking that somehow

she had gotten sucked into the game. But then I realized I was in one of the rooms at Rasmussem, lying on a total immersion couch.

"Welcome back, honey," the receptionist said.

How could they make it so real? It was over, but I could still feel Kenric's gentle arms around me. The sensation was so vivid, I had to turn to look.

And there was Kenric, still holding me. "Yikes," I said, but without much energy because I was incredibly tired.

The guy holding me smiled—same glorious smile—but his hair was shorter, and he was wearing jeans and a RASMUSSEM GAMING CENTER shirt. He was also the source of the popcorn aroma. He lowered my head back onto the couch's pillow.

"Tell me you're not Kenric," I said.

"I'm not Kenric," the guy said obligingly. "I'm Nigel Rasmussem."

"No, you're not." I was confused, but I wasn't *that* confused. "I've seen Nigel Rasmussem. He's a short, round guy with glasses."

"That's my uncle David. I used his image to talk to you because I thought he'd look more credible to you. I used *my* physical appearance for Kenric."

"You certainly did." I considered for a few moments, then said, "But you can't be more than..."

I hesitated, and he supplied, "Sixteen."

Sixteen. Rasmussem Enterprises had been around for two years, which meant he had started his company when he was no older than I was now. I will probably *not* be starting my own company in the coming months. "So what are you?" I asked: "Some kind of computer genius?"

310

He said, "You gotta do *something* when your parents saddle you with a name like Nigel."

"Wow," I said. "And you came here because I was in trouble?"

Nigel Rasmussem shook his head. "Rochester, New York, is world headquarters for Rasmussem Enterprises. My parents regulate how much time I can spend with computers, so I work here after school and on weekends." He added—though I guessed it a moment before he said it—"At the concession stand."

The receptionist said, "Sit her up."

At first I resented her speaking as though I was totally helpless—but I *was* totally helpless. Nigel did most of the work of getting me to a sitting position.

The receptionist handed me a cup of water. "You're fine," she assured me. "You might be a bit disoriented at first, but that will pass."

"It wasn't like this the other times I played," I said, worried despite her calming words.

"The other times you played, there would have been a cooldown period between the game stimulus and the waking state."

"Are you sure?" I asked. This was, after all, the woman who compared games to soups.

"That's what they pay me for."

I was reassured until she started speaking to someone who wasn't there, rattling off a bunch of numbers and techno-jargon, then ending with, "Signing off, unless you say otherwise."

Another voice said, "You're fine." Then I heard a dial tone.

The receptionist leaned over and touched something on the wall behind me, and the speaker went off.

"Do you want to rest a bit, honey?" she asked. "I can dim the lights and put on some soft music. We called your grandmother, and she should be here soon. And, of course, there'll be a media circus waiting outside. So I really recommend the rest now."

"Yes, please," I said. Then, maybe begging just a little, I asked Nigel, "Could you stay a bit?"

He pulled over a chair, while the receptionist dimmed the lights, put on the music, and then pulled the door shut behind her.

I asked, "She's a technician here?"

"Actually, a total immersion technologist—as well as an emergency medical technician. Do you want to talk about what happened, or do you want to sleep?"

"Both," I admitted.

"We'll compromise," he said. "Lie down. Close your eyes."

I did.

"May I?" Nigel had leaned over and was holding my hand.

Yes! Yes! Yes! I wanted to shout, but I managed a refined, "Mmmm."

Nigel spoke in a quiet, soothing voice. "You were in the game for eighty-seven minutes, which normally would have been totally safe, except for the damage the CPOC people did. They're going to get their asses fried for endangering the welfare of a minor. But you did fine. You did more than fine. You did"—was that admiration in his voice?—"you did things in that game that I didn't think could be done."

"Mmmm," I said again, pleased though I hardly knew the guy. Then his words sank in. My eyes flew open and I almost managed to sit up. "You were watching me?" I demanded.

"Giannine," he said, "there were technicians on both coasts and in England, Japan, and Ukraine following your readouts."

Horrified, I asked, "You could tell what I was thinking?"

Sounding just as horrified, he answered, "No, of course not. That's not the way the equipment works. Reading someone's thoughts?" He said it so contemptuously, I had to believe he was speaking the truth. "We couldn't even see or hear *you*. We were getting a steady stream of biofeedback statistics and data on how the characters and setting were changing, which let us interpret what you were doing. Sort of like watching a solar eclipse, which you can't do with your bare eyes, so you cast an image with a lens, and that's what you see—a reflection."

"I'll take your word for it," I said. "What do you mean I did things other people didn't do? Wasn't I playing right?"

"Of course, you were playing right. You were just making unusual choices."

I was getting irritated. All right, he was gorgeous and a sixteen-year-old genius who was CEO of his own multinational company, but that didn't give him the right to mock me. "Well, my choices made sense to me at the time."

"I didn't say they didn't make sense," he answered defensively.

I settled back down on the couch and closed my eyes once more, wondering if it was too rude to tell him I'd changed my mind and that he could go now and tend his concession booth.

"It's just," Nigel said, "trusting Kenric is almost always a bad choice. I kept thinking, *No, no, no,* but you did...twice...and the second time it worked out... Thank you for letting me be a good guy for once."

I opened my eyes again. "You..."—I amended that to—"Kenric...helped me so much at the very end, when I thought it was all over..."

"Heir Apparent is a game," Nigel said. "It's supposed to be fun. Frustrating, sure, but fun. If a player starts crying, that's a signal something has gone wrong. The characters become much more helpful. It's what the programmers call The Secret Weapon."

"Oh," I said. "Well, Kenric was nice before, just especially nice at the end. And I don't usually cry. It's only I was worn-out."

Nigel smiled. "I could tell. That you don't usually cry. You're incredibly brave. And creative. And you were about to win, when the equipment began overheating."

I shuddered, remembering the fireworks, realizing how close I'd come to not making it. Sometime, later, I might be able to ask what they would have done if I wasn't at the end of the game when the equipment started shorting out. But for the moment, that was too scary. So instead I asked, "What did I do wrong?"

"You didn't do anything wrong."

"What did I do differently from other people?"

Nigel considered. I guessed there were a lot of things he could have chosen from when he said, "Most players give the ring to Sister Mary Ursula, befriend Grimbold at his camp, and get Xenos Senior to take on the dragon, rather than handling it personally."

I wasn't even close.

"But your way worked, so it wasn't wrong."

The receptionist-technologist-technician knocked softly on the door, then came in with the miniature dragon on its leash. It settled on the couch-side table that held the pitcher of water. Close, but not close enough to nip. It opened its jaws, revealing many teeth and a tiny flame about the size you'd find on a match head right before it fizzles out.

"Your grandmother hasn't arrived yet," the receptionist said, "but there's a man who claims he's your father."

My father?

My father had come here?

She had apparently demanded his driver's license, and now she showed it to me.

Despite my amazement, I got my voice to work. "Yes, that's him."

The receptionist said, "And the second question is: Do you want to see him?"

Well, he wasn't Dexter the peat cutter, but neither was he King Cynric. I braced myself. "Sure," I told her.

And I told the tiny dragon with the butterfly wings, "Your mother has bad breath, even without the dead ox."

Then I let Nigel help me sit up, though this time I really didn't need him, and I waited for my father.

If you've decided that this book and others like it are dangerous, clip along this line, glue this page to cardboard, and fasten onto a stick. Start your own protest demonstration!

Don't corrupt the minds of our children!

Down with fantasy!

CHAPTER 1

The Dangers of Higher Education

My mother isn't normally the kind of parent who comes to school and has me yanked out of class because she needs to see me.

Never mind that the class I was pulled from was trigonometry, which is monumentally mind-numbing and—as far as I can tell—entirely useless to anyone except trigonometry teachers. It is rumored that, on a warm spring day three years ago, our trig teacher, Mr. Petersen, actually fell asleep during one of his own lectures. The speculation is that he has not awakened since, but is still droning on from memory, in a sleepwalking state.

I have never seen anything in Mr. Petersen's demeanor to make me doubt that rumor.

Generally speaking, I'd be eager for *any* excuse to get away from sine and cosine and whatever that third function is whose name I can never remember. But I felt a prickle of anxiety. Despite my mother's inability to come up with even one real-life situation where knowing the difference between opposite and adjacent, much less a hypotenuse would be a benefit to me, she does strongly believe in the theory of education. So I couldn't make sense of the note the messenger from the office interrupted the class to hand to me:

Grace Pizzelli
Go down to Mrs. Overstreet's
office right away.
Your mother is here

My brain instantly zipped to the West Coast, where Dad was attending a sales conference at a hotel I was suddenly convinced was the obvious target for arsonists, kidnappers, earthquakes, flash floods, outbreaks of Lyme disease, and/or killer bees.

My outlook wasn't improved by walking into Mrs. Overstreet's office. Mrs. Overstreet was wearing that I-smell-something-bad-and-I-suspect-it's-coming-from-you expression that must be taught in one of the required courses at principal college—a course that clearly would be more useful than trig.

But my mother had on sweatpants and a Milky Way Galaxy T-shirt she'd gotten when she'd chaperoned my Brownie troop's overnight at the Strasenberg Planetarium seven years ago. This is strictly at-home wear for her. Even for going to the grocery store, Mom's shoes need to match her purse. On this particular occasion, her shoes didn't match each other.

My prickly-all-over worry exploded into panic. "What's wrong? What's happened?" I asked. "Is Dad all right?"

My questions seemed to send my mother into a worse spiral than the one she was already in. "Dad?" she echoed. She glanced around the office, looking simultaneously dazed and frantic, as though not sure whether to level accusations at Mrs. Overstreet or the two strangers in the room—a man and a woman. She settled on the strangers and said in a squeaky voice, "You didn't tell me something happened to my husband!"

The man had a trim little beard, and excuse me, but if you were a casting director looking for someone to play the role of a debonair devil, you'd be giving this guy your card and asking him to come in for an audition. By contrast, the woman might well have been studying for that principal's course on intimidation through facial expression, but she was the one who spoke: "Mrs. Pizzelli, we don't even know where your husband is."

Mom's voice went even higher. "Tyler is *missing?*"

My feelings were bouncing all over the place because I didn't know if Mom was overreacting—which has been known to happen—or if she actually had a reason to suspect the worst.

Mrs. Overstreet went with option number one. "Mrs. Pizzelli, I'm sure your husband is fine." She didn't give my mother a chance to say more than "But—" before she continued, "When I go to conferences, the presenters always ask everyone to turn off their phones. I'm sure once they break for lunch, your husband will check his messages and return your call."

The other woman was nodding as though those were her thoughts exactly. "Please," she said, "now that your younger daughter is here, let's talk about Emily."

Emily?

Before I could ask "What's wrong with Emily?" the woman had stood up and offered me her hand to shake. She was very business-chic and sophisticated. "Hello, Grace. I'm pleased to meet you. Though not under these circumstances, of course."

The man, still sitting, smoothly interjected: "By which we do not mean to imply that Rasmussem Corporation or any of its employees is in any way responsible for those circumstances."

Ah, I thought, putting together that suave but slightly sinister look with his precise wording. *Lawyer.*

I finally noticed that they both had Rasmussem Corporation nametags, as well as school visitor badges.

The woman continued, "My name is Jenna Bennett, and I'm the chief technical engineer at the Lake Avenue Rasmussem facility. This is Alexander Kroll, from our legal department."

Mr. Kroll showed some of his teeth and added, "By which we do not mean to imply that this is a matter requiring adjudication."

Apparently, my principal didn't like lawyers. She leveled an I-am-picturing-doing-you-bodily-harm expression at him and said to my mother, "Yeah, yeah, so it's much too early to talk about suing the pants off them, but that's always a possibility."

Kroll's expression didn't change: proof, if anyone had needed it, about the sincerity of his smile.

Suing didn't sound good. People sue when something goes terribly wrong, and what did all this have to do with Emily—or me?

Ms. Really-I'm-an-Engineer-Despite-the-Fact-That-I-Look-Like-a-Principal-in-Training Bennett put on a pained expression.

But, fashionable and pretty as she was, she didn't know *pained*. My mother's eyes were red-rimmed and scared—*that* was pain. She took my hand and worked it like someone trying to soften up putty.

What a terrible person I am, I realized. *Something awful has happened to Emily, and here I am mentally moaning about a few squished fingers.*

Mom said to me, "Emily's playing a game at the arcade."

"Okay . . ." I said, knowing there had to be more. Emily is a student at RIT—Rochester Institute of Technology. She's studying technical engineering and is in a work co-op program at Rasmussem, which, long story short, means she's slave labor for them this semester, though I'm guessing Mr. Lawyer Kroll would try to qualify that statement. Rasmussem is the company that developed total immersion, the next step beyond virtual reality. When you play their games, sensations are fed directly into your brain: you can feel the warmth of the sun if it's daytime in the world you're playing in, just as you can feel cold and soaked to the bone if it's raining; you can taste the food and smell the flowers; and if you're riding a horse, after a while your butt goes to sleep. The difference between playing a Rasmussem game and a regular old virtual reality game is like the difference between watching an IMAX movie and one of those old black and white silent films.

I thought, *Of course Emily is playing games at the arcade.* No doubt most—if not all—of the people who work at Rasmussem are there because they love games. Well, maybe excepting the lawyers. But if the company wasn't going to pay their interns salaries, they couldn't be surprised at an unauthorized game or two. I assumed Emily was playing while she was supposed to be working, which apparently I didn't take as seriously as the legal department did. Was she getting fired? Was she getting expelled?

But surely that wasn't enough to account for Mom's distress, or for my getting called out of class.

Mom still seemed intent on kneading all my fingers into mush. She said, "They can't get it to stop."

Confused, I said, "The games last a half-hour. While you're playing, you feel like it's hours, but it's only thirty minutes." I figured my mother wasn't sure whether to believe me. She's not a gamer—hard as that is to conceive of these days. She's not into technology and can barely get her cell phone to cooperate. I said, "When the time runs out, the game just stops."

"Yes," Ms. Rasmussem-Engineer-Lady agreed. "Normally."

Okay, well, granted, something was not normal or we wouldn't all be here.

She continued, "Emily hooked herself into the game she was developing, and . . . she did something. She bypassed safety protocols. But the half-hour is up. The half-hour was up more than four hours ago."

"Can't you just . . ."—of course I *have* played Rasmussem's games, but Emily is the tech-type in the family—". . . unhook her?" I finished lamely, thinking of the wires they stick to your head when you lie down on a total immersion couch. Duh. Like the people who could think up total immersion weren't smart enough to think of that?

"We did," Ms. Bennett said, without sounding impatient or condescending at my obviousness. "She didn't revive."

Mom said, "I asked them to just pull the plug on the whole thing, but they won't." Pulling the plug is Mom's cure-it technique for *all* of our computer's ills.

Ms. Bennett said—and I could tell she'd said it before—"It doesn't work like that."

"There should be safeguards," Mom said.

"There are," Mr. Kroll told her. "Your older daughter, intentionally, with forethought, for her own reasons, disabled them. Leaving behind a note clearly showing her culpability."

From his briefcase, he pulled out a piece of paper in a clear plastic bag hand-labeled EVIDENCE.

Evidence? Like from courts and trials and cop shows? What sort of trouble was Emily in?

The note was in my sister's neat rounded penmanship. It said:

Not anybody's fault.
This is MY choice.

While the word *evidence* had set off all sorts of alarm bells in my head, now I think my body temperature dropped ten degrees.

Emily had *chosen* to go into a game and not come out? *Why?*

Mr. Kroll was still talking to my mother. "There may well be loss to company revenues because of her actions, beyond the time of the techs who have been trying to help her, beyond the time taken by Ms. Bennett and myself to explain things to you at your home, and now here again at your younger daughter's school because you wanted to consult with her." His expression clearly showed what he thought of a woman who would seek her fourteen-year-old's opinion.

"Be that as it may . . ." Principal Overstreet said.

We all looked at her, but she didn't really have anything to say; I guess she just didn't like our bickering.

Ms. Bennett stepped into the breach, too elegant to put up with bickering, either. "Be that as it may, we can tell, approximately, where in the Rasmussem-created scenario she is. I myself went in and tried to talk her out. She refused to listen to me."

This was so weird, so . . . *more* than weird. I couldn't even tell what I should be thinking.

I saw Ms. Bennett looking at me, waiting for me to realize she was looking at me. She said, "We're hoping she'll listen to you."

Me? Somehow this was coming down to *me*?

I had caught that part where Ms. Oh-So-Well-Dressed Bennett had said she'd *gone in* to talk to Emily.

"I think it's insane," Mom said. "First one of my daughters gets stuck in their crazy game; then they want my other daughter to just step right in after her."

"Mrs. Pizzelli," Ms. Bennett said, "I've already explained: there's no danger. I told you that I went into the game and was perfectly capable of coming back out again. Emily could come out, too. She's simply choosing not to. We're hoping Grace can get her to see reason."

Liking a game is one thing. Playing into the wee hours of the morning even though it's a school day is one thing. Shouting "Just a minute" when your mother hollers at you to get off the computer *now* because she's called you for dinner twice already—all of that is one thing.

Emily wouldn't come out?

"If," Mom said, "*if* someone from the family needs to do this, it should be me."

Ms. Bennett shook her head. "You're not a gamer. You'd be overwhelmed. Without experience, you wouldn't know where to begin, how to get around, what's important and what's only background. We'd lose valuable time. The programs are meant to last from thirty to sixty minutes. The equipment is rated safe for eight times that exposure. But it's not meant for sustained immersion."

Everything she said made sense, too much sense.

There was no way I could hope Mom would insist on being the one to go—not when I could see so clearly it would be better for Emily to have me there.

In the movies, the good guys always fight each other for the opportunity to do the dangerous stuff. The Rasmussem people were saying this *wasn't* dangerous. And *still* the responsibility was enough to freeze me solid.

Mrs. Overstreet, as a principal in charge of her students' safety, said to me, "Grace, you don't have to do this if you don't want to."

For the first time in my life, I wanted to hug her.

"No," Ms. Bennett agreed. "Of course she doesn't *have to*. But there's no reason she shouldn't. It's not like we're asking her to donate a kidney or something."

Suddenly we were into donating body parts? *Would* I donate a kidney? I wondered. Much as I loved Emily, I wasn't sure I could.

"Oh, I wish your father would pick up the damn phone," Mom said, "and tell me what we should do."

Somehow, that cleared my head. *We SHOULD*, I thought, *be able to make up our minds on our own*.

"No danger of me getting stuck in there?" I asked.

"Absolutely none," Ms. Engineer and Mr. Lawyer said in unison.

"Then," I had to admit, "I guess I don't see any reason why not."

My mother sniffled but didn't try to talk me out of it.

Mr. Kroll smiled his non-smile smile and opened his briefcase again. "Fine. We just have one or two papers for you to sign . . ."

ƎUᴛHOᴚ BIO

Vivian Vande Velde has written many acclaimed books for teen and middle grade readers, including two other books about virtual reality games created by the Rasmussem Corporation, *Heir Apparent* and *Deadly Pink*, as well as the Edgar Award–winning *Never Trust a Dead Man*. She lives in Rochester, New York.

www.vivianvandevelde.com